MATHEMATICAL TECHNIQUES

in Electronics and Engineering Analysis

J. W. HEAD, M.A.(CANTAB.), F.INST.P., A.M.I.E.E.

LONDON   ILIFFE BOOKS LTD
PRINCETON, NEW JERSEY
D. VAN NOSTRAND COMPANY, INC.

© J. W. HEAD, 1964

First published in 1964 by Iliffe Books Ltd
Dorset House, Stamford Street, London, S.E.1

Published in the U.S.A. by
D. Van Nostrand Company, Inc. 120 Alexander Street,
New Jersey

Printed and bound in England by
The Chapel River Press Ltd., Andover, Hants

BKS 4433

CONTENTS

PREFACE

Much of the material of this book is taken from articles by 'Computer' in *Electronic and Radio Engineer* and *Electronic Technology*, written between February 1957 and August 1962. Almost all these articles (except those between March 1960 and August 1961, which have not been included here) were written by the present author alone, and were intended to make various techniques available to the user of mathematics in practical applications rather than to the individual interested in mathematics for its own sake. The articles have been rearranged and further co-ordinating material added, to form the present book. (A second, related book, is in course of preparation. This deals mainly with Heaviside's operational calculus and techniques related thereto. It is the joint work of the present author and Mr. C. G. Mayo, and is based upon a lecture given by the present author at the College of Aeronautics at Cranfield in September 1961 and a recent paper on operational calculus published by the Journal of the British Institution of Radio Engineers (see Reference 7, page 262).)

The subjects discussed are mainly those which have arisen naturally in the course of the author's work as Mathematical Consultant in the Research Department of the BBC Engineering Division. For the most part, really useful and applicable mathematics is surprisingly elementary. The main need is that the problem under consideration be adequately specified and formulated. It is hoped that the reader who understands the techniques discussed here is adequately equipped to overcome the fear of mathematics which grips so many engineers, whose main interest is in applications, and also adequately equipped to understand the essential nature of a practical situation—to understand what the problem is really about. Full explanation has been given of all the techniques discussed; thus the book is completely self-contained, so that it is not essential for the reader to have any other book with him. References are included, however, partly to disclaim originality, but also to permit a more detailed study of particular techniques which may be of special interest to particular readers. Throughout, the emphasis is on ordinary, straightforward cases and general methods rather than the borderline, special and awkward cases which are so often the delight of professional mathematicians, but only confuse the issue for the would-be user of mathematics in practical applications.

Preference has been given to techniques where the object of each step can be easily understood, rather than to those where the number of operations to be carried out is as small as possible. In numerical calculations, so much time is wasted in chasing silly mistakes that the priority should go to making the process as automatic as possible, rather than as short as possible.

To sum up, the object of this book might be described as to give 'mathematical self-confidence' to the reader whose main interest is in practical applications.

J. W. H.

Kingswood Warren
Tadworth, 1963

Chapter I

INTRODUCTION

The present book is concerned with a number of mathematical tricks and techniques which are not very closely related, and which are in fact very much easier to understand, apply and use than the average non-mathematician thinks. Most specific examples will be related to electrical circuits, but the techniques illustrated by these examples are very generally applicable. Chapter 2 deals wih methods of solving linear simultaneous equations, and Chapters 3 and 4 with methods of solving algebraic equations. The main merit claimed for the methods put forward (in these and other chapters) is that they are easily understood in principle. The processes described may be somewhat tedious in the worst possible cases (which are usually the delight of professional mathematicians) but in practice we are more often concerned with cases which are either straightforward (though they may be tedious) or of moderate difficulty. For example, an algebraic equation of degree greater than 7 is comparatively rare, and it is therefore hardly appropriate for this book to include methods which really come into their own for an equation of degree 15 or 20. Equations of very high degree require the attention of a mathematical specialist, just as in the medical world, really difficult cases are referred to Harley Street specialists, although a remarkable number of cases which are reasonably straightforward are successfully handled by general practitioners.

Chapter 5 deals with the use of series, both finite and infinite, and includes the question of expressing the quotient of two polynomials in partial fractions. Series, like algebraic and simultaneous equations, have a way of occurring in almost any problem under the sun; very often one can make progress, particularly in the exploratory stage where one has only a vague idea of the type of answer to be expected, if a complicated mathematical entity is replaced by a

1

few terms of a suitable series expansion. A 'suitable' series expansion means one in which the important terms come near the beginning. Only a few very simple tests of convergence (i.e. ensuring that the important terms do come near the beginning) are mentioned briefly, as the author believes that genuine borderline cases occur with zero probability. In practice, a series or other approximation either works, or obviously fails to do so, in which case one need not pursue the matter further but it is necessary to start again with a different series expansion obtained by an alternative but mathematically equivalent set of manipulations.

Chapter 6 is concerned with the fundamental processes of differentiation and integration. It should be noted that while one can almost always find explicitly the differential coefficient of any given expression (and in a physical problem, all entities involved are in fact continuous and differentiable any number of times, however convenient it may sometimes be to represent them in terms of step, impulse or other discontinuous expressions) it is not always possible to express an integral in closed form. In practice there is no sharp distinction between functions explicitly integrable and those which are not. Approximations (of which Simpson's Rule is a remarkably useful example, easily adapted to a computer programme) are available so that in a particular (numerical) case we can obtain an effective substitute for the integral of an expression not explicitly integrable. It is thus not worthwhile to devote enormous efforts to finding explicit integrals; nevertheless, a few straightforward techniques for doing this, such as substitution, are discussed.

Chapter 7 is devoted to a number of generally useful but elementary techniques. First, it is important to realise that the obvious way to tackle a problem is often not the best. Ways of saving labour in numerical calculations by performing them in a well-chosen sequence are therefore discussed, and a case is included where it was very much easier to 'work backwards', and proceed as if we were given the quantity B in fact required, and as if we had to deduce the quantity A which was in fact given. In this way, we can obtain values of A in the neighbourhood of the A actually given, and by graphical or other interpolation of the corresponding values of B obtain the value of B actually required. This raises the question of interpolation generally, which is considered next. It is remarkable also how important the process of algebraic division is, for example, in evaluating a polynomial of moderately high degree for a complex value of the argument; this, and difficulties and anomalies associated with careless cancelling, are therefore carefully considered. Finally, the question of methods for obtaining suitable smooth curves from experimental data is discussed. Chapter 8 deals with versors (i.e. quantities of the form $x + jy$ considered mainly as vectors, or quantities having a magnitude and direction). Trigonometrical considerations naturally are very relevant here, and the subject is closely related to analytical geometry which is surprisingly useful in many electrical and circuit problems.

All the foregoing techniques are reasonably straightforward and generally applicable, and indeed one or more of them is likely to be required in making almost any calculation associated with a practical problem. The remaining chapters are devoted to somewhat more difficult (or at any rate less well-known) techniques specifically related to circuit problems. Outstanding among these are matrices (Chapter 10), particularly those having not more than two rows and columns, which alone we shall consider here. By means of such matrices it is frequently possible to write down equations in matrix form involving only the major features of a circuit, instead of having to bother about every individual node, mesh, internal current or voltage. The rules of matrix algebra make it possible to reduce these matrix equations to explicit equations expressing required quantities in terms of given quantities.

Operational calculus may be needed to reduce these explicit equations to results expressing the required quantities as functions of time. Only an outline discussion of the subject is included in Chapter 9 of this book, so that the way in which the various techniques discussed make their contribution to understanding circuit problems by means of operational calculus may be made clear. Operational calculus will be more fully discussed in a forthcoming book entitled 'Unified Circuit Theory'.

One often wishes to design a circuit so that some quantity (such as the rate of change of phase with frequency) shall be as constant as possible for a given range of the variable concerned. It is not possible (without an infinite amount of apparatus) to make this quantity exactly constant, and the question is what can be achieved in this direction in a practicable manner. Conditions for minimum variation of a function therefore are discussed in Chapter 11.

In Chapter 8 the usefulness of analytical geometry in relation to circuit theory was mentioned, and this is considered more fully in Chapter 12, where a geometrical approach to impedance calculations is discussed in some detail.

Chapter 13 is devoted to the important question of stability criteria. In the case of a network consisting of lumped elements only, there is usually an algebraic 'characteristic equation', of degree n say, which must be free from roots with positive real parts for stability. To determine stability, it is not necessary to solve the characteristic equation itself, but only (at worst) to determine whether two associated equations of degree about $\frac{1}{2}n$ have all their roots real and interlaced. On the other hand, in connection with sampled-data control systems, conditions for stability can be that a certain algebraic equation must have all its roots with modulus less than unity. These conditions are related and are carefully compared. A somewhat different kind of stability criterion was suggested by Liapunov in Russia; this is not as well known or understood in this country as it should be, and a brief discussion of fundamental principles associated with it, and applied to very simple cases only, is therefore included.

Chapter 2

SOLUTION OF SIMULTANEOUS EQUATIONS

In almost any kind of practical problem, there may be a requirement to solve a number n of linear simultaneous equations in n unknowns. If $n = 2$, the problem reduces to one familiar in our school days, and theoretically there is a unique solution, whatever the value of n may be. Text books generally make much mention of a certain exceptional case; we shall briefly indicate how this can arise when $n = 3$, but we shall not devote much attention to it, since essentially what has happened when such a case arises, is that we have made a mistake—we thought we had n equations' worth of information, but one of the equations we have written down is in fact (or is nearly) a linear combination of the remainder, so that our information is deficient. We really have only $(n - 1)$ equations, and we should devote our efforts to seeking a genuine, independent nth equation rather than to trying with enormous difficulty to extricate ourselves from the mess into which we have fallen by having n equations which are not really independent.

THREE EQUATIONS AND THREE UNKNOWNS: GENERAL CASE

If then we have three equations in three unknowns x, y, and z, say

$$
\left.
\begin{aligned}
a_1x + b_1y + c_1z &= d_1 \\
a_2x + b_2y + c_2z &= d_2 \\
a_3x + b_3y + c_3z &= d_3
\end{aligned}
\right\}
\tag{2.1}
$$

the obvious way to start, in theory, is to take the z-terms over to the right-hand side in the first two of Equations 2.1, and solve these for x and y in the schoolboy way as if z were a known number. We thus find

$$\left. \begin{array}{l} x = \dfrac{(d_1b_2 - d_2b_1) - (c_1b_2 - c_2b_1)z}{a_1b_2 - a_2b_1} \\[2mm] y = \dfrac{(c_1a_2 - c_2a_1)z - (d_1a_2 - d_2a_1)}{a_1b_2 - a_2b_1} \end{array} \right\} \qquad (2.2)$$

and substitution into the third of Equations 2.1 will give the value of z. The exceptional case already mentioned arises if the coefficient of z, when this substitution is made, is zero, and similarly we run into trouble with Equations 2.2 if $a_1b_2 = a_2b_1$. If the coefficients in Equations 2.1 arise from a physical problem, we shall only know their values approximately, not exactly, and thus we shall only know the value of the coefficient of z after substitution from Equations 2.2 approximately also. The probability that this coefficient is exactly zero is itself exactly zero, and the right procedure from the practical point of view is to forget this borderline case (and in fact most borderline cases, for similar reasons) but to be warned that if the said coefficient of z is small, the value of z deduced will be inaccurate, and so will the corresponding values of x and y deduced by substituting back into Equations 2.2. A small coefficient of z after substitution from Equations 2.2 indicates that Equations 2.1 are, in effect, only two distinct equations and the right procedure is to seek a further linear equation involving x, y and z not subject to this defect.

The above discussion has reduced the case $n = 3$ to the case $n = 2$, and clearly we could proceed similarly to reduce the case $n = 4$ to the case $n = 3$ and so on indefinitely. In fact, the solution for the general case can be written down in terms of 'determinants'. For purely theoretical work, such a solution (which can be found in many mathematical textbooks, and is commonly known as 'Cramer's rule') may be of some value, but the evaluation of determinants, particularly those of high order, is a tedious process subject to serious 'rounding-off' errors when only approximate values of the coefficients are available.

In this chapter, we are primarily concerned with the solution of linear simultaneous equations with numerical coefficients, which will usually be rounded-off to so many places of decimals. If the number of unknowns is very large, say 10 or more, the best course is probably to obtain a solution by means of an electronic computer, which is well adapted for this purpose.

THE 'ESCALATOR' METHOD

Here we shall discuss the matter, first in terms of a simple example of three equations for three unknowns where all the quantities required for the working are exact, and then in terms of a typical system of four equations for four unknowns where the coefficients and solutions are not conveniently exact. Both systems of equations are symmetrical; the method can be adapted to unsymmetrical sets of equations, or alternatively unsymmetrical sets of equations can be 'normalised' as indicated below. The procedure is explained in a perfectly general way, applicable to any number of equations and unknowns, and applicable whether the coefficients and solutions are exact or (as is more usual) not. A desk calculating machine is highly desirable, though not absolutely essential.

Various well-known methods are available for the numerical solution of equations; we have chosen the 'Escalator' method described below, due to Morris[1], because it can easily be reduced to a standard computational routine involving only elementary arithmetical processes, and because there are many points in the process where checks have to be satisfied so that errors can be discovered before too much time is wasted. If the obvious method of 'pivotal condensation' is used, so that one variable is successively eliminated from all the equations in turn, a numerical error may remain undetected until the whole process of solution is complete, and every number may have to be examined before the incorrect one is discovered. In the 'Escalator' process to be described, the search for the error is more restricted, as will be explained.

THREE SYMMETRICAL EQUATIONS AND THREE UNKNOWNS: INTEGER COEFFICIENTS

Consider first the symmetrical set of three equations in three unknowns

$$\left.\begin{array}{r} x + 3y + 5z - 9 = 0 \\ 3x + 19y + 10z - 32 = 0 \\ 5x + 10y + 28z - 43 = 0 \end{array}\right\} \tag{2.3}$$

for which the solution is in fact $x = y = z = 1$.

If the normal 'pivotal condensation' procedure is used, the first of Equations 2.3 is multiplied first by 3 and subtracted from the second equation, and then by 5 and subtracted from the third. We thus obtain a set of two simultaneous equations in y and z which can be solved in the well-known way. But if an error is made at any stage, it will not be discovered until we have found y and z, substituted back into one of Equations 2.3 to obtain x, and checked in both the remaining equations, and we shall also have no clue as to where the error occurred.

The 'Escalator' process to be described works in the opposite direction. The complete working for Equations 2.3 is given in Table 2.1, and the various quantities which occur are either labelled in Table 2.1 when they first occur, or defined in Equations 2.4 immediately following, in terms of quantities which have arisen earlier. In these equations, a_{11} means the coefficient of x in the first of Equations 2.3, a_{12} means the coefficient of y in the first of Equations 2.3 or the coefficient of x in the second, a_{13} means coefficient of z in the first of Equations 2.3 or the coefficient of x in the third, and a_{14} means the number term of the first equation (brought over to the left hand side), and so on.

$$
\left.
\begin{aligned}
-X_2 &= a_{12}/a_{11} \\
-X_3 &= (a_{13}/a_{11}) + s_{23}(X_2/q_2) \\
-Y_3 &= (s_{23}/q_2) \\
-X_4 &= (a_{14}/a_{11}) + s_{24}(X_2/q_2) + s_{34}(X_3/q_3) \\
-Y_4 &= (s_{24}/q_2) + s_{34}(Y_3/q_3) \\
-Z_4 &= s_{34}/q_3
\end{aligned}
\right\} \quad (2.4)
$$

etc.

In the above example, the procedure is quite straightforward provided that the operations are carried out in the right order. At frequent intervals there are checks on the accuracy of the working; thus the zeros in rows 3, 7 and 12 are not accidental; if they did not appear, an error would be indicated requiring correction before proceeding to the next stage. Further, there is an alternative formula for the quantities we have called q_2, q_3 etc., namely

$$
\left.
\begin{aligned}
q_2 &= a_{22} - (a_{12}^2/a_{11}) \\
q_3 &= a_{33} - (a_{13}^2/a_{11}) - (s_{23}^2/q_2) \\
q_4 &= a_{44} - (a_{14}^2/a_{11}) - (s_{24}^2/q_2) - (s_{34}^2/q_3)
\end{aligned}
\right\} \quad (2.5)
$$

Table 2.1. SOLUTION OF EQUATIONS 2.3 BY THE 'ESCALATOR' METHOD

Row No.	Column No. 1	Column No. 2	Column No. 3	Column No. 4	Remarks
1	−3	−9	−15	27	Coefficients of first of Equations $2.3 \times X_2 = -3$
2	3	19	10	−32	Coefficients of 2nd Equation 2.3
3	0	$10 = q_2$	$-5 = s_{23}$	$-5 = s_{24}$	Row 1 + Row 2
4	−6·5	−19·5	−32·5	58·5	Coefficients 1st Equation $\times X_3 = -6.5$
5	1·5	9·5	5	−16	Coefficients 2nd Equation $\times Y_3 = +0.5$
6	5	10	28	−43	Coefficients 3rd Equation.
7	0	0	$0.5 = q_3$	$-0.5 = s_{34}$	Row 4 + Row 5 + Row 6
8	1	3	5	Not needed	Coefficients 1st Equation $\times X_4 = 1$
9	3	19	10		Coefficients 2nd Equation $\times Y_4 = 1$
10	5	10	28		Coefficients 3rd Equation $\times Z_4 = 1$
11	−9	−32	−43		Number Terms
12	0	0	0		Rows 8–11 summed

and so on; for Equations 2.3 we have of course only q_2 and q_3 to consider.

The first step is to calculate X_2 from the first of Equations 2.4; for Equations 2.3 we thus find $X_2 = -3$, and this enables us to complete Row 1 of Table 2.1. Row 3 is the sum of Rows 1 and 2, and begins with a zero in Column 1. The quantities q_2, s_{23} and s_{24} are simply names for the numbers turning up to the right of the zero in row 3; further, the value of q_2 agrees with the first of Equations 2.5. At this stage it is only q_2, s_{23} and X_2 which we need to calculate X_3 and Y_3 from the next two of Equations 2.4; s_{24} is kept in cold storage, until we need it to find X_4, Y_4 and Z_4 from the last three of Equations 2.4 in order to complete Rows 8–12. Knowing X_3 and Y_3 we can complete Rows 4–7, and the two initial zeros are a check that we have made no error so far, and q_3 also agrees with the second of Equations 2.5 as it should.

Having completed Row 8, we know all the quantities required for determining X_4, Y_4 and Z_4, from Equations 2.4 which in this case are the required solutions; the fact that three zeros duly turn up

2

in Row 12 is a completely adequate check, and we do not have to bother about column 4 as we would have to if there were more unknowns.

We shall only discuss the case where the equations are symmetrical, that is to say, the coefficient of the rth unknown in the sth equation is the same as the coefficient of the sth unknown in the rth equation. Equations not having this property can easily be replaced by an equivalent symmetrical set as explained below.

FOUR SYMMETRICAL EQUATIONS: ARBITRARY NUMERICAL COEFFICIENTS

We shall now solve the symmetrical equations:

$$\left.\begin{array}{l} x + 0\cdot08711\,y + 0\cdot42521\,z + 0\cdot37688\,t + 0\cdot28009 = 0 \\[4pt] 0\cdot08711\,x + y + 0\cdot16249\,z + 0\cdot14094\,t + 0\cdot23215 = 0 \\[4pt] 0\cdot42521\,x + 0\cdot16249\,y + z + 0\cdot91117\,t - 0\cdot40936 = 0 \\[4pt] 0\cdot37688\,x + 0\cdot14094\,y + 0\cdot91117\,z + t - 0\cdot26253 = 0 \end{array}\right\} \quad (2.6)$$

If the normal 'pivotal condensation' procedure is used, the first of Equations 2.6 is multiplied first by $0\cdot08711$ and subtracted from the second equation, then by $0\cdot42521$ and subtracted from the third equation and, lastly, by $0\cdot37688$ and subtracted from the last equation. We thus obtain a set of three new linear simultaneous equations in y, z and t from which x is absent. Then y is eliminated from these equations, and we derive two simultaneous equations in z and t for which the solution is straightforward. But the values of z and t thus derived, and the values of x and y which can be deduced from these, must be checked in all the original equations, and if there is an error, we have 14 coefficients to check when trying to trace the error ($\frac{1}{6} n\,(n-1)\,(n+4) - 2$ such coefficients if originally we had n equations for n unknowns).

The first step, as with Equations 2.3, is to determine X_2 from the first of Equations 2.4; the actual value of X_2 is -0.08711. It is the result that would be obtained if in the first of Equations 2.6 the number term $0\cdot28009$ was omitted, z and t were both replaced by zero, and y by 1.

Row 1 of Table 2.2 is simply the coefficients of the various terms of the first of Equations 2.6 multiplied by X_2; row 2 of Table 2.2 is the coefficients of the second equation in order as they stand. Row 3 is obtained by adding rows 1 and 2. Again, the zero in the

Table 2.2. INITIAL STAGE OF 'ESCALATOR' TABULATIONS

Row No.	Column No. 1	Column No. 2	Column No. 3	Column No. 4	Column No. 5	Remarks
1	−0·08711	−0·007588	−0·037040	−0·032830	−0·024399	Coefficients of the first of Equations 2.6 × X_2
2	0·08711	1	0·16249	0·14094	0·23215	Coefficients of the second of Equations 2.6
3	0	$0·992412 = q_2$	$0·125450 = s_{23}$	$0·108110 = s_{24}$	$0·207751 = s_{25}$	Row 1 + Row 2

Table 2.3. SECOND STAGE OF 'ESCALATOR' TABULATIONS

Row No.	Column No. 1	Column No. 2	Column No. 3	Column No. 4	Column No. 5	Remarks
4	−0·414199	−0·036081	−0·176122	−0·156103	−0·116013	Coefficients of the first of Equations 2.6 × X_3
5	−0·011011	−0·126409	−0·020540	−0·077816	−0·029346	Coefficients of the second of Equations 2.6 × Y_3
6	0·42521	0·16249	1	0·91117	−0·40936	Coefficients of the third of Equations 2.6
7	0	0	$0·803338 = q_3$	$0·737251 = s_{34}$	$−0·554719 = s_{35}$	Sum

first column of row 3 is not an accident; it is our guarantee that we have obtained X_2 correctly. The quantities in the other columns of row 3 are given names q_2, s_{23}, s_{24} and s_{25} because they will be required at a later stage.

As in the case of Equations 2.3, the value of q_2, namely 0·992412, agrees with the first of Equations 2.5.

For the next stage, as before, we have to complete Rows 4–7 as in Table 2.3; X_3 and Y_3 come from Equations 2.4 and their numerical

Table 2.4. ORDERLY ARRANGEMENT OF THE QUANTITIES X_2, Y_3, ETC.

Row No.	Column No. 1	Column No. 2	Column No. 3	Column No. 4	Column No. 5
1	1	−0·08711	−0·414199		
2	0	1	−0·126409		
3	0	0	1		
4	0	0	0	1	

values are −0·414199 and −0·126409 respectively. The rows are numbered 4–7 because they are a continuation of Table 2.2; Row 4 consists of the coefficients of the first of Equations 2.6 multiplied by $X_3 = -0·414199$ while row 5 consists of the coefficients of the second of Equations 2.6 multiplied by $Y_3 = -0·126409$. Row 6 is merely the coefficients of the third of Equations 2.6. Row 7 is the sum of Rows 4–6, as in Table 2.1. If the first two columns do not have zeros as they should, the most likely trouble is an incorrect value of s_{23}; an incorrect value of x_2 or of q_2 would have been detected earlier. As indicated in Equations 2.5, the value of q_3 can be checked from

$$q_3 = a_{33} - \frac{a_{13}{}^2}{a_{11}} - \frac{s_{23}{}^2}{q_2} \tag{2.7}$$

where a_{33} is the coefficient of the third unknown z in the third Equation 2.6, here 1, and the quantities named q_3, s_{34} and s_{35} will all be required later.

We are now ready to proceed to the next stage, for which we require the values X_4 of x, Y_4 of y and Z_4 of z satisfying the first three Equations 2.6 if t is taken as unity and the number term is omitted.

X_4, Y_4 and Z_4 are given by Equations 2.4 and we know all the quantities needed to determine them. Although the determination of X_4, Y_4 and Z_4 is perfectly straightforward, it is easy to make mistakes, and the arrangement of Table 2.4, which includes various quantities we have obtained so far, is helpful.

In Table 2.4 the number in Row 1 and Column 1 is always unity; the table has one more column than the number of unknowns and the same number of rows as the number of unknowns. All rows of Column 1 below Row 1 contain zero. The number X_2 is placed in Row 1, Column 2, and the number 1 in Row 2, Column 2 and in all other places where the row-number and column-number are equal; zeros occupy any position where the row-number is greater than the column-number. In Column 3, the successive entries are X_3, Y_3 1 and 0, and X_4, Y_4, Z_4 will be entered in Column 4, Rows 1, 2 and 3 when they have been calculated as explained below. The quantities to be entered in Column 5 will be the respective values of x, y, z and t satisfying Equations 2.6, and they will be derived by means of Equations 2.14 which are similar to Equations 2.4.

It is convenient to tabulate separately (in Table 2.5) the quantities obtained by dividing Column 1 of Table 2.4 by a_{11}, Column 2 by q_2, Column 3 by q_3, and so on; at this stage we only know the first three columns of Table 2.5 which gives the results of this division.

In Table 2.5 the number of rows and columns is the same as the number of unknowns; as Column 5 of Table 2.4 is the solution, we do not need to proceed further and divide by a quantity to be called q_5, though this would be done if there were more equations and unknowns. Finally, we construct Table 2.6, which also has the same number of rows and columns as there are unknowns; at this

Table 2.5. ELEMENTS OF TABLE 2.4 WITH FIRST COLUMN DIVIDED BY a_{11}, SECOND BY q_2, THIRD BY q_3, AND SO ON

Row No.	Column No. 1	Column No. 2	Column No. 3	Column No. 4
1	1	−0·087776	−0·515597	
2	0	1·007646	−0·157355	
3	0	0	1·244806	
4	0	0	0	

stage we can complete all of it except the number s_{45} in the bottom right-hand corner. Column 1 is the coefficients of the first of Equations 2.6 in order, including the number-term but omitting a_{11}, the coefficient of x. Column 2 has a zero in the first row (and zeros likewise occupy all places in which the column-number exceeds the row-number) but the remaining entries are the quantities we have already determined in Table 2.2 and labelled s_{23}, s_{24} and s_{25};

the non-zero elements of Column 3 of Table 2.6 are already determined in Table 2.3 and labelled s_{34}, s_{35}. Table 2.6 at this stage is thus

Table 2.6. ORDERLY ARRANGEMENT OF COEFFICIENTS OF EQUATION 2.6, AND THE QUANTITIES NAMED S_{23}, S_{34}, ETC.

Row No.	Column No. 1	Column No. 2	Column No. 3	Column No. 4
1	0·08711	0	0	0
2	0·42521	0·125450	0	0
3	0·37688	0·108110	0·737521	0
4	0·28009	0·207751	−0·554719	

and the point of this tabulation is that Equations 2.4 can be handled most easily by aligning a row of Table 2.6 with a row of Table 2.5, multiplying numbers in the same column of the two chosen rows, adding the results of these multiplications and changing the sign of the sum. This operation can be performed on a calculating machine without recording anything except the numbers in Tables 2.5 and 2.6 and the final answer, and when a number of divisions by the same divisor are required, as in the columns of Table 2.5, time can be saved by multiplying by the reciprocal of that divisor which is itself an entry in Table 2.5. Thus, to obtain X_3 take Row 2 of Table 2.6 with Row 1 of Table 2.5

$$- X_3 = 0{\cdot}42521 \times 1 + 0{\cdot}125450 \times (-0{\cdot}087776) \qquad (2.8)$$

and to obtain Y_3, take Row 2 of Table 2.6 with Row 2 of Table 2.5 so that

$$- Y_3 = 0{\cdot}42521 \times 0 + 0{\cdot}125450 \times (1{\cdot}007646) \qquad (2.9)$$

Similarly, to obtain X_4 take Row 3 of Table 2.6 with Row 1 of Table 2.5, so that

$$- X_4 = 0{\cdot}37688 \times 1 + 0{\cdot}108110 \times (-0{\cdot}087776)$$
$$+ 0.737521 \times (-0{\cdot}515597) \qquad (2.10)$$

X_4 is thus 0·012734.

To obtain Y_4, take Row 3 of Table 2.6 with Row 2 of Table 2.5 which gives

$$- Y_4 = 0{\cdot}108110 \times 1{\cdot}007646 + 0{\cdot}737521 \times (-0{\cdot}157355)$$
$$(2.11)$$

so that Y_4 is 0.007074. The row in Table 2.6 has the number one less than the suffix of the quantity sought, thus it is the third row when we seek X_4, Y_4 or Z_4 and the second when we seek X_3 or Y_3. The row in Table 2.5 is 1 if we seek an X, 2 if we seek a Y, 3 if we seek a Z, and so on.

Having obtained X_4, Y_4 and Z_4, we can complete Table 2.7, which is a continuation of Tables 2·2 and 2·3 so that the rows are numbered from 8 upwards.

As at the corresponding point of earlier stages, we now have powerful checks on the calculation. If the first three columns of Row 12 of Table 2.7 are not zero, there is an error in X_4, Y_4 or Z_4. The most likely cause of this is that s_{24} or s_{34} is wrong, since an error in X_3, Y_3, q_3 or s_{23} would have been detected at an earlier stage. There is also a check on the value of q_4 as indicated in Equations 2.5, namely

$$q_4 = a_{44} - \frac{a_{14}{}^2}{a_{11}} - \frac{s_{24}{}^2}{q_2} - \frac{s_{34}{}^2}{q_3} \qquad (2.12)$$

a_{44} being the coefficient of the fourth unknown t in the fourth equation. (Those familiar with determinants may like to know that the determinant of the coefficients of the unknowns of Equations 2.6 is $a_{11}q_2q_3q_4$.) The numerators of the terms in Equation 2.12 are in Row 3 of Table 2.6 just as those of the terms in Equation 2.7 are in Row 2 of Table 2.6; the relevant row number in Table 2.6 is one less than the suffix of the q concerned. The quantity s_{45} is next written in the blank space (Row 4, Column 4) of Table 2.6. We are now ready to calculate the solution, which is

$$x = X_5,\, y = Y_5,\, z = Z_5,\, t = T_5 \qquad (2.13)$$

where X_5, Y_5, Z_5 and T_5 are given by equations analogous to the last three of Equations 2.4, namely

$$\left. \begin{aligned} - X_5 &= (a_{15}/a_{11}) + (s_{25}X_2/q_2) + (s_{35}X_3/q_3) + (s_{45}X_4/q_4) \\ - Y_5 &= \qquad\qquad (s_{25}/q_2) + (s_{35}Y_3/q_3) + (s_{45}Y_4/q_4) \\ - Z_5 &= \qquad\qquad\qquad\qquad (s_{35}/q_3) + (s_{45}Z_4/q_4) \\ - T_5 &= \qquad\qquad\qquad\qquad\qquad\qquad (s_{45}/q_4) \end{aligned} \right\} \qquad (2.14)$$

a_{15} being the number-term in the first of Equations 2.6, here 0·28009. X_5, Y_5, Z_5 and T_5 can be obtained direct from Equations 2.14, but it simplifies the calculation and avoids errors to complete Table 2.4 by writing X_4, Y_4 and Z_4 in Column 4, and to complete

Table 2.7. THIRD STAGE OF 'ESCALATOR' TABULATIONS

Row No.	Column No. 1	Column No. 2	Column No. 3	Column No. 4	Column No. 5	Remarks
8	0·012734	0·001109	0·005415	0·004799	0·003567	Coefficients of the first of Equations 2.6 × X_4
9	0·000616	0·007074	0·001149	0·000997	0·001642	Coefficients of the second of Equations 2.6 × Y_4
10	−0·390230	−0·149123	−0·917734	−0·836212	0·375684	Coefficients of the third of Equations 2.6 × Z_4
11	0·37688	0·14094	0·91117	1	−0·26523	Coefficients of the fourth of Equations 2.6
12	0	0	0	0·169584 = q_4	0·118363 = s_{45}	Sum

Table 2.8. FINAL CHECK OF THE 'ESCALATOR' SOLUTION

Row No.	Column No. 1	Column No. 2	Column No. 3	Column No. 4	Column No. 5	Remarks
13	−0·556754	−0·048499	−0·236737	−0·209829	Not	Coefficients of the first of Equations 2.6 × X_5
14	−0·026269	−0·301564	−0·049001	−0·042502	Needed	Coefficients of the second of Equations 2.6 × Y_5
15	0·565980	0·216284	1·331061	1·212823		Coefficients of the third of Equations 2.6 × Z_5
16	−0·263048	−0·098371	−0·635961	−0·697961		Coefficients of the fourth of Equations 2.6 × T_5
17	0·28009	0·23215	−0·40936	−0·26253		Number terms
18	0	0	0	0		Sum

Table 2.5 by dividing these quantities by q_4 and putting the results

$$X_4/q_4 = 0.075090$$

$$Y_4/q_4 = 0.041714$$

$$Z_4/q_4 = -5.411677$$

in the first three rows of Column 4, and $1/q_4 = 5.896782$ in the fourth row. X_5, Y_5, Z_5 and T_5 are then obtained by multiplying elements of the fourth row of Table 2.6 (now completed with the value 0.118363 of s_{45} in the fourth column) in turn by corresponding elements of the first, second, third and fourth rows of Table 2.5 (in which there is now a fourth column as just explained) summing the products and reversing the sign. To check the final solution, it is easiest to complete the first four columns only of Table 2.8, which is a continuation of Tables 2.2, 2.3 and 2.7 so that the rows are numbered 13 to 18. The zeros in Row 18 are the final check: if they do not appear, the error is most likely to be in s_{25}, s_{35} or s_{45}, since errors in other quantities would have been detected earlier. Row 17 has the number-term of the first of Equations 2.6 in Column 1, that of the second in Column 2, and so on.

'NORMALISING' UNSYMMETRICAL EQUATIONS TO MAKE THEM SYMMETRICAL

Suppose that the original unsymmetrical equations are

$$\left.\begin{aligned} a_1x + b_1y + c_1z = d_1 \\ a_2x + b_2y + c_2z = d_2 \\ a_3x + b_3y + c_3z = d_3 \end{aligned}\right\}$$

Multiply each of these equations by the coefficient of x in that equation and add; the resulting equation is

$$(a_1{}^2 + a_2{}^2 + a_3{}^2)x + (a_1b_1 + a_2b_2 + a_3b_3)y + (a_1c_1 + a_2c_2 + a_3c_3)z$$
$$= a_1d_1 + a_2d_2 + a_3d_3$$

Now multiply each of the given equations by the coefficient of y in that equation and add, to obtain

$$(a_1b_1 + a_2b_2 + a_3b_3)x + (b_1{}^2 + b_2{}^2 + b_3{}^2)y + (b_1c_1 + b_2c_2 + b_3c_3)z$$
$$= b_1d_1 + b_2d_2 + b_3d_3$$

and, finally, multiply each of the given equations by the coefficient of z in that equation and add, to obtain

$$(a_1c_1 + a_2c_2 + a_3c_3)x + (b_1c_1 + b_2c_2 + b_3c_3)y + (c_1{}^2 + c_2{}^2 + c_3{}^2)z$$
$$= c_1d_1 + c_2d_2 + c_3d_3$$

and we have a symmetrical set equivalent to the original equations·

The 'Escalator' process described in the main text can be adapted[1] to unsymmetrical equations, but is simpler with symmetrical equations. It should, however, be noted that the checks on the arithmetic which have been explained are only effective on the assumption that the symmetrical equations are correctly derived. Although the process of derivation is straightforward, mistakes are easily made, and therefore the normalised equations must be very carefully checked in a numerical case before the 'Escalator' process is begun.

A SHORT CUT FOR A SPECIAL CASE

The 'Escalator' method of solving linear simultaneous equations just discussed is generally applicable to any numerical coefficients, but sometimes special relations between the coefficients make a short-cut possible.

We shall consider an illustrative example which is not in itself of great practical importance, but enables us to explain the labour-saving trick without unnecessary complications; thereafter it will be much easier to see how this trick can be applied more generally. Suppose therefore that we have a circuit in which the output current $I(t)$ satisfies the differential equation

$$\frac{\mathrm{d}^3I}{\mathrm{d}t^3} + 6\frac{\mathrm{d}^2I}{\mathrm{d}t^2} + 11\frac{\mathrm{d}I}{\mathrm{d}t} + 6I = 0 \ (t > 0) \tag{2.15}$$

and that we know that I has the value y_0, $\mathrm{d}I/\mathrm{d}t$ has the value y_1 and $\mathrm{d}^2I/\mathrm{d}t^2$ has the value y_2 when $t = 0$. We shall here adopt the classical approach, and ask no questions about how the circuit came to be in this condition. Our first duty is therefore to solve the 'auxiliary equation'

$$x^3 + 6x^2 + 11x + 6 = (x + 1)(x + 2)(x + 3) = 0 \tag{2.16}$$

and we thus know that the current $I(t)$ is of the form

$$I(t) = Ae^{-t} + Be^{-2t} + Ce^{-3t} \tag{2.17}$$

where A, B and C are arbitrary constants which have to be found from the initial conditions, so that we have to solve the linear simultaneous equations

$$\left.\begin{array}{l} A + B + C = y_0 \\ - A - 2B - 3C = y_1 \\ A + 4B + 9C = y_2 \end{array}\right\} \qquad (2.18)$$

This particular set of equations could be solved equally well by several different methods; the trick which follows, however, happens to be widely applicable. Multiply the first of Equations 2.18 by $\alpha\beta$, the second by $(\alpha + \beta)$ and add to the third. The coefficient of A becomes

$$\alpha\beta - (\alpha + \beta) + 1 = (1 - \alpha)(1 - \beta) \qquad (2.19a)$$

and the coefficient of B becomes

$$\alpha\beta - 2(\alpha + \beta) + 4 = (2 - \alpha)(2 - \beta) \qquad (2.19b)$$

and the coefficient of C becomes

$$\alpha\beta - 3(\alpha + \beta) + 9 = (3 - \alpha)(3 - \beta) \qquad (2.19c)$$

so that Equations 2.18 reduce to

$$A(1 - \alpha)(1 - \beta) + B(2 - \alpha)(2 - \beta) + C(3 - \alpha)(3 - \beta)$$
$$= y_0\alpha\beta + y_1(\alpha + \beta) + y_2 \qquad (2.20)$$

and Equation 2.20 is true whatever the values of α and β may be. Equation 2.20 will give us information about A only, if we can so choose α, β that the coefficients of B and C are both zero. This happens if we take $\alpha = 2$ and $\beta = 3$ (or $\alpha = 3$ and $\beta = 2$; we do not care which is which of α and β, so in what follows, permutation possibilities of this kind will be disregarded). Putting $\alpha = 2$ and $\beta = 3$ everywhere in Equation 2.20 we thus find

$$2A = 6y_0 + 5y_1 + y_2 \qquad (2.21)$$

Similarly, if we take $\alpha = 3$ and $\beta = 1$, the coefficients of A and C will both be zero in Equation 2.20 and we thus find

$$- B = 3y_0 + 4y_1 + y_2 \qquad (2.22)$$

Lastly, if we take $\alpha = 1$ and $\beta = 2$ in Equation 2.20, the coefficients of A and B are both zero, and we thus obtain

$$2C = 2y_0 + 3y_1 + y_2 \qquad (2.23)$$

It is easily verified that these values of A (Equation 2.21), B (Equation 2.22) and C (Equation 2.23) satisfy all of Equations 2.18, and of course exactly the same solution would be obtained if any other method of solution was used.

Now Equation 2.15 was deliberately chosen, for purposes of illustration, so that the corresponding 'auxiliary equation' Equation 2.16 had simple roots, but the method of solution does not depend for its effectiveness either on the simplicity of the roots of the 'auxiliary equation' Equation 2.16 or on the number of these roots. What makes the method effective is that in Equation 2.18, the ratio of the coefficient in any column on the left-hand side to the coefficient above it (or below it) is constant, and the constant arises in the example we have considered from the differentiation of an exponential. In the A-column of Equations 2.18 the constant multiplier in question is -1, in the B-column it is -2 and in the C-column it is -3. It is not an accident that -1, -2 and -3 are the roots of the 'auxiliary equation' Equation 2.16. Equations having essentially the same nature as Equations 2.18 are likely to occur frequently in connection with linear systems having 'lumped' elements, but there is no reason why the 'auxiliary equation', analogous to Equation 2.16, should be a cubic or have simple roots like -1, -2 and -3. We shall therefore next consider the solution of the simultaneous equations

$$\left.\begin{aligned}
A + B + C + D &= y_0 \\
Aa + Bb + Cc + Dd &= y_1 \\
Aa^2 + Bb^2 + Cc^2 + Dd^2 &= y_2 \\
Aa^3 + Bb^3 + Cc^3 + Dd^3 &= y_3
\end{aligned}\right\} \qquad (2.24)$$

which would arise in a linear system for which we knew that the current $I(t)$, instead of having the form of Equation 2.17, had the form

$$I(t) = Ae^{at} + Be^{bt} + Ce^{ct} + De^{dt} \qquad (2.25)$$

and a, b, c and d are perfectly general—there is no reason why some of them should not be complex conjugate pairs, though for a stable system they will have negative real parts. The principle on which we work is the same as before; it is only the detail that appears to be different. We first have to find a way of getting rid of unwanted arbitrary constants from the set A, B, C and D as effective as Equation 2.20. This is done by multiplying the first of Equations 2.24 by $\alpha\beta\gamma$, the second by $(\beta\gamma + \gamma\alpha + \alpha\beta)$, the third by $(\alpha + \beta + \gamma)$ and adding to the fourth. The coefficient of A is

$$\alpha\beta\gamma + a(\beta\gamma + \gamma\alpha + \alpha\beta) + a^2(\alpha + \beta + \gamma) + a^3$$
$$= (a + \alpha)(a + \beta)(a + \gamma) \qquad (2.26)$$

and the coefficients of B, C and D are similar expressions in which b, c and d are successively substituted for a. It follows that

$$A(a + \alpha)(a + \beta)(a + \gamma) + B(b + \alpha)(b + \beta)(b + \gamma)$$
$$+ C(c + \alpha)(c + \beta)(c + \gamma) + D(d + \alpha)(d + \beta)(d + \gamma)$$
$$= \alpha\beta\gamma y_0 + (\beta\gamma + \gamma\alpha + \alpha\beta)y_1 + (\alpha + \beta + \gamma)y_2 + y_3 \qquad (2.27)$$

and that Equation 2.27 is true for all values whatsoever of a, b, c, d, α, β and γ. To obtain A, we put $\alpha = -b$, $\beta = -c$, and $\gamma = -d$; this makes a clean sweep of the B, C and D terms on the left-hand side of Equation 2.27 and leaves us with the value of A, namely

$$A = \frac{y_3 - (b + c + d)y_2 + (cd + db + bc)y_1 - bcdy_0}{(a - b)(a - c)(a - d)} \qquad (2.28)$$

A similar expression can be obtained for B by putting $\alpha = -c$, $\beta = -d$, and $\gamma = -a$; for C by putting $\alpha = -d$, $\beta = -a$ and $\gamma = -b$ and for D by putting $\alpha = -a$, $\beta = -b$ and $\gamma = -c$ in Equation 2.27. Once again, it must be emphasised that Equation 2.28 and the similar expressions for the other quantities B, C and D are valid whatever the values of a, b, c and d may be.

FEAR NOT 'BOUNDARY CASES'

If any two of a, b, c and d are exactly equal, we look like running into trouble with Equation 2.28, but it should be carefully noted that, in practice two quantities like a, b, c, d in the above context may be 'metrically' equal, differing by a small quantity, but will not be exactly equal. If two of a, b, c, d, say a and b, are close together, then Equation 2.28 shows that A will be large. The corresponding expression for B in such a case will be found to be nearly equal and opposite to A, whereas C and D will not be abnormally large. It may therefore be possible to express $I(t)$ in Equation 2.25 in an alternative form from which the large parts of A and B have been cancelled, leaving residual terms of normal size which seem to be of an unusual type. Although this is usually done in textbooks, we suggest that it is not really worth doing. Suppose, for example

$$y_0 = y_1 = y_2 = 0, a = -1, b = -1 \cdot 01, c = -2, d = -3$$

$$(2.29)$$

Then from Equation 2.28 the A-term of Equation 2.25 is $50y_3 \, e^{-t}$ and the B-term is similarly $-50 \cdot 759 y_3 \, e^{-1 \cdot 01 t}$; these two terms can be combined to yield

$$50 y_3 \, e^{-t} [1 - 1 \cdot 0152 e^{-0 \cdot 01 t}] \qquad (2.30)$$

As long as t is small compared with 100 (but not necessarily small compared with unity) the term $e^{-0.01t}$ can be satisfactorily replaced by $(1 - 0 \cdot 01 t)$, and we thus can replace expression 2.30 by

$$y_3 \, e^{-t} (0 \cdot 508 t - 0 \cdot 759) \qquad (2.31)$$

and this is the type of result usually given in textbooks on the assumption that the quantities a and b are exactly equal. In the C and D terms, no serious error will be committed by taking a and b as both equal to -1; the reason for this is that in these terms the expression $(a - b)$ does not occur in the denominator. This means that there is no critical comparison. To sum up, we have shown that in this special but typical case, Equation 2.30 is equivalent to Equation 2.31 for times likely to be of interest (since when $t = 20$ all the terms of I in Equation 2.25 are negligible, and 20 is still small compared with 100). Equation 2.30 can be obtained by the general procedure of using Equation 2.28 as when all of the quantities a, b, c and d are appreciably different, but has the disadvantage that it contains two large terms which are nearly equal and opposite. In Equation 2.31, there are no abnormally large terms, but one is left with the false impression that the case in which two of the quantities a, b, c and d are very close together is radically different from the case in which they are not. The balance of advantage surely lies in doing away with special cases, and putting up with the fact that large terms nearly equal and opposite may then occasionally have to be watched and handled with special care.

It appears to be something of a disadvantage that the expressions like $(bc + cd + db)$ which occur in Equation 2.28 and similar expressions may be somewhat tedious to calculate when some or all of the quantities a, b, c and d are complex. But here again, there is a short cut.

In our original example, the quantities corresponding to a, b, c

and d in Equation 2.24 were the numbers -1, -2 and -3 which arose as the roots of the 'auxiliary equation' Equation 2.16. Equation 2.16 was deliberately chosen to have nice, simple roots for purposes of illustration, but in practice the auxiliary equation itself will always look nice and simple, even if its roots are complex and require careful calculation. Let us therefore suppose that the auxiliary equation, whose roots we have called a, b, c and d, in the more general example discussed from Equation 2.24 onwards, is

$$x^4 + q_3x^3 + q_2x^2 + q_1x + q_0 = 0 \qquad (2.32)$$

Then if we divide the left-hand side of Equation 2.32 by $(x - a)$, there should only be a very small remainder if a is calculated accurately, and the quotient is a cubic expression in x. The coefficient of x^2 in this quotient is equal to $-(b + c + d)$, the coefficient of x is $(cd + db + bc)$ and the number term is $-bcd$, and these are just the expressions that turn up in Equation 2.28 if the denominator is multiplied out in descending powers of a. Similarly, we can divide the left-hand side of Equation 2.32 by $(x - b)$ to get the expressions that turn up in the equation for B corresponding to Equation 2.28 and so on.

Division directly by $(x - a)$ is quite straightforward if a is real. If a is complex, and a^* is its conjugate, division by $(x - a)$ is equivalent to multiplication by $(x - a^*)$, followed by division by the real quadratic divisor $x^2 - (a + a^*)x + aa^*$; it is thus rather more tedious, but still possible, as explained in Chapter 7.

In general, the 'Escalator' method discussed in the earlier part of this chapter is recommended for the solution of numerical linear simultaneous equations, but equations of the special type considered in Equation 2.24 occur quite frequently enough (especially in connection with linear systems having lumped elements) to justify the intensive search carried out here for special labour-saving devices.

Chapter 3

SOLUTION OF
ALGEBRAIC EQUATIONS

In almost any problem there may be a requirement to solve an
algebraic equation. If the degree of the equation is 1 or 2, this is
quite straightforward. Equations of very high degree (say 10 or
more) should be at least discussed with a mathematician, but it is
much more possible than is usually realised for the engineer whose
interest is mainly practical to deal with equations of moderate
degree, say up to 6 or 7. Three main methods of attack will be
discussed in this chapter. First, we consider a special but important
case, when the equation is of the form

$$x^n = N \tag{3.1}$$

and this is followed by a discussion of the 'root-locus method'[4]
which can in principle be carried out graphically and is applicable
to equations of any degree, whether the roots are real or complex.
The author considers that the 'root-locus method', which was
invented to meet the needs of servomechanism engineers rather than
mathematicians, is supreme in giving a means of locating complex
roots roughly. In many cases it alone will be quite sufficient to
determine the roots accurately enough for practical purposes. In
the later part of the chapter, however, iterative processes are discussed, by means of which a starting approximation to the root of
an equation which is 'in the right street' can be improved. The
main emphasis is on Lin's[2] iterative process, not so much because
from the mathematical specialist's point of view it is necessarily the
best but because it is successful in almost all cases not deliberately
concocted to be awkward (when the properties of the successive
approximations are fully exploited, as will be explained) and the

24

computational processes to be carried out are easy to understand. The effectiveness of Lin's process is greatly increased if we have initially a rough idea of the location of the roots, and this is obtainable by the 'root-locus' method as already indicated.

EXTRACTION OF ROOTS

Let us therefore start by considering Equation 3.1. It may be suggested that in this simple case a slide-rule or tables of logarithms are all that is needed, but it sometimes happens that we need to know the solution of Equation 3.1 to a greater degree of accuracy than is easily provided by such means. Suppose that the true solution of Equation 3.1 is $x = a + \xi$, where ξ is small compared to a, so that a is a good approximation, such as would be provided by slide-rule or logarithm tables. Then a better approximation is b given by the formula

$$b = \frac{1}{n}\left\{(n-1)a + \frac{N}{a^{n-1}}\right\} \tag{3.2}$$

which can easily be evaluated with or without a desk calculating machine.

For example, if $n = 2$ and $N = 2$, and we start with 1·4 as an approximation to $\sqrt{2}$, so that $a = 1\cdot4$ in Equation 3.2, the next approximation b_1 is

$$b_1 = \frac{1}{2}\left\{1\cdot4 + \frac{2}{1\cdot4}\right\}$$

$$= \tfrac{1}{2}\{1\cdot4 + 1\cdot428571..\}$$

$$= 1\cdot41429$$

which agrees with the value 1·4142 given in five-figure tables with an error of only 1 in the fifth significant figure. If we now put 1·41429 for a in Equation 3.2 and repeat the process, we find that the next approximation b_2 is

$$b_2 = \frac{1}{2}\left\{1\cdot41429 + \frac{2}{1\cdot41429}\right\}$$

$$= \tfrac{1}{2}\{1\cdot41429 + 1\cdot41413713\}$$

$$= 1\cdot414213565$$

and $b_2{}^2 = 2\cdot0000000074.$

3

Again, if we require $\sqrt[6]{800}$, and start with the crude approximation $a = 3$ (since $3^6 = 729$), we find from Equation 3.2 with $n = 6$, $a = 3$ and $N = 800$ that the first approximation b_1 is given by

$$b_1 = \frac{1}{6}\left\{5 \times 3 + \frac{800}{243}\right\} = \frac{1}{6}[18\cdot29218] = 3\cdot048697$$

Repeating the process with $a = 3\cdot048697$, we find

$$a^6 = 802\cdot944596; \quad a^5 = 263\cdot373040; \quad b_2 = 3\cdot046834$$

and

$$(3\cdot046834)^6 = 800\cdot0051.$$

Thus the second approximation b_2 is such that $b_2{}^6$ is in error by about 1 part in 160,000, and b_2 is therefore in error by about $\frac{1}{6}$ of this, say 1 in 10^6. Our starting approximation was here quite crude, and an approximation at least as good can be obtained by means of a table of higher powers of integers up to 100, which is included, for example, in Attwood's[3] 5-figure tables on p. 52.

The proof of Equation 3.2 depends on the binomial theorem, which will be discussed in more detail in Chapter 4. Here it is sufficient to say that if as we have supposed the true value of $\sqrt[n]{N}$ is $(a + \xi)$ where a is the starting approximation, the expression on the right-hand side of Equation 3.2 reduces to

$$b \approx (a + \xi) + (n - 1)\xi^2/2a \tag{3.3}$$

so that the absolute error is $(n - 1)\xi^2/2a$, and is an overestimate if $n > 1$. This means that roughly speaking b in Equation 3.2 is accurate to twice as many significant figures as a.

In Equation 3.2 there is actually no need for n to be an integer or for n to be positive; we could therefore put $n = 1\cdot5$ in Equation 3.2 to obtain $N^{2/3}$ or $n = -4$ in Equation 3.2 to obtain $N^{-\frac{1}{4}}$. Clearly it is an advantage to start with a good approximation for a, but the penalty for failure to do so is merely that we may have to repeat the process one or two extra times.

For example, to calculate $\pi^{2/3}$, we note that $1\cdot4^3 = 2\cdot744$ and $1\cdot5^3 = 3\cdot375$, so $\sqrt[3]{\pi}$ is about $1\cdot47$ and we can thus start with $a = 3\cdot142/1\cdot47 = 2\cdot14$ and $n = 1\cdot5$. We thus find the second approximation b_1 is given from Equation 3.2 by

$$b_1 = \frac{2}{3}\left\{\frac{2\cdot14}{2} + \frac{3\cdot14159265}{\sqrt{2\cdot14}}\right\} \tag{3.4}$$

We can obtain $\sqrt{2\cdot14}$ sufficiently accurately from tables at this stage; if necessary Equation 3.2 can be applied, starting with $n = 2$, $N = 2\cdot14$ and $a = 1\cdot46$, say. This gives a second approximation $1\cdot462877$ to $\sqrt{2\cdot14}$, and $(1\cdot462877)^2 = 2.1400091$. Substituting into Equation 3.4 gives $b_1 = 2\cdot145029$, which is correct to 6 places. Alternatively, we could have calculated $\pi^{1/3}$ from Equation 3.2 with $N = \pi$, $n = 3$ and $a = 1\cdot47$ and squared the result; in this particular case putting $n = 1\cdot5$ as above appears to be superior.

To obtain $e^{-1/4}$, we note that $1\cdot2^4 = 2\cdot0736$; $1\cdot3^4 = 2\cdot8561$ so that $e^{1/4}$ is about $1\cdot28$; we can thus take a as $1/1\cdot28 = 0\cdot781$. We have $N = 2\cdot71828183$ and $n = -4$, so that Equation 3.2 gives the second approximation b as $0\cdot778785$, whereas the correct value of $e^{-1/4}$ is $0\cdot778801$.

THE ROOT-LOCUS METHOD: GENERAL IDEAS

We now come to consider the general algebraic equation of degree n, say, for which the special tricks already discussed are not available.

In the above discussion we only considered the real root, say r, of Equation 3.2; the equation has n roots altogether, namely

$$r, \; re^{j2\pi/n}, \; re^{j4\pi/n}, \; \ldots \; re^{j(2n-2)\pi/n}$$

so that if we have an equation in which the x^n term and the number term (say a_0) are much more important than any of the intermediate terms, we know that the roots are roughly equally spaced round a circle of radius $|a_0|^{1/n}$. In practice, however, we do not often encounter equations where the location of the roots is as obvious as this, and we therefore have to find a clue as to their whereabouts in the general case.

If the equation to be solved is of even degree, say

$$p^{2n} + a_{2n-1}p^{2n-1} + a_{2n-2}p^{2n-2} + \ldots + a_2p^2 + a_1p + a_0 = 0$$
$$(3.5)$$

one possible procedure is to divide through by the terms of even degree and write it in the form

$$1 + \frac{p[a_{2n-1}p^{2n-2} + a_{2n-3}p^{2n-4} + \ldots + a_3p^2 + a_1]}{p^{2n} + a_{2n-2}p^{2n-2} + a_{2n-4}p^{2n-4} + \ldots + a_2p^2 + a_0} = 0$$
$$(3.6)$$

so that Equation 3.6 is in the form

$$1 + K\frac{N(p)}{D(p)} = 0 \quad (K \text{ constant}) \tag{3.7}$$

for which the 'root-locus method' is specifically designed. Division by the even-degree terms is not the only way of reducing Equation 3.5 to the form 3.7, and in feedback problems the form 3.7 arises naturally.

As far as the root-locus method to be discussed is concerned, it does not very much matter how the equation is reduced to the form 3.7; what matters is how we proceed having got the form 3.7. In what follows, we shall assume that we know the factors of $N(p)$ and $D(p)$, as we do in all the examples discussed. In the worst possible case, when we are given Equation 3.5 'out of the blue', without any knowledge of how it was derived so that there is no obvious way of getting it into the form 3.7 except via Equation 3.6, it must be noted that the numerator and denominator of Equation 3.6 contain only even powers of p (apart from the factor p outside the numerator). They are thus effectively of about half the degree of the original equation. Furthermore, if Equation 3.5 is associated with a stable system, and is thus free from roots with positive real parts, we shall see (in Chapter 13) that both the numerator and denominator of Equation 3.6 must have only real roots in p^2. Now real roots can always be located approximately by drawing a graph, so that even in this worst case we are better off with Equation 3.6 than the original Equation 3.5.

In the above discussion we only assumed that the equation was of even degree for clarity; if it is of odd degree, $2n + 1$ we divide through by the terms of odd degree and Equation 3.6 is replaced by

$$1 + \frac{a_{2n}p^{2n} + a_{2n-2}p^{2n-2} + \ldots + a_2p^2 + a_0}{p[p^{2n} + a_{2n-1}p^{2n-2} + a_{2n-3}p^{2n-4} + \ldots + a_3p^2 + a_1]} = 0 \tag{3.8}$$

and this is still of the required form 3.7, but the factor p is now outside the denominator instead of the numerator. As an equation of odd degree always has one real root, it is always possible to locate this root graphically and if necessary improve the approximation by the iterative procedure discussed later, and then divide out the corresponding factor, leaving a residual equation of even degree. It will therefore simplify the argument if we confine our attention to equations of even degree when discussing matters concerning algebraic equations in general, though specific numerical examples may have either odd or even degrees.

THE ROOT-LOCUS METHOD: A CUBIC EXAMPLE

The 'root-locus method', devised by servomechanism engineers to solve feedback problems which naturally gave rise to equations of the form 3.7, is essentially a way of finding the roots of Equation 3.7 assuming that those of $N(p) = 0$ (called *zeros*) and those of $D(p) = 0$ (called *poles*) are known. The method is discussed fully by Savant[4]. The procedure is most easily explained in terms of specific examples, so we shall begin with the case in which Equation 3.7 has to be solved with

$$\left. \begin{array}{l} N(p) = p + 2 \\ D(p) = (p + 4)\,(p + 3 + j5)\,(p + 3 - j5) \end{array} \right\} \quad (3.9)$$

so that there is one zero $-2 + j0$, and three poles $-4 + j0$ and $-3 \pm j5$. These are first plotted as in Fig. 3.1; it is customary to indicate a pole by a cross on the point and a zero by a circle round it. The same scale must be used along the horizontal or α–axis as up and down the vertical or ω–axis. Now let X or $\alpha + j\omega$ be any other point, so that in Fig. 3.1 α is negative and ω positive. Then if X is joined to Z, and $XZ = r$ and $\angle OZX = \phi$, we have

$$\alpha - (-2) + j\omega = re^{j\phi} \quad (3.10)$$

If X is also joined to the poles, and these are at distances R_1, R_2, R_3 and in directions determined by θ_1, θ_2, and θ_3 as indicated in Fig. 3.1, we also have

$$\left. \begin{array}{l} \alpha - (-5) + j\omega = R_1 e^{j\theta_1} \\ \alpha - (-3) + j(\omega - 5) = R_2 e^{j\theta_2} \\ \alpha - (-3) + j(\omega - (-5)] = R_3 e^{j\theta_3} \end{array} \right\} \quad (3.11)$$

and therefore, if $(\alpha + j\omega)$ is substituted for p in Equations 3.9

$$\left. \begin{array}{l} \text{magnitude of } K(N(p)/D(p)) = Kr/R_1 R_2 R_3 \\ \text{phase of } K(N(p)/D(p)) \quad = \phi - \theta_1 - \theta_2 - \theta_3 \end{array} \right\} \quad (3.12)$$

If the point X corresponds to a root of Equation 3.7 the magnitude of $K(N(p)/D(p))$ must be unity and its phase must be an odd multiple of 180° when $\alpha + j\omega$ is substituted for p. We therefore have

$$\theta_1 + \theta_2 + \theta_3 - \phi = \text{odd multiple of } 180° \qquad (3.13)$$

$$K = R_1 R_2 R_3 / r \qquad (3.14)$$

Now the 'root locus' is the locus of points X such that Equation 3.13 is true, and the essential point of the root-locus method is

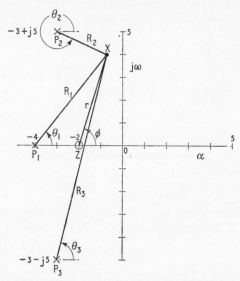

Fig. 3.1. Poles and zeros associated with Equations 3.7 and 3.9, together with a typical point X or $\alpha + j\omega$ (α negative)

that this locus is independent of K. We have to find positions of X on this locus first, which can be done by trial and error, and only when we have found them do we need to bother about whether the corresponding value of K given by Equation 3.14 is correct. Points on the 'root-locus' can be found by measurement of the distances and angles in Fig. 3.1 if we wish, or by calculation if we prefer it or need accuracy greater than that obtainable by plotting and measurement.

The easiest points of the root-locus to find are those for which X is on the real or α–axis. At such points the angles θ_2 and θ_3 will necessarily add up to zero (or 360°) so that Equation 3.13 effectively reduces to the fact that ($\phi - \theta_1$) is an odd multiple of 180°. Now if X is on the real axis to the left of P_1, both ϕ and θ_1 will be 180°, and if X is to the right of Z and on the real axis, both ϕ and θ_1 will be zero, so X can only be on the real axis between P_1 and Z, when θ_1 is zero but ϕ is 180°. In fact, the portion P_1Z is a complete branch of the root-locus; if K is small, there will be a root near P_1 while if K is large, there will be a root near Z.

Since when $K = 0$ there is a root at P_2, there must be a branch of the root locus starting at P_2, and our next task is to find out what happens to this branch. If X is near P_2, θ_2 will be very sensitive to small variations in the position of X, but the angles θ_1, θ_3 and ϕ_3 will differ little from their values when X is actually at P_2, namely $\theta_1 = \tan^{-1} 5 = 78°41'$; $\theta_3 = 90°$ and $\phi_1 = 180° - \tan^{-1} 5 = 101°19'$. Hence from Equation 3.13, the branch beginning at P_2 leaves P_2 so that $\theta_2 = 112°38'$. Further, if X is a long way off in a direction making an angle θ with the real axis $O\alpha$, then θ_1, θ_2, θ_3 and ϕ will all be equal to θ, and therefore to satisfy Equation 3.13 we must have $\theta = 90°$ or 270°. The branch of the root-locus which starts at P_2 therefore goes to infinity along an asymptote which is parallel to the imaginary or ω–axis. More accurately, if X is a long way off in the direction of the imaginary axis,

$$\tan \theta_1 = \omega/(\alpha + 4)$$

and for large ω this means that θ_1 is

$$90° - \tan^{-1}\{(\alpha + 4)/\omega\}$$

or

$$\{90 - 180(\alpha + 4)/\pi\omega\}$$

degrees. Similarly,

$$\tan \theta_2 = (\omega - 5)/(\alpha + 3)$$

and for large ω this means that θ_2 is

$$90 - \{180(\alpha + 3)/\pi(\omega - 5)\}$$

degrees, and likewise θ_3 is

$$90 - \{180(\alpha + 3)/\pi(\omega + 5)\}$$

degrees, and ϕ is

$$90 - \{180(\alpha + 2)/\pi\omega\} \text{ degrees.}$$

If we neglect $1/\omega$ altogether, we obtain the result we have already had, that X must go to infinity parallel to the imaginary axis; if however, we retain $1/\omega$ but neglect $1/\omega^2$, which means that in the denominators of the above expressions for θ_1, θ_2, θ_3 and ϕ we regard ω, $\omega + 5$ and $\omega - 5$ as all equal to ω, we find that to satisfy Equation 3.13

$$\frac{180}{\pi\omega}\ [(\alpha + 4) + (\alpha + 3) + (\alpha + 3) - (\alpha + 2)] = 0 \qquad (3.15)$$

so that α is -4. Hence the branch of the root-locus beginning at P_2 glides on to an asymptote parallel to the imaginary or ω–axis

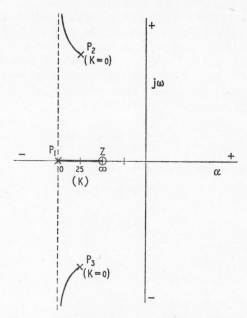

Fig. 3.2. *Rough sketch of root-locus associated with Equations 3.9 and 3.7*

and a distance 4 to the left of it. (The fact that this asymptote goes through P_1 is an accident.) The complete root-locus is therefore as in Fig. 3.2. In this case there is no point in taking much trouble to determine any additional points, but if it was for any reason necessary to do so, α can be taken to have successive values say $-3\cdot3$ and $-3\cdot6$ and the corresponding values of ω for X to be on the root-locus can then be found by trial and error. If $\alpha = -3\cdot3$, we know that ω must be somewhat greater than $5 + [\alpha - (-3)] \times \tan 112°38' = 5\cdot72$, since the branch of the root-locus we are considering starts from $-3 + j5$ at the angle $112°38'$ and ends at $-4 + j\infty$ and is therefore concave upwards. We therefore start with a trial value $\omega = 5\cdot8$, in which case

$$\left.\begin{array}{l} \theta_1 = 83°7' \ \theta_2 = 110°33' \ \theta_3 = 91°35' \ \phi = 102°38' \\ \theta_1 + \theta_2 + \theta_3 - \phi = 182°37' \end{array}\right\} \qquad (3.16)$$

and the correct value of ω is in fact very close to $5\cdot95$, for when $\omega = 5\cdot95$, $\theta_1 + \theta_2 + \theta_3 - \phi = 180°3'$. It is quite sufficient to obtain ω within say $\pm 0\cdot1$ by measurement, because at this stage we only need to know the salient features of the root-locus.

The complete root-locus for the case of Equation 3.9 is thus as in Fig. 3.2. We already know that the branches begin at the poles when $K = 0$ and end at the zero Z or at infinity when K is large; if we require to know more accurately the value of K at any other point of the root-locus, we can obtain it from Equation 3.14, and graphical accuracy will be sufficient. It is much easier to choose a point of the root-locus and determine K from Equation 3.14 than to choose K and determine the corresponding root. If therefore what we really require is the approximate value of the root associated with a particular value K_0 of K, on a particular branch, we can find a point X_1 on that branch where K is slightly less than K_0, and another where K is slightly greater than K_0 and then interpolate graphically between them.

In this particular case, the equation 3.7 was only cubic in p, and therefore an alternative procedure was possible, namely to choose a real negative value of p between -2 and -4 (which we already know is on the locus), determine the corresponding value of K (by calculation) from Equation 3.14, and then we have only a quadratic equation to solve to find the remaining two roots associated with the same K. Thus if we take $p = -3$, $R_1 = 1$, $R_2 = R_3 = 5$ and $r = 1$, so that $K = 25$. Hence

$$1 + K(N(p)/D(p)) = 1 + 25 \frac{(p+2)}{(p+4)[(p+3)^2 + 5^2]} \qquad (3.17)$$

so that the equation we actually have to solve for the roots is

$$(p+4)(p^2 + 6p + 34) + 25(p+2) = 0 \qquad (3.18)$$

knowing that one of the roots is $p = -3$. In fact

$$(p + 4)(p^2 + 6p + 34) + 25(p + 2) = p^3 + 10p^2 + 83p + 186$$
$$= (p + 3)(p^2 + 7p + 62) \qquad (3.19)$$

so that the remaining two roots for $K = 25$ are $-3 \cdot 5 \pm j7 \cdot 0534$. But the root-locus method is available whatever the degrees of $N(p)$ and $D(p)$ may be, whereas the method just described would not work if the Equation (3.7) was of high degree, and especially if most of the roots were complex.

ANOTHER TYPICAL CUBIC EXAMPLE

The above example does not have all the features which commonly occur, so we next consider the case in which

$$N(p) = 1 \quad D(p) = (p + 1)(p + 2)(p + 5) \qquad (3.20)$$

There are therefore no zeros, and three poles at -1, -2 and -5 respectively; if these are plotted in Fig. 3.3 and X or $\alpha + j\omega$ is any point of the root-locus, and X is joined to the three poles so that $XP_1 = R_1$ and XP_1 makes an angle θ_1 with the positive direction $O\alpha$ in the sense indicated by the arrow and R_2, θ_2, R_3, θ_3 are defined similarly, we have, as the condition for X to be on the root-locus

$$\theta_1 + \theta_2 + \theta_3 = 180° \qquad (3.21)$$

$$R_1 R_2 R_3 = K \qquad (3.22)$$

If, as before, we first seek places where X can be on the real or α–axis, it is clear that X can either be to the left of P_3 (θ_1, θ_2 and θ_3 all 180°), or between P_1 and P_2 ($\theta_1 = 180°$ and $\theta_2 = \theta_3 = 0°$). But this example differs from the previous example because P_1 and P_2 are both poles, whereas there the corresponding limited portion of the real axis went from a pole to a zero. Now suppose that X is at $-1 - x + j0$ where x is between 0 and 1. Then we have

$$K = R_1 R_2 R_3 = x(1 - x)(4 - x) \qquad (3.23)$$

and this expression is zero for $x = 0$ and for $x = 1$ and positive for all values of x in between. It therefore has a maximum, which is easily found to be $0 \cdot 8794$ for $x = 0 \cdot 4648$. If therefore K is between 0 and $0 \cdot 8794$, there will be one root between -1 and $-1 \cdot 4648$ and a second between $-1 \cdot 4648$ and -2; as K increases these two roots will approach each other along the real or α-axis until when K reaches the 'breakaway value' 0·8794, the two roots coincide at the 'breakaway point' $-1\cdot4648 + \text{j}0$. In fact, when K has the 'breakaway value',

$$D(p) + KN(p) = p^3 + 8p^2 + 17p + 10\cdot8794$$
$$= (p + 1\cdot4648)^2\,(p + 5\cdot0704) \qquad (3.24)$$

and this squared factor in Equation 3.24 is not an accident but an asset, of which good use can be made to determine roughly the position of the breakaway point in more difficult cases, as will be explained later. The important point to notice immediately, however, is that if K is increased beyond the 'breakaway value', the root-locus leaves the real axis at the breakaway point at right angles. To find what happens to it after that, we can find by trial and error a root for which $\alpha = -1\cdot7$ or $-1\cdot3$, say, but it will save much vain searching for roots in unpromising areas if we first consider, as in the preceding section, what happens when X is a long way off in direction θ, so that $\theta_1 = \theta_2 = \theta_3 = \theta$. To satisfy Equation 3.21, θ must either be $\pm\ 60°$ or $180°$. If θ is $180°$, this simply means that the corresponding root is real and negative, and that the whole of the real or α-axis to the left of P_3 is part of the root-locus. As however θ can also be $\pm\ 60°$, there is an asympote of the root-locus making $60°$ with the real axis. In our last example the asymptote was parallel to the imaginary axis, and we were easily able to find its actual position by taking $1/\omega$-terms into account and neglecting $1/\omega^2$-terms in that case. In our present case it is in fact possible to turn the whole diagram of Fig. 3.3 anticlockwise through $30°$ and apply a similar argument, but the resulting rule is so simple that it is not worth doing more than quoting it and noting that a proof is given by C. J. Savant[4]. Asymptotes always go through the 'centre of gravity', that is to say, the point $G + \text{j}0$ determined by the expression

$$G = \frac{(\text{sum of poles}) - (\text{sum of zeros})}{(\text{number of poles}) - (\text{number of zeros})} \qquad (3.25)$$

so that in our case $G = -2\frac{2}{3}$. As complex zeros and poles occur in conjugate pairs, G is always on the real axis.

Since there is an asymptote making $60°$ with the real axis, it is clear that for large values of K, there must be roots to the right of the imaginary axis, and therefore there must be a place where the root-locus crosses the imaginary axis, which will be of critical importance in relation to stability. Further, it must be the upper branch of the root-locus that breaks away from the real axis at $-1.4648 + j0$, joins this asymptote and crosses the imaginary axis eventually; this branch therefore curves to the right and it is useless to look for a complex root with real part -1.7 but there will be a complex root with real part -1.3. Actually, in this particular case, there is no need to use trial and error to find the imaginary part associated with a complex root having given real part, for if $\alpha + j\omega$ is the complex root we are seeking,

$$0 = \tan (\theta_1 + \theta_2 + \theta_3)$$

$$= \frac{\tan \theta_1 + \tan \theta_2 + \tan \theta_3 - \tan \theta_1 \tan \theta_2 \tan \theta_3}{1 - \tan \theta_2 \tan \theta_3 - \tan \theta_3 \tan \theta_1 - \tan \theta_1 \tan \theta_2} \qquad (3.26)$$

and therefore the numerator of the last member of Equation 3.26 is zero, which gives

$$\frac{\omega}{\alpha + 1} + \frac{\omega}{\alpha + 2} + \frac{\omega}{\alpha + 5} = \frac{\omega^3}{(\alpha + 1)(\alpha + 2)(\alpha + 5)} \qquad (3.27)$$

so that, as $\omega \neq 0$ for the complex root,

$$\left.\begin{aligned}
\omega^2 &= (\alpha + 2)(\alpha + 5) + (\alpha + 5)(\alpha + 1) + (\alpha + 1)(\alpha + 2) \\
&= 3\alpha^2 + 16\alpha + 17 \\
&= 3(\alpha + 1.4648)(\alpha + 3.86853)
\end{aligned}\right\} \qquad (3.28)$$

This checks that $\omega = 0$ at the breakaway point $-1.4648 + j0$. The fact that $\omega^2 = 0$ when $\alpha = -3.86853$ is irrelevant; although this value genuinely satisfies Equation 3.26, the value of $\theta_1 + \theta_2 + \theta_3$ is there not $180°$ but zero. In particular Equation 3.28 shows that $\omega^2 = 17$ when $\alpha = 0$, and we reach the borderline of instability. From Equation 3.22, the corresponding value of K is $(18 \times 21 \times 42)^{\frac{1}{2}}$ or 126. This checks with the fact that when Equation 3.7 (with $N(p)$ and $D(p)$ given by Equation 3.20) is cleared of fractions, it becomes

$$p^3 + 8p^2 + 17p + (10 + K) = 0 \qquad (3.29)$$

and it is well known that for critical stability (that is, a purely imaginary root) in the case of a cubic equation, the condition is that the product of the coefficients of p and p^2 must equal the product of the coefficient of p^3 and the number term. This confirms that the critical value of K is 126 in the case of Equation 3.29.

More generally, if $N(p)$ is 1, but $D(p)$ is

$$(1 + pT_1)\,(1 + pT_2)\,(1 + pT_3)$$

instead of as in Equation 3.20, the critical value of K is

$$T_2/T_3 + T_3/T_2 + T_3/T_1 + T_1/T_3 + T_1/T_2 + T_2/T_1 + 2 \qquad (3.30)$$

so that, if the main consideration is to make the expression 3.30 as large as possible, T_1 and T_2 should be made nearly equal and T_3 should be very different—many times larger or smaller than T_1 and T_2.

As Equation 3.29 is only a cubic, we can easily obtain a formula for the value of K when we know the real part α of a root; when this formula is combined with Equation 3.28 it means that in this particular case (or indeed any case where the roots are given by a cubic equation) we do not in fact need to use trial and error to determine the root-locus or any part of it. But the root-locus trial-and-error technique is available whatever the degree of the equation giving the root whereas a formula for the value of K in

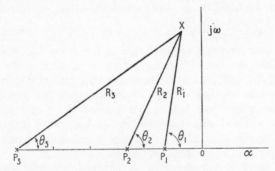

Fig. 3.3. A general point of the root-locus associated with Equations 3.20 and 3.7, and its relation to the poles

terms of α rapidly becomes more difficult to obtain as the degree of the equation rises.

If in Equation 3.29, there are two conjugate complex roots $\alpha + j\omega$ and $\alpha - j\omega$, the third root is $-8 + 2\alpha$, since the sum of the three roots must be -8, that is, minus the ratio of the coefficient of p^2 to that of p^3. Hence the factors of the left-hand side of Equation 3.29 must be

$$[p^2 - 2\alpha p + (\alpha^2 + \omega^2)] [p + 8 + 2\alpha] \qquad (3.34)$$

It follows, by equating coefficients of p and the constant terms, that

$$\alpha^2 + \omega^2 - 2\alpha(8 + 2\alpha) = 17 \qquad (3.35)$$

$$\alpha^2 + \omega^2 = (10 + K)/(8 + 2\alpha) \qquad (3.36)$$

and, substituting for ω^2 from Equation 3.36 into Equation 3.35 and rearranging, we thus find

$$K = 126 + 162\alpha + 64\alpha^2 + 8\alpha^3 \qquad (3.37)$$

A rough diagram of the root-locus is given in Fig. 3·4.

ROOT-LOCUS METHOD: GENERAL RULES

It now remains to express the ideas we have used to determine the positions of key portions of the root-locus in a more general form, so that the locus can be determined when we have not the comforting help of explicit formulae like Equation 3.28 and Equation 3.37, with as little trial-and-error determination of complex roots as possible.

First, if Equation 3.7 is cleared of fractions and K is zero, it is obvious that the roots are the same as the poles, so the root-locus consists of a number of branches which begin at the poles.

Second, in both examples we found that certain portions of the real or α-axis belonged to the root-locus while the remainder did not. The general rule here is that a point of the real axis belongs to the locus if and only if there is an odd number of real poles and/ or zeros to the right of it. Complex poles or zeros, which occur in conjugate pairs, are irrelevant in this connection.

Next, there is the question of the position and direction of asymptotes to branches that go to infinity. The rules here are quite simple: asymptotic directions are obtained by dividing any odd multiple of 180° by the difference between the number of poles and the number of zeros. In the last example, this difference was 1, so there was only one asymptote at 180°, and when this happens the asymptote is always the real axis itself. But in this example (*see* Fig. 3.4) there were three poles and no zeros, so asymptotic directions occur at odd multiples of 60°. The rule for finding the position of G, the centre of gravity of the roots, where the asymptotes meet the real axis, has already been given in Equation 3.25.

Next, we have to consider how to determine the breakaway point roughly and easily.   Now we noticed that in Fig. 3.4 and Equation

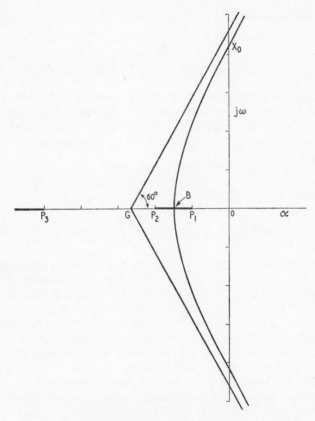

Fig. 3.4.   Rough diagram of root-locus associated with Equations 3.20 and 3.7 (and with Equation 3.41 for $T_a = 0$)

3.24, K had a maximum value (for real roots) at the breakaway point.   It follows that log K also has a maximum and therefore its derivative is zero.   (This is equally true in cases where a portion of the real axis belonging to the root-locus joins two zeros instead of two poles as in Fig. 3.4; in such cases K has a minimum (for real

roots) at the breakaway point between those zeros.) Now it can
be shown that

$$\frac{d}{dp} \log K = \frac{1}{p - p_1} + \frac{1}{p - p_2} + \frac{1}{p - p_3} + \cdots$$

$$- \frac{1}{p - z_1} - \frac{1}{p - z_2} - \frac{1}{p - z_3} - \cdots \qquad (3.38)$$

where p_1, p_2, p_3 etc. are the various poles (real or complex) and z_1,
z_2, z_3 etc. are the various zeros. Hence the right-hand side of
Equation 3.38 can be equated to zero if p_b, corresponding to the
breakaway point, is substituted for p. The real poles and zeros
present no difficulty in Equation 3.38 except insofar as care must
be taken to get the signs right. Complex poles (and zeros) must
be taken together in conjugate pairs; if for example $p_2 = \alpha + j\omega$
and $p_3 = \alpha - j\omega$, we have

$$\frac{1}{p_b - \alpha - j\omega} + \frac{1}{p_b - \alpha + j\omega} = \frac{2(p_b - \alpha)}{(p_b - \alpha)^2 + \omega^2}$$

$$= \frac{2(p_b - \alpha)}{R^2} \qquad (3.39)$$

R being the distance from p_b to $\alpha \pm j\omega$, which is easily measured.

It is not usually necessary to determine the breakaway point very
accurately, and if in Equation 3.39 ω is large, the contribution
from the two complex conjugate poles is small. A good idea of
the position of the breakaway point can therefore often be obtained
graphically by applying Equation 3.38 with only real or nearly
real poles and zeros taken into account. The determination of K
for any *real* value of p is not difficult, so if greater accuracy is
required, the variation of K for real values of p near the value
obtained graphically can be checked to see that there really is a
maximum or minimum in that neighbourhood, but usually in
Equation 3.38 one or two terms on the right-hand side are much
more sensitive to small variations of p near the suspected breakaway
point than the remainder, and Equation 3.38 thus gives p_b easily.

The only remaining points that help in drawing the root-locus
are, that at the breakaway point the root-locus always leaves the
real axis at right angles, and that the direction in which it leaves
complex poles (or reaches complex zeros) can be determined, as in
the last example, by finding the phase angles of all the lines joining
the particular pole (or zero) to the remaining poles and zeros, and

thus determining the angle of departure or arrival which will make the phase of $N(p)/D(p)$ equal to an odd multiple of 180°.

It will be seen that all the above rules have been applied in the two examples given: Equation 3.38 tells us that in the particular example discussed here, the breakaway point is given by

$$\frac{1}{p_b + 1} + \frac{1}{p_b + 2} + \frac{1}{p_b + 5} = 0 \qquad (3.40)$$

and this agrees with Equations 3.27 and 3.28, although in this case it was quite easy to obtain the breakaway point directly from the fact that K was a maximum there. The application of the remaining rules to the two examples given is straightforward.

ROOT-LOCUS METHOD: A QUARTIC EXAMPLE

We have now gone through all the motions necessary for seeking approximately the roots of an algebraic equation in the form 3.7 when the zeros of $N(p)$ and $D(p)$ are assumed known. In the examples which follow, no new principle is involved. They are included mainly to show how much can be achieved by means of the root-locus method, whose essential ideas are, as we have seen, easy to understand.

An equation of the form 3.7 with $N(p) = 1$ and $D(p)$ cubic in p could arise in connection with a three-stage RC feedback amplifier. If such an amplifier failed to meet the stability conditions required, one possibility would be to add capacitance in the feedback loop. If this was done for the system defined by Equations 3.20 just discussed, the modified 'characteristic equation' to be considered would no longer be Equation 3.7 with $N(p)$ and $D(p)$ defined by Equations 3.20, but

$$1 + \frac{K}{\beta_0} \frac{p + (10/T_a)}{(p + 1)(p + 2)(p + 5)(p + [10/T_a\beta_0])} = 0 \qquad (3.41)$$

where β_0 is the low-frequency gain in the feedback loop and T_a is a time-constant associated with the added capacitance. From our present point of view, the precise meaning of T_a and β_0 is irrelevant; they are positive constants at our disposal. To fix our ideas we shall take β_0 to be 0·1 henceforward; the question is then whether we can choose T_a (which in effect means choosing the value of the capacitance introduced into the feedback loop) so that the system defined by Equation 3.41 is an improvement on that defined by

Equations 3.20 and 3.7; the two systems are the same if T_a is sufficiently small. From the practical point of view, the system defined by Equation 3.41 would be an improvement if a higher value of K could be obtained without instability (that is, without allowing Equation 3.41 to have roots with positive real parts) than when T_a is zero. From our present point of view, however, we are mainly concerned with the effect of varying T_a on the root-locus associated with Equation 3.41. We shall consider the cases $T_a = 1$, $T_a = 2$ and $T_a = 4$ (for which the root-loci are given in Figs. 3.5, 3.6 and 3.7 respectively) and $T_a = 5$.

If $T_a = 1$, Equation 3.41 reduces to

$$1 + \frac{K}{\beta_0} \frac{p + 10}{(p + 1)(p + 2)(p + 5)(p + 100)} = 0 \qquad (3.42)$$

As there are 4 poles and one zero, the parts of the real axis that belong to the root locus are those where an odd number of poles and zeros lie to the right, that is to say $p < -100$, $-10 < p < -5$ and $-2 < p < -1$. For any value of K, there will be one real root less than -100 and one between -5 and -10; if K is sufficiently small, there will be two real roots between -1 and -2 but these will be replaced by a complex conjugate pair for larger values of K.

As there are three more zeros than poles, the asymptotic directions of the locus remain $180°$ and $\pm 60°$ as in Fig. 3.5, but the major change is in the position of the centre of gravity, which is at $-32\frac{2}{3} + 0j$ instead of $-2\frac{2}{3} + 0j$ as in Fig. 3.4. Hence the locus is as in Fig. 3.5; it consists of the part of the real axis to the left of P_4 or $-100 + 0j$, the part joining Z_1 to P_3, the part joining P_2 to P_1 and the curve labelled $C_1 C_2$. We are obliged to use one-fifth of the scale of Fig. 3.4 in order to show all the poles and zeros. The breakaway point occurs at $p = -1.478 + 0j$; it is easily obtained by trial and error from the equation

$$\frac{1}{p + 1} + \frac{1}{p + 2} + \frac{1}{p + 5} + \frac{1}{p + 100} - \frac{1}{p + 10}$$

$$= \frac{d}{dp} \log \left(\frac{K}{\beta_0} \right) = 0$$

which is the analogue for the case under discussion of Equation 3.38. The first two terms are much more sensitive to variations of p in the neighbourhood of -1.5 than any of the other terms. We now have sufficient information to draw the root locus as in Fig. 3.5

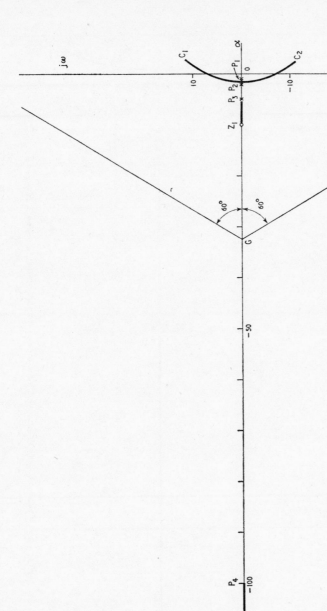

Fig. 3.5. Rough diagram of complete root-locus associated with Equation 3.41 when $T_a = 1$, $\beta_0 = 0.1$

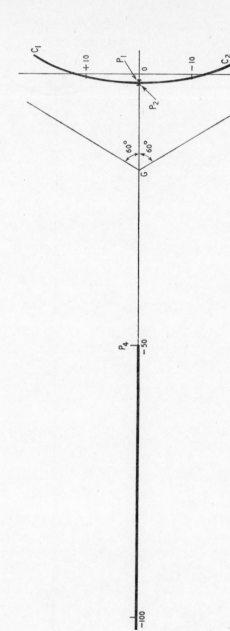

Fig. 3.6. Rough diagram of complete root-locus associated with Equation 3.41 when $T_a = 2$, $\beta_0 = 0 \cdot 1$

provided that we can find the position of one point on the complex part of this locus. Clearly the most useful point to determine is that on the imaginary axis (and above the real axis). Assuming that this part of the curve is not very different from the corresponding part of Fig. 3.5, we can start exploring near $p = 5j$, and the correct value of p is thus found to be 7·2j. The corresponding value of K/β_0 is found to be 3874 by substituting 7·2j for p in Equation 3.42 (or by drawing and measurement from a sufficiently accurate version of Fig. 3·5, since K/β_0 is the product of the distances from 7·2j to the various poles, divided by the distance to the zero at $-10 + 0j$) and the maximum value of K consistent with stability has thus risen from 126 when $T_a = 0$ to 387·4 when $T_a = 1$ μsec.

If T_a is now increased to 2 μsec, Equation 3.41 reduces to

$$1 + \frac{K}{\beta_0} \frac{1}{(p+1)(p+2)(p+50)} = 0 \qquad (3.43)$$

instead of Equation 3.42. It is surprising how little change this makes in the essential nature of the root locus. The pole that we called P_4 in Fig. 3.6 is now at $-50 + 0j$ instead of $-100 + 0j$, and the short segment Z_1P_3 disappears because Z_1 now coincides with P_3. The point G is now at $-17\frac{2}{3} + 0j$, but the oblique asymptotes are still at $\pm 60°$ as before. The breakaway point occurs when

$$\frac{1}{p+1} + \frac{1}{p+2} + \frac{1}{p+50} = 0 \qquad (3.44)$$

and in this case Equation 3.44 can be solved as a quadratic in p to give the breakaway point as $-1·497 + 0j$ and the point where the root-locus crosses the imaginary axis can be expected somewhere in the region of 8j (that is, somewhat above the corresponding point of Fig. 3.5) and it is in fact at about 12·3j. Substitution into Equation 3.43 for K/β_0 gives the value of this quantity as 7945, so that the maximum value of K consistent with stability is now one-tenth of this or 794·5; this is in remarkably good agreement with the more accurate value of 795·6 obtained by taking advantage of the fact that Equation 3.43 is a cubic. A rough diagram of the complete root locus is therefore as given in Fig. 3·6 (which is drawn to the same scale as Fig. 3.5).

If we now increase T_a to 4 μsec, Equation 3.6 reduces to

$$1 + \frac{K}{\beta_0} \cdot \frac{p + 2·5}{(p+1)(p+2)(p+5)(p+25)} = 0 \qquad (3.45)$$

so the point G has moved to $- 10\frac{1}{6} + j0$ and the zero Z_1 is now to the right of P_3. In drawing the root-locus (Fig. 3.7) we can therefore adjust the scale so that we are only obliged to omit the part of the real axis to the left of $-25 + j0$ as the price of having the diagram near the original poles clearer. The breakaway point is given by

$$\frac{1}{p+1} + \frac{1}{p+2} + \frac{1}{p+5} + \frac{1}{p+25} - \frac{1}{p+2\cdot5} = 0 \qquad (3.46)$$

and is therefore about $p = -1\cdot592 + j0$. As before, the only other point worth reasonably accurate determination is the point on the imaginary axis; if we start looking for this in the region of 20j, we find that it is in fact at $11\cdot87j$. The corresponding value of K is $477\cdot2$ (from Equation 3.45).

If T_a is now increased to 5 μsec, Equation 3.40 again has cancelling factors, $(p + 2)$ in this case, in numerator and denominator, and if we clear of fractions, the relevant cubic becomes

$$(p + 1)(p + 5)(p + 20) + 10K = 0 \qquad (3.47)$$

and the critical value of K becomes $315\cdot0$. The curved part of the root locus will have much the same general shape as in Fig. 3.7, so we have not determined it; the procedure is exactly the same as for Figs. 3.5, 3.6 and 3.7. It thus appears that the greatest possible value of K consistent with stability is obtained when T_a is near, but slightly above 2 μsec; the values of maximum permissible K we have obtained are plotted against T_a in Fig. 3.8. To complete Fig. 3.8 we have used the fact that when T_a is 10 μsec, Equation 3.41 reduces to the cubic

$$(p + 2)(p + 5)(p + 10) + 10K = 0 \qquad (3.48)$$

so that the maximum value of K consistent with stability is given by the rule for cubics mentioned after Equation 3.41 and again, if $T_a \to \infty$, Equation 3.41 reduces to Equation 3.7 (with $N(p)$ and $D(p)$ given by Equation 3.20) except that $10K$ now takes the place of K. The maximum value of K is therefore $12\cdot6$, one-tenth of the value 126 found in connection with Equation 3.20.

Thus the common-sense idea of adjusting T_a so as to cancel out the factor $(p + 5)$ in Equation 3.41 appears to be very close to the best possibility available, but the root-locus technique shows us that a sufficiently small variation of T_a from the value of 2 μsec associated with exact cancellation is not significant.

AN EQUATION OF DEGREE 13

In the earlier part of this chapter, we have considered the application of the root-locus method to cubic and quartic equations associated with feedback problems. The great usefulness of the method will now be demonstrated by applying it to an equation of degree 13; this just shows what can be done with it.

Part of the point is to pay a mathematician's grateful tribute to the workers in the field of servomechanisms and control devices for

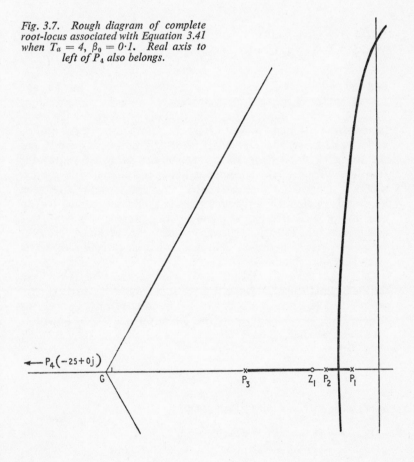

Fig. 3.7. Rough diagram of complete root-locus associated with Equation 3.41 when $T_a = 4$, $\beta_0 = 0.1$. Real axis to left of P_4 also belongs.

producing this method of locating approximately the roots, and especially the complex roots, of equations.

The root-locus method provides just this information, and provides it in such a way that all computations are performed on the original equation instead of on a derived equation, for example, one in which roots already found have been factored out. Hence if there is an error in the calculation of a particular root, this will not affect the calculation of any other root.

The equation to be solved arose in connection with a problem of filter design: it was originally written in the form

$$1 + K \;\frac{(1 - \omega^2)^2(1 - 0 \cdot 8\omega^2)^4}{\omega^2 A^2 B^2}$$

where $A = (1 - 8\omega^2)(1 - 4\omega^2)(1 - 2\omega^2)$

$\qquad B = (1 - 1 \cdot 5\omega^2)(1 - 1 \cdot 2\omega^2)(1 - 1 \cdot 1\omega^2)$ (3.49)

and the case we really wish to consider is when $K = 1$. To take full advantage of the root-locus procedure, however, we shall allow K to have other values also when necessary. Without the root-locus method, Equation 3.49 defied the joint efforts of the author and his assistant for several days. With the root-locus method and the straightforward interpolation techniques indicated below, the roots given here were determined in about the same length of time; accuracy achieved is discussed later. Accuracy could have been improved by iterative processes (which would be tedious for an equation of such high degree, though straightforward) but this was considered unnecessary, especially when the practical problem which gave rise to Equation 3.49 had lost priority before the roots given here were obtained.

Our object here is simply to show what can be done if we have sufficient 'mathematical faith'. Equation 3.49 must first be rearranged so that the coefficient of ω^2 is unity in each factor; we shall regard ω^2 and not ω as the unknown quantity. Equation 3.49 thus becomes

$$1 + \frac{K}{39204} \;\frac{(1 - \omega^2)^2(1 \cdot 25 - \omega^2)^4}{\omega^2 C^2 D^2} = 0$$

where $C = (0 \cdot 125 - \omega^2)(0 \cdot 25 - \omega^2)(0 \cdot 5 - \omega^2)$

$\qquad D = (\tfrac{2}{3} - \omega^2)(\tfrac{5}{6} - \omega^2)\,(\tfrac{10}{11} - \omega^2)$ (3.50) and the arrangement of poles and zeros is thus as in Fig. 3.9, *P* being an arbitrary point.

As ω^2 is the unknown quantity being sought, the origin P_0 is a simple pole, $P_1, P_2 \ldots P_6$ are all double poles, Z_1 is a double zero

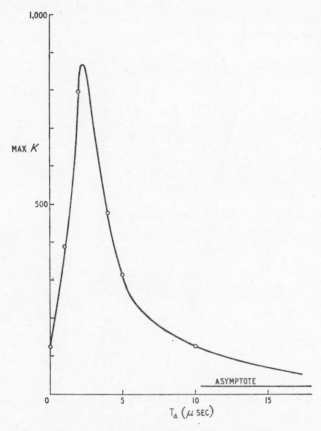

Fig. 3.8. Rough graph of maximum K against T_a

and Z_2 is a quadruple zero. Only the part of the real ω^2-axis to the left of P_0 belongs to the root-locus, for if ω^2 is real and positive, there is always an even number of poles and zeros to the right. As all the poles and zeros except P_0 and Z_2 are double, the root-locus must leave the real axis vertically at the poles P_1 to P_6 and approach it vertically at Z_1. It will cross the real axis at these places, and

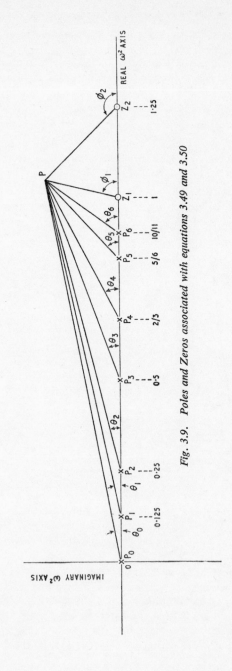

Fig. 3.9. Poles and Zeros associated with equations 3.49 and 3.50

short vertical lines can be drawn through them as a first step in sketching the root-locus.

At P_0 there is a single pole, and the root-locus leaving P_0 is the negative real axis as already mentioned. At Z_2 there is a quadruple zero, and we must determine next how the root-locus reaches Z_2. An arbitrary point P (*see* Fig. 3.9) will be on the root-locus if the sum of the angles formed when P is joined to each pole (counting double poles twice) differs from the sum of the angles formed when P is joined to each zero (counting Z_1 twice and Z_2 four times) by an odd multiple of 180°; in other words, in the notation of Fig. 3.9, the critical quantity is

$$X = \theta_0 + 2\theta_1 + 2\theta_2 + 2\theta_3 + 2\theta_4 + 2\theta_5 + 2\theta_6 - 2\phi_1 - 4\phi_2 \quad (3.51)$$

and X must be an odd multiple of 180° for P to be on the root-locus. In Fig. 3.9 all the angles mentioned are significant, but if P is very close to Z_2, the only angle which differs significantly from zero is ϕ_2, and therefore when P is near Z_2, $4\phi_2$ must be an odd multiple of 180° for P to be on the locus. Hence ϕ_2 must be $\pm 45°$ or $\pm 135°$, and short lines at these angles through Z_2 are included in Fig. 3.10.

The next step is to draw in the asymptotes from the centre of gravity G. The position of G is obtained by adding together the co-ordinates of all the poles, subtracting those of all the zeros, and dividing by 7, the difference between the number of poles (13) and the number of zeros (6). The co-ordinates of the poles and zeros are clear from Equation 3.50, so that the sum of the co-ordinates of the poles is

$$0 + 2\left(0.125 + 0.25 + 0.5 + \tfrac{2}{3} + \tfrac{5}{6} + \tfrac{10}{11}\right) = 6\tfrac{25}{44}$$

while the sum of the co-ordinates of the zeros is

$$2 \times 1 + 4 \times 1.25 = 7$$

The position of G is therefore specified by

$$\left(6\tfrac{25}{44} - 7\right) / 7 = -19/308$$

so that G is at $-0.0617 + 0j$.

Since there are 13 poles and 6 zeros, the asymptotes, which all pass through G, are in directions θ such that

$$(13 - 6)\,\theta = \text{odd multiple of } 180°$$

so that θ must be $\pm 25\tfrac{5}{7}°$, $\pm 77\tfrac{1}{7}°$, $\pm 128\tfrac{4}{7}°$ or 180°. The asymptotes

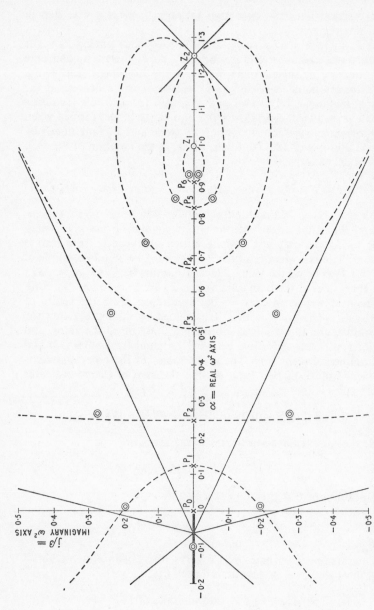

Fig. 3.10. Pole-zero plot with asymptotes and the root locus at the poles and zeros (for Equation 3.50) drawn in. The dotted curves are the rough root-loci drawn freehand, and the doubly-ringed points are the actual roots for $K = 1$ found later

can therefore be drawn as in Fig. 3.10; they make angles of $51\frac{3}{7}°$ with each other.

We now know that the root-locus consists of the real axis to the left of P_0, branches crossing the real axis at right angles at P_1, P_2, P_3, P_4, P_5, P_6 and Z_1, and, that it crosses the real axis twice (at angles $\pm 45°$) at Z_2, and we know the positions of the asymptotes. We can therefore sketch it in roughly. From a pole the locus must terminate on a zero or approach an asymptote, so the most probable form is as in Fig. 3.10. The loci through P_1 and P_3 are easily sketched, while that joining P_6 to Z_1 and that connecting P_4 and P_5 to Z_2 have a fairly obvious general shape. The branch through P_2 is the most difficult to guess, but we do not need a very accurate guess. Our purpose is to find the roots of Equation 3.49 when $K = 1$; this is done by trial and error, and even the rough root-locus of Fig. 3.10 gives us sufficient guidance as to where to try. The dotted curves have been drawn in freehand by guesswork, guided only by the known crossing points of the real axis and asymptotes. We have anticipated somewhat by plotting the positions of the roots finally obtained in Fig. 3.10, surrounded by double rings. They are remarkably close to the guessed curves. This shows how informative such easily drawn curves can be.

To obtain further points on the root-locus, we must revert to Fig. 3.9 and Equation 3.51; any point where X is an odd multiple of $180°$ is on the root-locus and vice versa. At such a point, the corresponding value of K is given by

$$K = 39204 \; \frac{PP_0 \cdot PP_1{}^2 \cdot PP_2{}^2 \cdot PP_3{}^2 \cdot PP_4{}^2 \cdot PP_5{}^2 \cdot PP_6{}^2}{PZ_1{}^2 \cdot PZ_2{}^4} \qquad (3.52)$$

where PP_0, etc., are the lengths of the lines joining P to the poles and zeros.

To achieve our ultimate objective of finding a root where $K = 1$, we start with a trial point Q_1 as in Fig. 3.11 which appears to be suitable from the general lie of the appropriate branch of the root-locus. For Q_1 we compute the value of X, say X_1, from Equation 3.51. If it is not widely out, we take another point Q_2, near Q_1, and determine the corresponding value X_2 of X. By interpolation we can deduce a third point Q_3 which will usually be very close indeed to the root-locus. For this point we can find the corresponding value K_3 of K from Equation 3.52. By repeating the process with a neighbouring pair of points Q_4 and Q_5, we can determine a second interpolated point Q_6 which should again be very close to the root-locus. If K_6 is the value of K associated with Q_6,

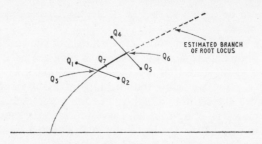

Fig. 3.11. Systematic determination of points on the root-locus, and roots of Equation 3.50

we can do a further interpolation to find the wanted point Q_7, which is not only on the root-locus but has $K = 1$ and therefore determines a root of Equation 3.50.   This procedure we now apply in simplified form to determining the real root, and we also give in detail the determination of the root of Equation 3.50 on the branch of the root-locus through P_1.

Unless the root-locus is drawn on a very large scale, no great accuracy can be obtained geometrically, and it is usually best to compute the relevant angles and lengths.   If P is at $\alpha + j\beta$, we have

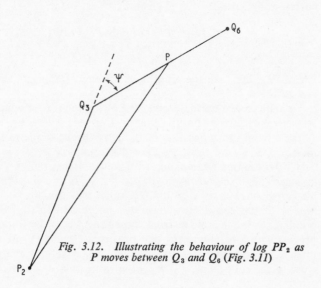

Fig. 3.12.   Illustrating the behaviour of log PP_2 as P moves between Q_3 and Q_6 (Fig. 3.11)

$$\tan \theta_2 = \frac{\beta}{\alpha - 0.25} \; ; PP_2{}^2 = (\alpha - 0.25)^2 + \beta^2 \qquad (3.53)$$

with similar equations for the other poles and zeros.

If we seek first the root for which ω^2 is real and negative, we do not have to consider the value of X which is automatically $180°$, so that in effect in Fig. 3.12 we have only to determine Q_3 and Q_6 and the interpolation of the wanted point Q_7 from them. If Q_3 is at $-0.1 + 0j$, then $Q_3P_0 = 0.1$, $Q_3P_1 = 0.225$, $Q_3P_2 = 0.35$, $Q_3P_3 = 0.6$, $Q_3P_4 = 0.767$, $Q_3P_5 = 0.933$, $Q_3P_6 = 1.009$, $Q_3Z_1 = 1.1$ and $Q_3Z_2 = 1.35$; substitution of these values in Equation 3.52 gives $K_3 = 1.135$. This is not far from the required value of unity, so we try Q_6 at $-0.09 + 0j$ and find, from Equation 3.52, that $K_6 = 0.840$.

We now find the position of Q_7, where $K = 1$, by interpolation. This means that we suppose, in this neighbourhood,

$$\log K = x \, \alpha + y \qquad (3.54)$$

where $\alpha + 0j$ is the position of any point P between Q_3 at $-0.1 + 0j$ and Q_6 at $-0.09 + 0j$, and x and y are constants obtained by solving the simultaneous equations

$$\log K_3 = 0.05520 = -0.1 \, x + y$$
$$\log K_6 = \bar{1}.92453 = -0.09 \, x + y$$

so that $x = -13.067$ and $y = -1.2515$. (The values of $\log K$ given were obtained by working to five-figure accuracy, but this is in general an unnecessary refinement.) Since $\log 1$ is zero, the required value of α at Q_7 is $-y/x$ or -0.0958. This value can be checked by direct substitution for K in Equation 3.52 and if necessary the value of K obtained could be used for further interpolation.

It may be asked why in Equation 3.54 we assumed that $\log K$ rather than K varied linearly with α. The explanation is that Equation 3.50 involves many multiple poles and zeros. If we seek a point on the root-locus which is very near P_2, say, then Equation 3.52 shows that for arbitrary variations of P near P_2, K is approximately proportional to $PP_2{}^2$, since the other distances like PP_0, PP_1, PZ_1 will not differ significantly from P_2P_0, P_2P_1, P_2Z_1, etc., and can therefore be regarded as sensibly constant. Thus the relation between K and PP_2 is non-linear, whereas $\log K$ is $2 \log PP_2$ plus a constant, in other words, $\log K$ is linearly related to log PP_2. In Fig. 3.12, P is shown at an arbitrary point between Q_3 and Q_6. If Q_3Q_6 make an angle ψ with P_2Q_3 as indicated, and Q_3Q_6 is small compared to Q_3P_2, then PP_2 is approximately equal to $P_2Q_3 + PQ_3 \cos \psi$, and therefore

$$\log_e PP_2 = \log_e Q_3P_2 + \log_e \left(1 + \frac{PQ_3}{P_2Q_3} \cos \psi\right)$$

$$\approx \log_e Q_3P_2 + \frac{PQ_3}{P_2Q_3} \cos \psi$$

so that $\log_e PP_2$, or $\log_{10} PP_2$, is, in general, linearly related to PQ_3 as P moves along Q_3Q_6. If we seek a root which is not near a multiple pole or zero, much the same result will be obtained whether we use linear interpolation with respect to $\log K$ as suggested above, or with respect to K in the ordinary way. It is easier to have the same rule for all cases, since we have no means of telling in advance how near the poles and zeros the various roots of Equation 3.50 are going to be. We have therefore interpolated logarithmically in all cases; the above argument is clearly unaffected if we are looking for a complex root instead of a real negative one as here.

For the root of Equation 3.50 on the branch through P_1 and above the real axis, we try Q_1 (in the notation of Fig. 3.11) on the imaginary axis at $0 + 0{\cdot}2j$. The corresponding value of X_1 is $-173° \; 8'$. Q_2 can therefore usefully be taken at $0 + 0{\cdot}21j$ and the corresponding value X_2 of X is $-181° \; 44'$. It happened to be convenient in this case to make Q_1Q_2 parallel to the imaginary ω^2-axis, but this need not be done; Q_1Q_2 can be in any direction, and in general it is useful to have it approximately normal to the estimated root-locus. We now determine the interpolated point Q_3 on the root-locus by assuming that the value of X at any point Q on the line Q_1Q_2 varies linearly with QQ_1; in other words, we assume that at the point Q whose co-ordinates are $\alpha + j\beta$ where

$$\alpha + j\beta = k (0 + 0{\cdot}2j) + (1 - k) (0 + 0{\cdot}21j) \qquad (3.55)$$

the value of X is given by

$$X = k (-173° \; 8') + (1 - k) (-181° \; 44') \qquad (3.56)$$

and since we want X in Equation 3.56 to be $-180°$, we can find k uniquely. Obviously

$$-180° = k (-180°) + (1 - k) (-180°) \qquad (3.57)$$

and if we subtract Equation 3.57 from Equation 3.56 with X on the left-hand side replaced by 180°,

$$0 = k(6°52') - (1 - k)(1°44')$$

Working in minutes, this gives

$$412k - 104(1 - k) = 0, \text{ or } k = \frac{104}{516} = 0.2016$$

The position of Q_3 is thus obtained by substituting this value for k in the expression for $\alpha + j\beta$ in Equation 3.55. α is clearly zero and β is 0.2080, but Equation 3.55 has been written as above so that this interpolation process can easily be applied when Q_1Q_2 is in any direction. We here take Q_3 as being on the root locus; if necessary the value X_3 of X at Q_3 could be checked by substitution in Equation 3.51 and the interpolation process repeated.

Next, the value of K_3 of K at Q_3 is obtained from Equation 3.52 and found to be 1.535; as this is above unity, the point Q_4 in Fig. 3.11 should for this case be taken nearer P_1 (where $K = 0$) so we take Q_4 at $0.02 + 0.18j$, guessing the $0.18j$ from the general lie of the estimated curve of Fig. 3.10. X_4 is then $-177°52'$, so Q_5 was taken as $0.02 + 0.182j$ and X_5 was found to be $-179°38'$. This was considered at the time accurate enough, so Q_5 was regarded as Q_6; a better position for Q_6 would have been $0.02 + 0.1824j$. If Q_6 is taken as $0.02 + 0.182j$, K_6, from Equation 3.52 is 0.7812.

Once again, we assume that if Q' (with co-ordinates $\gamma + j\delta$) is any point on the line Q_3Q_6, log K varies linearly with $Q'Q_3$; we also assume that the short chord Q_3Q_6 of the root locus is indistinguishable from the locus itself. This means that we take the value of K at Q' where

$$\gamma + j\delta = k'(0 + 0.2080j) + (1 - k')(0.02 + 0.182j) \qquad (3.58)$$

to be given by

$$\log K = k'\log 1.535 + (1 - k') \log 0.7812 \qquad (3.59)$$

so that at Q_7, where $K = 1$ and log $K = 0$, we have

$$k' = \frac{-\log 0.7812}{\log 1.535 - \log 0.7812} = \frac{0.10723}{0.29334} = 0.3655$$

Thus we finally obtain the root of Equation 3.50 on the branch

5

through P_1 of the root-locus by substituting the value 0·3655 for k' in Equation 3.58; it is 0·0127 + 0·1915j. This was regarded as sufficiently accurate.

The roots of Equation 3.50 associated with the remaining branches of Fig. 3.10 were determined in like manner; one set of points Q_1-Q_7 was considered sufficient to enable each root of Equation 3.50 to be determined, and these roots, plotted on Fig. 3.10 surrounded by double circles, could have been used to improve our estimate of the root-locus as a whole. This, however, is not worth doing unless we are interested in several different values of K: the crude estimate of Fig. 3.10 is, as we have seen, obtainable quickly and is all that is needed. For the root near 0·92, advantage was taken of the fact that θ_6 is much more sensitive to small changes in the position of the trial point P (necessarily near P_6) than any other angle. The collected values of ω^2 for the roots of Equation 3.50 thus obtained are:

$$- 0·0958; \quad 0·0127 \pm 0·1915j; \quad 0·2679 \pm 0·2746j;$$

$$0·5427 \pm 0·2359j; \quad 0·7366 \pm 0·1363j; \quad 0·8565 \pm 0·0513j;$$

$$0·9230 \pm 0·0160j.$$

and it now remains to discuss the overall accuracy achieved.

For the particular root-pair 0·5427 ± 0·2359j, Equation 3.49 was cleared of fractions (with $K = 1$) and the left-hand side was then divided by the corresponding quadratic factor in ω^2, namely $\omega^4 - 1·0854\omega^2 + 0·35017$, with the astonishing result that this root-pair checked to four significant figures! When Equation 3.49 is cleared of fractions, the number-term is 1, the coefficient of ω^2 is $-4·2$, the coefficient of ω^{24} is $-105,471·5904$ and the coefficient of ω^{26} is 16,057·9584. Overall accuracy is thus checked by evaluating the following:

Sum of roots (in ω^2) is 6·5832, when it should be

$$105,471·5904/16,057·9584 = 6·5681$$

Product of roots is $-6·3903 \times 10^{-5}$, when it should be

$$- 1/16,057·9584 = -6·2274 \times 10^{-5}$$

Sum of reciprocals of roots is 4·128, when it should be 4·2/1 or 4·2.

Now in the evaluation of the sum of reciprocals of the roots, the result 4·128 arises as the difference between the negative reciprocal of $-0·0958$ and the positive reciprocals associated with the remaining roots; an error in the first place of decimals is therefore not surprising.

Thus we contend that it is not at all necessary for an engineer to be frightened when he sees a cubic or quartic equation, as the equation of degree 13 here considered has been solved by means of processes (notably that illustrated in Fig. 3.11) which are within the capacity of any competent engineer.

Chapter 4

LIN'S ITERATIVE PROCESS FOR IMPROVING APPROXIMATIONS TO ROOTS OF ALGEBRAIC EQUATIONS

At this stage we have seen how powerful the root-locus method is as a means of locating approximately the roots (particularly complex roots) of algebraic equations, and in principle it is a method which can be carried out graphically. It remains to consider how, having obtained an approximation to a root of an equation, we can improve this approximation if we wish to do so. For this purpose we suggest that Lin's iterative process is easy to understand, especially when full advantage is taken of the way in which successive approximations converge to or diverge from the true value.

REAL ROOTS

Lin's process involves only algebraic division and works for equations having real or complex roots, and we therefore explain it first in terms of a cubic equation having three real roots, namely

$$f(x) = x^3 + 18x^2 + 78.75x + 81 = 0 \qquad (4.1)$$

In reality, this equation has three real negative roots whose exact values are -1.5, -4.5 and -12; we know this because we have constructed the equation to have these roots! We shall not make use of this knowledge in solving the equation, however, but merely reserve it to check our solution.

The first step is to obtain approximate values for the roots. By trying some extreme values, we find

$$f(0) = 81; \; f(-2) = -12.5; \; f(-10) = 93.5; \; f(-\infty) = -\infty \quad (4.2)$$

and from this we can see that there must be one real root between 0 and -2, for $f(x)$ changes sign between these values. By taking further values and plotting a *rough* graph (Fig. 4.1) we can easily discover that there are, in fact, three real roots, that the one between 0 and -2 is the smallest numerically and that the other two lie between -2 and $-12\cdot5$. We may also estimate from this rough graph that the value of this smallest root is about $-1\cdot7$. We take this value as a starting point and use it to obtain a more accurate value.

The first step is to divide $f(x)$ in Equation 4.1 by $x(x + 1\cdot7)$; incidentally, this same divisor would be used whatever the degree of $f(x)$. Performing the division, the quotient is $x + 16\cdot3$ with the remainder $51\cdot04x + 81$, which we express as $51\cdot04(x + 1\cdot587)$.

The process is now repeated, but using $x(x + 1\cdot587)$ as the divisor of $f(x)$. The quotient is now $x + 16\cdot413$ with remainder $52\cdot70x + 81 = 52\cdot70(x + 1\cdot537)$.

In this, quite simple, way we have obtained three successive approximations to the required root. They are, first, the value $-1\cdot7$ which we obtained from a rough graphical solution; secondly, $-1\cdot587$ as a result of the first division; and thirdly, $-1\cdot537$ as a result of the second division.

We can now use these to obtain a closer approximation. This is given by Aitken's well known formula

$$P = \frac{p_1{}^2 - p_0 p_2}{2p_1 - p_0 - p_2} = p_0 + \frac{\delta_1{}^2}{2\delta_1 - \delta_2} \qquad (4.3)$$

where

$p_0 =$ the original approximation (here $-1\cdot7$)

$p_1 =$ the number arising out of the first division (here $-1\cdot587$)

$p_2 =$ the number arising out of the second division (here $-1\cdot537$)

$\delta_1 = p_1 - p_0$ (here $0\cdot113$)

$\delta_2 = p_2 - p_0$ (here $0\cdot050$)

Inserting values in (3) we find $P = -1\cdot497$ and, since in this case we know that the exact value of the root is $-1\cdot5$, we see that the process has actually given us quite a close approximation to it.

For numerical work it is preferable to use the form of (4·3) involving δ_1 and δ_2. The validity of (4·3) depends upon the fact that if p_0, p_1 and p_2 are all sufficiently close to the true root (say, p) then the quantities $(p_0 - p)$, $(p_1 - p)$, $(p_2 - p)$ are theoretically expected to form a geometric progression. In numerical working, the original quantity p_0 can be rounded off to any convenient number of decimal places, but p_1 and p_2 should be calculated to as many decimal places as are required for the true root.

Having obtained the value $-1\cdot497$ for the root, if we do not consider this to be accurate enough we can repeat the whole process using this value for the initial value p_0. Doing this, we find $p_1 = -1\cdot49875$ and $p_2 = -1\cdot49948$. The use of equation (4·3) then gives $P = -1\cdot50000$.

In this way, we have found the smallest root of the equation and by dividing by $x + 1\cdot5$ we can obtain a new equation of one degree lower. Since our equation is a cubic, the new one is a quadratic and can be at once solved by formula for the remaining two roots. If it had been of higher degree, however, the new one would have been at least a cubic and we should then have to tackle this in the same way as Equation 4.1.

If, for any reason, we are primarily interested in the largest root of Equation 4.1 instead of the smallest, we rewrite the equation in a different 'reciprocal' form before starting to find the root. The drill is to replace x by $1/y$ and multiply the resulting expression by y^3 (y^n in the general case of an equation of degree n). The root-finding process is then actually applied to

$$y^3 f(1/y) = 81y^3 + 78\cdot75y^2 + 18y + 1 \qquad (4.4)$$

We can if we like divide through by the coefficient (81) of the highest power of y.

The process described is now applied to find the smallest root of Equation 4.4 and this is, of course, the reciprocal of the largest root of Equation 4.1.

The procedure for finding the smallest and largest roots of any equation having negative real roots has now been explained.

A cubic equation can always be solved by the procedure given here, and so can any equation having not more than one pair of complex conjugate roots and all its real roots distinct. It may be necessary to use the 'reciprocal' equation, derived as Equation 4.4 was derived from Equation 4.1, rather than the original equation, but with either the original or the 'reciprocal' equation or both we can obtain real roots in succession and divide by the corresponding linear factors until the degree of the residual equation is reduced to 2, so that the complex conjugate pair can be obtained from formula.

COMPLEX ROOTS

For an equation having some complex conjugate root pairs and some real roots, the process described will not work for the original equation if we seek the numerically smallest real root and there is a complex conjugate root pair of much smaller modulus, or if we use the 'reciprocal' equation and seek the numerically largest real root when there is a complex conjugate root pair having much larger modulus.

For an equation having more than one pair of complex conjugate roots, however, the procedure is the same in principle, but different in detail. We shall explain it in terms of the quartic equation

$$F(x) = x^4 + 3x^3 + 12x^2 + 11x + 9 = 0 \qquad (4.5)$$

which has two pairs of complex-conjugate roots, and can be solved in a very similar manner.

As before, it is the root-pair which has least modulus which should be sought first. An adequate starting approximation can often be

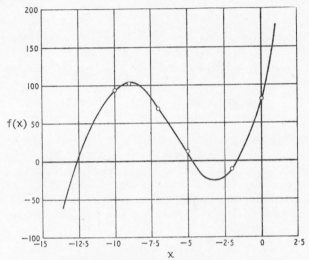

Fig. 4.1. Rough plot of Equation 4.1, made in order to determine the approximate values of the roots

obtained by taking the last three terms of $F(x)$ and dividing through by the coefficient of x^2. Rounding this off to two places, our starting approximation to the factor corresponding to the root-pair having least modulus is

$$D_1(x) = x^2 + 0.92x + 0.75 \qquad (4.6)$$

This is not as good a starting approximation as can be obtained by the root-locus method, but starting approximations obtained in this crude way are often adequate. If the starting approximation is crude, the iterative process to be described will have to be applied a few extra times before the roots of Equation 4.5 are obtained to a given degree of accuracy; on the other hand, it is not necessary to determine the root-locus. It is worth-while to use the root-locus method in almost all cases because this gives information about the rough location of all the roots, whereas extra iterations only give information about one root or root pair.

Having decided to start with the approximate factor $D_1(x)$, $F(x)$ is divided by $x(x^2 + 0.92x + 0.75)$ and, as in the real-root case, the same divisor would be used whatever the degree of $F(x)$. The quotient is $(x + 2.08)$ and the remainder $9.3364x^2 + 9.44x + 9$, which we write as

$$9.3364(x^2 + 1.01110x + 0.97468) \qquad (4.7)$$

We next divided $F(x)$ by $x(x^2 + 1.01110x + 0.97468)$; the quotient is $x + 1.98890$ and the remainder $9.01434x^2 + 9.06146x + 9$. Again, we divide out by the coefficient of x^2 in this remainder, and obtain

$$D_2(x) = x^2 + 1.00523x + 0.99841 \qquad (4.8)$$

Alternative Steps

There are now two possible ways to proceed. The easier way, which is the more effective in this particular case, is to repeat the same process with Equation 4.8 instead of Equation 4.6 and then with the resulting remainder, and so on.

The successive divisors obtained in this way for the particular Equation 4.5 are thus

(a), $x^2 + 1.00133x + 1.00040$;

(b), $x^2 + 1.00065x + 1.00059$;

(c), $x^2 + 1.00008x + 1.00014$;

(d), $x^2 + x + 1.00002$

and the next repetition gives the actual factor $(x^2 + x + 1)$ correct to 5 places. But convergence is not always as rapid as this and there may even be divergence. The following procedure, analogous to what was done when seeking real roots, is safer, though it has the disadvantage of requiring complex numbers to be substituted in a formula we have already used in connection with real roots.

First, find the zeros, by formula, of the quadratic expressions in

Equations 4.6, 4.7 and 4.8 which have positive imaginary parts. These zeros, which we shall call p_0, p_1 and p_2 are given by

$$p_0 = -0.46 + 0.73376j; \quad p_1 = -0.50555 + 0.84800j;$$

$$p_2 = -0.50261(5) + 0.86359j \qquad (4.9)$$

Then, a good approximation to the root we are seeking is

$$P = \frac{p_1{}^2 - p_0 p_2}{2p_1 - p_0 - p_2} = p_0 + \frac{(p_1 - p_0)^2}{2p_1 - p_0 - p_2} \qquad (4.10)$$

Equation 4.10 represents the same relationships of terms as Equation 4.3, but the values of p_0, p_1 and p_2 to be substituted are the complex numbers derived from Equation 4.9 instead of real numbers.

The value of P obtained by substitution from Equations 4.9 into Equation 4.10 is $-0.50092 + 0.86513j$; the corresponding real quadratic factor is

$$x^2 + 1.00184x + 0.99937 \qquad (4.11)$$

which is only in error in the third decimal place. A repetition of the whole process with expression 4.11 replacing expression 4.6 as the starting divisor, two divisions, determination of new values of p_0, p_1 and p_2 as in Equations 4.9, and substitution in Equation 4.10 will often give the required complex conjugate root-pair having least modulus with sufficient accuracy. Two repetitions would very seldom fail to do so.

As in the case of real roots, we can find the complex root-pair of largest modulus by using the 'reciprocal' equation; that is, putting $(1/y)$ for x and multiplying through by y^4 in the case of Equation 4.5, y^n in the general case of an equation of degree n.

Difficulties

There are two main causes of difficulty which we can now discuss briefly, but adequately for most practical purposes. The first is relatively easy to overcome. We may find that, having selected the trial divisor in Equation 4.6, the division process is violently divergent. This indicates that the given equation has a single real root of smaller modulus than any complex conjugate pair, and we should therefore start again and seek a real root; having divided out the corresponding linear factor, the divergence will have been removed for the residual equation. If we seek a quadratic factor as above for an equation which has two or more real roots small in modulus compared to any complex roots, we shall succeed in obtaining a quadratic factor but, instead of having complex conjugate zeros, it will have two real zeros.

The other case of difficulty occurs when the equation has a number of repeated or nearly-repeated roots. On the rare occasions when such cases occur in practice, the following procedure will usually remove the difficulty. If it fails to do so, a mathematician should be consulted at an early stage. We can test, by means of the H.C.F. process, whether an equation has repeated or closely clustered roots. Consider as an illustrative example the equation

$$G(x) = (x^2 + 2x + 2)^2 - 0 \cdot 01 = 0$$

or

$$x^4 + 4x^3 + 8x^2 + 8x + 3 \cdot 99 = 0 \tag{4.12}$$

We have

$$G'(x) = 4(x^3 + 3x^2 + 4x + 2)$$

Now divide $G(x)$ by $G'(x)$, or preferably, to avoid unhelpful fractions, by $\frac{1}{4} G'(x)$, and we find

$$G(x) = \tfrac{1}{4} G'(x) \{x + 1\} + (x^2 + 2x + 1 \cdot 99)$$

Next divide $(x^2 + 2x + 1 \cdot 99)$ into $\frac{1}{4}G'(x)$, and we have

$$\tfrac{1}{4}G'(x) = (x^2 + 2x + 1 \cdot 99) (x + 1) + (0 \cdot 01x + 0 \cdot 01)$$

and the remainder $(0 \cdot 01x + 0 \cdot 01)$ has remarkably small coefficients. This indicates that the preceding divisor, $(x^2 + 2x + 1 \cdot 99)$, has factors $x + 1 \pm 0 \cdot 995\text{j}$ which are, or are nearly, repeated factors of $G(x)$. We now put $x = -1 + 0 \cdot 995\text{j} + Z$ (which we shall round off to $-1 + \text{j} + Z$) in Equation 4.10, and it reduces to

$$Z^4 + 4\text{j}Z^3 - 4Z^2 - 0 \cdot 01 = 0 \tag{4.13}$$

This implies $Z = \pm 0 \cdot 05\text{j}$ if we neglect powers of Z above the second in Equation 4.13. It follows that Equation 4.12 has one root $x \approx -1 + 1 \cdot 05\text{j}$ and another $x \approx -1 + 0 \cdot 95\text{j}$. The conjugates of these quantities are also roots so, as Equation 4.12 is a quartic, we have found all the roots.

To obtain the root near $-1 + 1 \cdot 05\text{j}$ more accurately, transpose the $4Z^2$ term to the right-hand side of Equation 4.13, and substitute $0 \cdot 05\text{j}$ for Z on the left-hand side; only the positive sign is relevant after taking the square root. Then, to obtain the root near

$-1 + 0.95j$ more accurately, transpose the $4Z^2$ term again, substitute $-0.05j$ for Z on the left-hand side, and use only the negative sign after taking the square root.

In the general case, if the original polynomial has a squared factor, the lowest power of Z genuinely represented in the equation corresponding to Equation 4.11 will be Z^2; if the original polynomial has a cubed factor, the lowest power of Z will be Z^3, and so on. There may be terms involving lower powers of Z but, if so, they will have small coefficients and they can be neglected to a first approximation; it is the lowest power of Z having a coefficient of normal size which alone should be transposed.

It thus appears that the procedure we have discussed is capable of solving almost all the algebraic equations with numerical coefficients likely to occur in practice. In many cases, the solution is obtained surprisingly quickly. At several points in the process we have to make a choice—for example, should we try for a real linear factor or a real quadratic factor, and do we continue the division process for several rounds, or for only two rounds and use Equation 4.10. We may sometimes make the wrong choice, but if so, we are soon aware that it is wrong and the number of possible alternatives is reasonably small. A preliminary investigation by means of the root-locus method makes a wrong choice much less likely, since it shows us whether we ought to be looking for a real root or a conjugate-complex pair, and whether other roots are all of greater modulus (the case most favourable to Lin's original process) or not. Equation 4.10, however, means that we need not worry whether Lin's original process (of carrying on successive divisions indefinitely) is convergent or not, as long as it is not so violently divergent that the quantity we have called p_2 is nowhere near the true value of the root being sought.

JORDAN'S ALTERNATIVE PROCEDURE

Broadbent[5] suggested that a better alternative iterative procedure to that of Lin just discussed was given by Jordan[6], especially in the case of root extraction, i.e. equations of the form 3.1. Jordan's method amounts to saying that if y_1 is an approximation to a root of an equation $F(y) = 0$, then

$$y_2 = y_1 - \frac{2F(y_1)F'(y_1)}{2\{F'(y_1)\}^2 - F(y_1)F''(y_1)} \tag{4.14}$$

is a much better approximation to the true value for y.

In Equation 4.14 $F'(y_1)$ means the derivative of $F(y)$ when $y = y_1$ and $F''(y_1)$ means the second derivative, also with y replaced by y_1 after differentiation.   There is little restriction upon the nature of $F(y)$, except that it must be continuous, and differentiable at least twice, in the neighbourhood of its zeros.   If Equation 4.14 is used

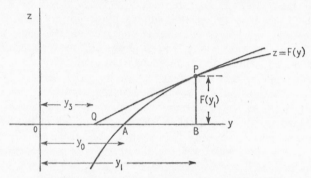

Fig. 4.2.   The geometry of Newton's approximation

for finding $\sqrt[n]{N}$, $F(y)$ is $y^n - N$, but Equation 4.14 can be used also when $F(y)$ is any polynomial.   It can even be used when we are seeking complex roots of algebraic equations, for $F(y) F'(y)$, $\{F'(y)\}^2$ and $F(y) F''(y)$ are then all polynomials in y.   If we require their value when $y = a + jb$, we divide by $(y^2 - 2ay + a^2 + b^2)$ and put $y = a + jb$ in the (linear) remainder.

If we wish to understand the essential nature of an object or abstract idea, comparison with something similar but not identical is often extremely helpful, and for that reason results obtained by applying Equation 4.14 are compared with those already discussed for some of the equations considered in this chapter.

The reason why y_2 is a better approximation than y_1 is fundamentally geometrical, when y_1 and y_2 are real.   Equation 4.14 is essentially an improvement of Newton's method of saying that a better approximation than y_1 to the zero y_0 of $F(y)$ is

$$y_3 = y_1 - \frac{F(y_1)}{F'(y_1)} \tag{4.15}$$

In Fig. 4.2, O is the origin and Oy, Oz are rectangular axes; the curve is $z = F(y)$.   The true zero of $F(y)$ is represented by the point A with co-ordinates $(y_0, 0)$ where the curve crosses the y-axis.   The improved approximation y_3 is obtained by finding where the tangent PQ to the curve at the point P meets Oy; P is the point whose co-ordinates are $(y_1, F(y_1))$, associated with the initial approximation y_1. Now the main error, represented by AQ in Fig. 4.2, introduced by Equation 4.15 is due to the curvature of $z = F(y)$. The object of Equation 4.14 is to 'straighten out' this curvature. Equation 4.14 is obtained from Equation 4.15 by replacing $F(y)$ by $G(y)$ where

$$G(y) = F(y)/\{F'(y)\}^{\frac{1}{2}} \tag{4.16}$$

$G(y)$ has the same zeros as $F(y)$, but has zero curvature at each of them.

Clearly, if the slope of the line PQ is small, it will be difficult to determine Q accurately and QA may be large. Equation 4.14 will therefore not be very satisfactory for an equation which has equal or nearly equal roots. Such roots are not common in practical equations of degree not exceeding 7, though in equations of high degree, say 12 or more, they often do occur. Hence, for the equations likely to occur in electrical engineering, Equation 4.14 must be regarded as obviously worth trying. Once y_1 is close to y_0, y_2 obtained from Equation 4.14 will be very close indeed when $F'(y_1)$ is not unduly small.

A disadvantage of Equation 4.14 for a general equation of degree n is that the numerator and denominator are respectively of degrees $(2n - 1)$ and $(2n - 2)$ whereas, with the Lin method, all manipulations consist of divisions of the original polynomial of degree n by a linear or quadratic expression. This disadvantage, however, does not apply in the case of square-root extraction, for then $F(y)$, $F'(y)$ and $F''(y)$ are all very simple expressions, as they are when a cube or higher root is extracted.

On the other hand, it is sometimes necessary to derive a square root to accuracy only slightly greater than that easily obtainable by means of slide rule or tables. If a is the approximation and it is divided into N whose square root we require, the result N/a of the division is on one register of the calculating machine, while a is on another; their averaging to obtain a better approximation to $\sqrt{N}$ can be done mentally, whereas the application of Equation 4.12, though straighforward, does involve a separate calculation. This will give $\sqrt{N}$ to an unnecessarily high degree of accuracy, and no advantage can be gained with the excessive accuracy.

We shall now apply Equation 4.14 to various equations already considered in this chapter. Comment will be purely explanatory, so that the reader is left free to choose the method he prefers. This choice is partly subjective—a matter of temperament.

Example 4.1

Extraction of $\sqrt{2}$ with 1·4 as starting approximation. This was discussed in Chapter 3. Two applications of the averaging process there used gave 1·414213565, whose square is $2 + 7 \times 10^{-9}$. The first application of Equation 4.14 gives

$$y_2 = y_1 \times \frac{y_1{}^2 + 3N}{3y_1{}^2 + N} = 1·4 \times \frac{7·96}{7·88} = 1·4142132$$

the square of which is $2 - 1 \times 10^{-6}$.

Example 4.2

Extraction of $\sqrt[6]{800}$ starting with 3. A result 3·046834, in error by about 1 in 10^6, was obtained from two applications of the process given in Chapter 3. The first application of Equation 4.14 with $y_1 = 3$ gives

$$y_2 = y_1 \left[1 - \frac{2(y_1{}^6 - 800)}{7y_1{}^6 + 5 \times 800}\right]$$

$$= 3 \left[1 + \frac{142}{9103}\right]$$

$$= 3·046798.$$

Example 4.3

Solving the cubic equation 4.1 starting with $y_1 = -1·7$.

We find from Equation 4.14

$$y_2 = -1·7 - \frac{2 \times (-5·768) \times (26·22)}{2 \times 687·4884 - (-5·768) \times (25·8)}$$

$$= -1·5015$$

Example 4.4

Solving Equation 4.5 starting with the quadratic-factor approximation of Equation 4.6.

Using Equation 4.14 with $y_1 = -0·46 + j\sqrt{0·5384} = -0·46 + j0·733757$, we have

$$F(y) = (y^2 + 0.92y + 0.75)(y^2 + 2.08y + 9.3364) + \\ + 0.850512y + 1.9977$$

$$F(y_1) = 1.9977 + 0.850512(-0.46 + 0.733757j) \\ = 1.606464 + 0.624069j$$

$$F'(y) = (y^2 + 0.92y + 0.75)(4y + 5.32) + 16.1056y + 7.01$$

$$F'(y_1) = 7.01 + 16.1056(-0.46 + 0.733757j) \\ = -0.398576 + 11.817597j$$

$$F''(y) = 12(y^2 + 0.92y + 0.75) + 6.96y + 15$$

$$F''(y_1) = 15 + 6.96(-0.46 + 0.733757j) \\ = 11.7984 + 5.106949j$$

so that

$$y_2 = y_1 - \frac{2(1.606464 + 0.624069j)(-0.398576 + 11.817597j)}{[2\{-139.496736 - 9.420421j\} - \{1.606464 \\ + 0.624069j\}\{11.7984 + 5.106949j\}]}$$
$$= -0.49901 + 0.86544j$$

and the corresponding quadratic factor is

$$y^2 + 0.99802y + 0.99800$$

which has errors only in the third significant figure.

Example 4.5

Solving Equation 4.12.

If the number term is raised to 4, $G(y)$ would become $(y^2 + 2y + 2)^2$, so we are dealing with a case of nearly equal roots. It was suggested that the presence of equal or nearly equal roots can be suspected by applying the 'H.C.F. process' to $G(y)$ and $G'(y)$ and that this indicates that $(y^2 + 2y + 1.99)$ is nearly a repeated factor of $G(y)$. We therefore apply Equation 4.14 with $y_1 = -1 + j\sqrt{0.99}$ or $-1 + j0.994987$ in an exploratory manner. We find, proceeding as in Example 4.4

$$G(y) = (y^2 + 2y + 2)^2 - 0.01$$

$$G'(y) = 4(y + 1)(y^2 + 2y + 2)$$

$$G''(y) = 12(y + 1)^2 + 4$$

and $y_1 + 1 = 0 \cdot 994987$j; $y_1{}^2 + 2y_1 = -1 \cdot 99$, so that $G(y_1) = -0 \cdot 0099$; $G'(y_1) = 0 \cdot 0397995$j; $G''(y_1) = -7 \cdot 88$ whence, from Equation 4.14, $y_2 = -1 + 0 \cdot 98728$j. Continuing the process defined by Equation 4.14 with y_2 instead of y_1, we obtain as our next approximation $y_3 = -1 + 0 \cdot 96696$j, and repeating the process twice more gives $y_4 = -1 + 0 \cdot 94968$j and $y_5 = -1 + 0 \cdot 948683$j, the last root being a root of $G(y) = 0$ correct to six places.

It thus seems to be roughly true that two applications of the root-extraction process given earlier (in Chapter 3) are equivalent to one of the Jordan process (Equation 4.14), and the same two-to-one ratio seems also to hold when equations have to be solved. The processes discussed above for solving equations, however, are confined to algebraic operations on the original polynomial, and it is not normally necessary to obtain its derivatives or their numerical values at particular points.   Example 4.5, however, was deliberately chosen to be unfavourable to the Jordan process, which has given an accurate result after four applications.   Any process for solving equations with equal or nearly equal roots involves consideration of $F'(y)$ as well as $F(y)$, and we took as our starting-point the factor $y^2 + 2y + 1 \cdot 99$ in Example 4.5, derived by using the 'H.C.F. process'.   Without this favourable start, a solution would have been difficult to obtain by any method.

The techniques discussed in Chapters 3 and 4 are sufficient to enable an engineer to cope with algebraic equations of moderate degree that are not deliberately chosen to be awkward.   The methods are straightforward in principle, and this has been regarded as the most important consideration.   In cases of difficulty, a mathematician should be consulted if possible, since mathematicians are constantly facing problems arising out of such matters as the solution of equations, whereas an engineer is faced with this sort of problem relatively seldom.   The above discussion, however, should show that there is no need to give up trying to solve a problem leading to an algebraic equation of degree higher than 2, or a set of linear simultaneous equations with several unknowns.

Chapter 5
SERIES AND PARTIAL FRACTIONS

So far we have considered mainly the solution of linear simultaneous equations and algebraic equations, as these are likely to arise in almost any problem. If any problem can be reduced to the form 'Find x so that some known function $f(x)$ shall have a given value (usually zero)', or to a system of linear equations, we are already adequately equipped to solve it. But quite often we may be able to simplify a practical problem by means of preliminary mathematical manipulation.

When we are set examples at school on algebraic manipulations of various kinds, we are often inclined to regard them as rather pointless. When such manipulations were the subject of the day, the author (who began his career as a schoolmaster) was often asked the very fair question: 'Please, sir, what is the use of this?'

The broad answer to this question is that algebraic and other manipulations make a change in the outward form of a mathematical expression without changing its essential inward nature. The object of the manoeuvre is to get the mathematical expression into the form most suitable for the particular problem in hand; when the expression is in the right form the solution, or at any rate the next step or two towards getting the solution, will usually be obvious. Hence the more possible equivalent ways of expressing the same mathematical entity, the better; we never know which one is going to be enormously useful to-morrow or the next day if not to-day.

In this and later chapters, we shall discuss some of the manipulations which seem to have a high probability of leading to solution of practical problems, and which are at the same time reasonably straightforward.

THE BINOMIAL THEOREM (INTEGER INDEX)

One of the most fundamental and widely applicable of these is known as the 'Binomial Theorem'; it is essentially an alternative way of writing the expression $(a + x)^n$. A simple example of its use is if we require to know (to an accuracy too great to permit the use of standard logarithm tables) the amount on £1 at $100x\%$ compound interest after n years; the answer is $£(1 + x)^n$. The simplest case is when n is a positive integer, and we shall consider this first; a and x may then have any values whatsoever. The case when n is not a positive integer is more difficult, and the values of a and x put into the alternative expression for $(a + x)^n$ have to be restricted in this case to make sure that the important terms in the alternative expression come near the beginning.

First, we can derive $(a + x)^2$ and $(a + x)^3$ and $(a + x)^4$ by direct multiplication; the working, though straightforward, is included because it makes clear the way in which the coefficient of the various terms of $(a + x)^n$ are built up.

$$
\begin{array}{r}
a + x \\
a + x \\
\hline
a^2 + ax \\
\end{array}
$$

$$
\begin{array}{r}
ax + x^2 \\
\hline
(a + x)^2 = a^2 + 2ax + x^2 \\
\end{array}
$$

$$
\begin{array}{r}
a + x \\
\hline
a^3 + 2a^2x + ax^2 \\
a^2x + 2ax^2 + x^3 \\
\hline
(a + x)^3 = a^3 + 3a^2x + 3ax^2 + x^3 \\
\end{array}
$$

$$
\begin{array}{r}
a + x \\
\hline
a^4 + 3a^3x + 3a^2x^2 + ax^3 \\
a^3x + 3a^2x^2 + 3ax^3 + x^4 \\
\hline
(a + x)^4 = a^4 + 4a^3x + 6a^2x^2 + 4ax^3 + x^4 \\
\end{array}
$$

Now let us arrange the various coefficients that have so far arisen in an orderly manner (known as Pascal's Triangle) and see how we can extend the triangle without actually having to do the work of multiplication, rather as a cricketer who hits a boundary scores his runs without actually having to run them.

We now notice that any number in Pascal's Triangle is the sum of the numbers in the row above which are immediately to the left and right of it, as indicated by the pairs of arrows and by the working of

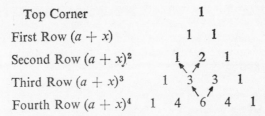

Top Corner | 1

First Row $(a + x)$ | 1 1

Second Row $(a + x)^2$ | 1 2 1

Third Row $(a + x)^3$ | 1 3 3 1

Fourth Row $(a + x)^4$ | 1 4 6 4 1

the multiplications. The law of formation persists indefinitely, and enables us to form successive rows. Thus, in the fifth row, we begin with a 1 half a place to the left of the initial 1 at the left-hand end of the fourth row, the next number, to the right of the 1 in the fourth row and to the left of the 4 is 5, the result of adding 1 and 4, then, below and to the right of the 4 and below and to the left of the 6 comes $4 + 6 = 10$, and the remaining entries are similarly $6 + 4 = 10, 4 + 1 = 5$, and finally a 1 half a place to the right of the 1 in the fourth row. Similarly the sixth row starts with a 1 on the left, followed by $1 + 5 = 6, 5 + 10 = 15, 10 + 10 = 20$, $10 + 5 = 15, 5 + 1 = 6$ and the usual 1 on the extreme right. Continuing this process as far as the eighth row, the arrangement becomes

$$
\begin{array}{c}
1 \\
1 \quad 1 \\
1 \quad 2 \quad 1 \\
1 \quad 3 \quad 3 \quad 1 \\
1 \quad 4 \quad 6 \quad 4 \quad 1 \\
1 \quad 5 \quad 10 \quad 10 \quad 5 \quad 1 \\
1 \quad 6 \quad 15 \quad 20 \quad 15 \quad 6 \quad 1 \\
1 \quad 7 \quad 21 \quad 35 \quad 35 \quad 21 \quad 7 \quad 1 \\
1 \quad 8 \quad 28 \quad 56 \quad 70 \quad 56 \quad 28 \quad 8 \quad 1
\end{array}
$$

and the significance of this is that the numbers in any row, say the nth row, give us the coefficients of the various powers in $(a + x)^n$, thus for $n = 5, 6, 7, 8$ we have

$$(a + x)^5 \equiv a^5 + 5a^4x + 10a^3x^2 + 10a^2x^3 + 5ax^4 + x^5$$

$$(a + x)^6 \equiv a^6 + 6a^5x + 15a^4x^2 + 20a^3x^3 + 15a^2x^4 \\ + 6ax^5 + x^6$$

$$(a + x)^7 \equiv a^7 + 7a^6x + 21a^5x^2 + 35a^4x^3 + 35a^3x^4 \\ + 21a^2x^5 + 7ax^6 + x^7$$

$$(a + x)^8 \equiv a^8 + 8a^7x + 28a^6x^2 + 56a^5x^3 + 70a^4x^4 \\ + 56a^3x^5 + 28a^2x^6 + 8ax^7 + x^8 \tag{5.1}$$

We are now in a position to appreciate that it may be possible to find a general formula for $(a + x)^n$ which will include all the Identities 5.1, and the lower powers of $(a + x)$ which we multiplied out, as special cases. This formula is well known as the 'Binomial Theorem', and is

$$(a + x)^n \equiv a^n + \frac{n}{1} \cdot a^{n-1}x + \frac{n}{1} \cdot \frac{(n - 1)}{2} a^{n-2}x^2 +$$

$$+ \frac{n}{1} \cdot \frac{(n - 1)}{2} \cdot \frac{(n - 2)}{3} a^{n-3}x^3 + \cdots \qquad (5.2)$$

The coefficient of the general term $a^{n-r} x^r$ in the Identity 5.2 is

$$^nC_r = \frac{n}{1} \cdot \frac{(n - 1)}{2} \cdot \frac{(n - 2)}{3} \cdots \frac{(n - r + 1)}{r} \qquad (5.3)$$

that is to say, it has r factors in numerator and denominator, and the sum of each numerator and its associated denominator is $(n + 1)$. The peculiar symbol ^nC_r is used for this coefficient because it happens to be the number of possible choices, or combinations, of r objects out of n when the objects are all different and we are not interested in the order in which the objects are chosen. The law of formation associated with Pascal's Triangle can be expressed in the form

$$^nC_r + {}^nC_{r-1} = {}^{n+1}C_r \qquad (5.4)$$

Hitherto we have assumed that n is a positive integer and that there is no restriction whatever on a and x. When n is a positive integer, we see from Equation 5.3 that putting $r = n$ gives us $^nC_n = 1$ as we should expect from Pascal's Triangle, and that if r has any value greater than n, one of the factors in the numerator of the right-hand side of Equation 5.3 will be zero and, therefore, the identity 5.2 gives us $(n + 1)$ terms on the right-hand side and no more. This again confirms what we have already found out for values of n up to 8 by means of Pascal's Triangle.

We now have to consider what use (if any) can be made of the Identity 5.2 when n is no longer restricted to being a positive integer. If we are thus to remove the restriction on n, the price we have to pay for it is that the expression on the right-hand side of Identity 5.2 becomes an infinite series instead of a finite one and, therefore, in order to obtain useful information, we must manipulate a and x in such a way that the series is convergent. The simplest way to ensure this is to say that a must be 1, and x if real must be between -1 and $+1$ (*not* equal to -1 or $+1$), or if complex must have its modulus less than (*not* equal to) 1. We shall show that certain preliminary manipulations are possible which make this restriction on a and x much less than it appears at first sight to be.

THE BINOMIAL THEOREM: ANY INDEX

When n is not a positive integer, the terms on the right-hand side of Equation 5.2 continue indefinitely, so the formula is of no use unless a good approximation can be obtained by stopping short after a reasonably small number of terms. When a series of terms is in theory infinite and has the property that a good approximation can be obtained by curtailing the series, the series is called 'convergent'. In a convergent series, the important terms come near (though not necessarily at) the beginning. If very few terms of the series are required to obtain a good approximation, the series is said to be 'rapidly convergent'.

Applying Equation 5.2 with $a = 1$, x restricted as just indicated, and various values of n, we obtain such series as

$$\left.\begin{aligned}
(1 + x)^{-1} &\equiv 1 - x + x^2 - x^3 + \cdots \\
(1 + x)^{-2} &\equiv 1 - 2x + 3x^2 - 4x^3 + \cdots \\
(1 + x)^{1/2} &\equiv 1 + \tfrac{1}{2}x - \tfrac{1}{8}x^2 + \tfrac{1}{16}x^3 - \cdots \\
(1 + x)^{0 \cdot 7} &\equiv 1 + 0 \cdot 7x - 0 \cdot 105x^2 + 0 \cdot 0455x^3 \cdots
\end{aligned}\right\} \quad (5.5)$$

All the series 5.5 are rapidly convergent if $|x|$, the modulus of x, is sufficiently small, and converge more slowly as $|x|$ approaches 1. If therefore we require an expansion for $(a + x)^n$, it is important to carry out preliminary manipulations as far as possible to make the series actually used rapidly convergent. Thus, if we are concerned with $(a + x)^n$ when $|a|$ is numerically greater than $|x|$, we take a outside the bracket and write

$$(a + x)^n = a^n \left(1 + \frac{x}{a}\right)^n \qquad (5.6)$$

The expansion actually used will then be

$$(a + x)^n = a^n \left[1 + \frac{n}{1} \cdot \frac{x}{a} + \frac{n}{1} \cdot \frac{n-1}{2} \cdot \left(\frac{x}{a}\right)^2 + \cdots\right] \qquad (5.7)$$

If however the modulus of x is greater than that of a, we have to write

$$(a + x)^n = x^n\left(1 + \frac{a}{x}\right)^n \tag{5.8}$$

and the expansion actually used, instead of the series 5.7 is

$$(a + x)^n = x^n\left[1 + \frac{n}{1}\cdot\frac{a}{x} + \frac{n}{1}\cdot\frac{n-1}{2}\cdot\left(\frac{a}{x}\right)^2 + \ldots\right] \tag{5.9}$$

but the series 5.9 differs from the series 5.7 in that descending powers of x are involved instead of ascending powers. Whether the appropriate series is given by Equation 5.7 or Equation 5.9, it will converge slowly if $|a|$ and $|x|$ are nearly equal. In such cases, convergence can often be made more rapid by writing

$$b = a + y; \;\; \xi = x - y \tag{5.10}$$

so that

$$a + x = b + \xi \tag{5.11}$$

and choosing y in such a way that $|b|$ and $|\xi|$ are not nearly equal. Then we can write

$$(a + x)^n = (b + \xi)^n$$

$$= b^n\left[1 + \frac{n}{1}\cdot\frac{\xi}{b} + \frac{n(n-1)}{1\cdot 2}\left(\frac{\xi}{b}\right)^2 + \ldots\right] \tag{5.12a}$$

or

$$= \xi^n\left[1 + \frac{n}{1}\cdot\frac{b}{\xi} + \frac{n}{1}\cdot\frac{n-1}{2}\left(\frac{b}{\xi}\right)^2 + \ldots\right] \tag{5.12b}$$

the first being used if $|\xi| < |b|$ and the second if $|\xi| > |b|$. If $x \approx ae^{j\theta}$, y can conveniently be taken as $ae^{j\theta}$; in this case

$$b = a(1 + e^{j\theta}) = 2a\cos\tfrac{1}{2}\theta \cdot e^{\frac{1}{2}j\theta}$$

and ξ will be small compared to b unless θ is nearly π, in which case the procedure of Equation 5.10 may have to be repeated with another value of y.

If we wish to use the Binomial Theorem to calculate $(2\cdot 1)^{1/3}$, then since

$$1\cdot 3^3 = 2\cdot 197, \;\; 1\cdot 28^3 = 2\cdot 097152$$

we can write $(2.1)^{1/3}$ in any of the following three forms:

$$1 \cdot 1^{1/3} \left(1 + \frac{1}{1 \cdot 1}\right)^{1/3}$$

$$1 \cdot 3 \quad \left(1 - \frac{0 \cdot 097}{2 \cdot 197}\right)^{1/3}$$

$$1 \cdot 28 \quad \left(1 + \frac{0 \cdot 002848}{2 \cdot 097152}\right)^{1/3}$$

before applying the series 5.7. The last form would be much the most effective, as the series is rapidly convergent, and the factor $1 \cdot 28$ outside is exact whereas, in the first form, the series for $\{1 + (1/1 \cdot 1)\}^{1/3}$ would be slowly convergent, and it would be necessary to determine $1 \cdot 1^{1/3}$ separately.

As long as care is taken, by manipulations of the kind indicated in Equations 5.7 and 5.10 where necessary, to make the binomial series actually used rapidly convergent, the Binomial Theorem can be satisfactorily used for any value of n, positive, negative, integral or fractional. When n is a positive integer, and not too large, Pascal's triangle is the easiest way to obtain the coefficients, and the number of terms has the finite value $(n + 1)$.

Thus the Binomial Theorem, Equation 5.2, is a means of changing the expression $(a + x)^n$ into a finite or infinite series of terms of the form $A_r a^r x^{n-r}$; if it is so handled that rapidly convergent series are actually used, there is little effective difference between the case when n is a positive integer and when n is not. The important point is that the two sides of Equation 5.2 are equally valid, alternative expressions for the same entity. For some problems, this entity may arise in the form $(a + x)^n$ and be easier to handle in series form, but it may also happen that from the data we are able to deduce a series expression which could preferably be reduced to the combination of a few terms like $(a + x)^n$.

PARTIAL FRACTIONS

In circuit theory involving lumped elements in linear systems, expressions of the form $F(p)/G(p)$, (where p is an abbreviation for d/dt and $F(p)$ and $G(p)$ are polynomials) frequently occur. The full equipment for dealing with such expressions by means of 'operational calculus' is provided in Chapter 9 below and elsewhere[7]. Here it is only necessary to discuss the fact that algebraically any expression of the form $F(p)/G(p)$ is equivalent to a set of 'partial fractions' of the form $A_r/(p + \alpha_r)$, together with a polynomial in p unless the degree of $G(p)$ is higher than that of $F(p)$. One possible way of handling the 'partial fractions' $A_r/(p + \alpha_r)$ is to express them in series form by means of the binomial theorem (with $n = -1$). Such series expansion can be the best procedure, as is indicated in Chapter 10, but this is not usually the case. In general, however, the form $F(p)/G(p)$ is not as easy to handle as the partial fraction form, and we therefore now consider the derivation of the appropriate partial fractions in a few simple but typical cases.

Consider first the expression

$$
\begin{aligned}
f_1(p) &= \frac{1}{p + 1} + \frac{1}{p + 2} \\
&= \frac{(p + 2) + (p + 1)}{(p + 1)(p + 2)} \\
&= \frac{2p + 3}{p^2 + 3p + 2}
\end{aligned} \tag{5.13}
$$

Proceeding downwards is quite well known and straightforward; it is exactly analogous to the procedure for adding numerical fractions like $\frac{1}{2}$ and $\frac{2}{3}$. But we now wish to be able to proceed upwards in Equation 5.13. It is therefore natural to enquire whether we can determine A and B so that

$$
\frac{A}{p + 1} + \frac{B}{p + 2} \text{ shall be the same as } \frac{2p + 3}{p^2 + 3p + 2} \tag{5.14}
$$

In such a situation, the first thing to do is to write down

$$
\frac{A}{p + 1} + \frac{B}{p + 2} = \frac{2p + 3}{p^2 + 3p + 2} \tag{5.15}
$$

which expresses this formally. The sign '$\equiv$' rather than '$=$' might be used, since it is intended that Equation 5.15 shall be true whatsoever p may be (even if p is not an ordinary number at all, but the operator d/dt). But

$$
\frac{A}{p + 1} + \frac{B}{p + 2} = \frac{A(p + 2) + B(p + 1)}{p^2 + 3p + 2} \tag{5.16}
$$

so that

$$
A(p + 2) + B(p + 1) = 2p + 3 \tag{5.17}
$$

The obvious way of making the two sides of Equation 5.17 agree is to ensure that the p-terms agree and that the number terms agree separately, so that

$$\left.\begin{array}{c} A + B = 2 \\ 2A + B = 3 \end{array}\right\} \tag{5.18}$$

By solving the simultaneous Equations 5.18, we duly find that $A = B = 1$. If we had more terms (as we would have had if $f_1(p)$ in Equation 5.13 had had a denominator of degree n instead of 2) we might have had to solve n simultaneous equations analogous to 5.18 for n unknowns like A and B. Theoretically this could be done with the help of the methods considered in Chapter 2, but there is a simple trick which greatly simplifies the working. We want Equation 5.17 to be true whatever p may be, and therefore in particular we want it to be true if p is replaced by -1 or -2 on both sides. Replacing p by (-1), Equation 5.17 becomes

$$(- 1 + 2)A = 2(- 1) + 3 = 1 \tag{5.19}$$

so that

$$A = \frac{2(-1) + 3}{(-1) + 2} = 1 \tag{5.20}$$

and, replacing p by (-2), Equation 5.17 similarly becomes

$$B = \frac{2(-2) + 3}{(-2) + 1} = 1 \tag{5.21}$$

Now the point is that replacing p by (-1) and (-2), the numbers that make the given denominator $(p^2 + 3p + 2)$ zero, works even if we have a large number of unknowns like A and B; the equations like 5.20 and 5.21 will always contain only one of these unknowns. Further, if we write the right-hand side of Equation 5.15 in the form

$$\frac{2p + 3}{(p + 1)(p + 2)} \tag{5.22}$$

we notice that in Equation 5.20, A is obtained by replacing p by (-1) everywhere in expression 5.22 after removing or covering up the factor $(p + 1)$ in the denominator which would thus be made zero. B is obtained similarly by putting (-2) instead of p everywhere in expression 5.22 after removing the factor $(p + 2)$ from the denominator. This is not an accident—it always happens, whatever the degree of the denominator of the expression we are trying to put into partial fractions.

Furthermore, in principle the situation is the same if this denominator has complex zeros instead of the simple, real zeros (-1) and (-2) of this case. The only snag is that it is more difficult to evaluate expressions like $(2p + 3)/(p + 2)$ if p is to be replaced by a complex number. But by judicious use of algebraic division, such evaluation, fully discussed in Chapter 7, is not as difficult as it looks.

Three minor points remain; first, that we have hitherto assumed that the degree of the denominator $G(p)$ of the expression to be put into partial fractions exceeds the degree of the numerator $F(p)$. If this is so, the job of splitting into partial fractions is complete when all the quantities we have called A and B are found. If however the numerator $F(p)$ is of the same degree as the denominator $G(p)$ or of higher degree, we have to add a polynomial obtainable by the simple process of dividing $G(p)$ into $F(p)$, finding the quotient, say $\phi(p)$, and ignoring the remainder. Thus in general we end the process with an explicit expression of the form

$$\frac{F(p)}{G(p)} = \phi(p) + \frac{A_1}{p + \alpha_1} + \frac{A_2}{p + \alpha_2} + \ldots + \frac{A_n}{p + \alpha_n} \qquad (5.23)$$

where $\phi(p)$ is the quotient when $F(p)$ is divided by $G(p)$, or zero if $G(p)$ is of higher degree, and $\alpha_1, \alpha_2 \ldots \alpha_n$ are the real or complex zeros of $G(p)$. The second minor point is that we may not know the zeros of $G(p)$ initially, but we can find them by means of the techniques discussed in Chapters 3 and 4. The third and last point is that we have assumed that these zeros are all different. In a practical problem, this can be taken as always true, since two physical quantities may be nearly equal, but exact equality occurs with probability exactly zero. The author therefore considers that existing textbooks tend to devote a disproportionate amount of space to this matter of so-called 'multiple-zeros', and that it is not necessary to devise special methods for such cases which are not essentially different. The point is that if some of $\alpha_1, \alpha_2 \ldots$ are close together, there will tend to be large and cancelling terms in Equation 5.23. The special techniques consist essentially in removing these cancelling terms at an early stage, whereas in the author's opinion it is better to proceed always by the same general method, and to avoid actually carrying out any cancellation until a very late stage of the proceedings, when the best way of carrying it out will probably be obvious.

SERIES

Although the Binomial Theorem is a fruitful source of series expansions by means of which the apparent shape of a mathematical expression may be changed, it is by no means the only such source. For example, another way of expressing $F(p)/G(p)$, instead of Equation 5.23, is to divide $G(p)$ into $F(p)$ and cancel the *lowest* power of p remaining at each stage. This will give a series for $F(p)/G(p)$ in ascending powers of p, equivalent to that obtained by applying the binomial theorem to each of the expressions on the right-hand side of Equation 5.23. Alternatively (and preferably for operational-calculus purposes) we can divide $G(p)$ into $F(p)$, and cancel out the highest power of p remaining at each stage, but continue the division indefinitely to give a series in descending powers of p.

Thus we may be faced with the situation that we can by some means express a mathematical entity in the form of a finite or infinite series, and we need guidance as to whether this series is any use. For an infinite series to be useful, it must be convergent, that is to say, the important terms must come near the beginning, so that the end-terms can be omitted without serious error. Even in the case of a finite series, it is a great advantage if all but a few early terms can be neglected.

Series are so useful for dealing with expressions that cannot otherwise be handled at all easily that we shall here consider their properties generally, and techniques for manipulating them advantageously.

A very useful collection of series whose sums (to n terms or to infinity) are known explicitly has been made by L. B. W. Jolley[8]. The proofs of many of these results are difficult, and here we shall not be much concerned with proofs, but rather with making the best use of well-known results.

Let us then first consider the simple geometric series

$$S_n = a + ar + ar^2 + ar^3 + \ldots + ar^{n-1} \qquad (5.24)$$

in which each term is obtained from the previous term by multiplying by a fixed number r. Both a and r may be complex numbers in Equation 5.24. If we multiply both sides of Equation 5.24 by r and subtract from Equation 5.24 itself, all the terms cancel on the right-hand side except the first and the last, so that

$$S_n (1 - r) = a (1 - r^n) \qquad (5.25a)$$

and therefore

$$S_n = a\frac{1 - r^n}{1 - r} \tag{5.25b}$$

The geometric series is unusual in having an explicit sum to n terms, given by Equation 5.25b for all values of r, real or complex, with the single exception of $r = 1$. If $r = 1$, 5.25b takes the form $0 \div 0$; one way of dealing with this situation is to go back to 5.24 which gives immediately that if $r = 1$, then $S_n = na$. There is also a useful rule for dealing with expressions like 5.25 which are, in general, 'well-behaved' (i.e., continuous and differentiable any number of times), but become indeterminate at isolated points. To find the limiting value of S_n when r tends to 1, differentiate the numerator $(1 - r^n)$ and put $r = 1$ after differentiation, giving the value $-n$, and differentiate the denominator $(1 - r)$ putting $r = 1$ after differentiation, giving -1. Then

$$\lim_{r \to 1} S_n = a\frac{(-n)}{(-1)} = na \tag{5.26}$$

in complete agreement with the commonsense result already obtained. In symbols, this rule is usually expressed by saying that if $f(x)$, $g(x)$ are two well-behaved functions such that $f(a) = g(a) = 0$, and $f'(x)$, $g'(x)$ are the first derivatives of $f(x)$ and $g(x)$ respectively, then

$$\lim_{x \to a} \frac{f(x)}{g(x)} = \lim_{x \to a} \frac{f'(x)}{g'(x)} \tag{5.27}$$

When a series has a sum to n terms for which there is an explicit formula, like 5.25, this formula can be differentiated (or integrated) any number of times. (With adequate safeguards, as we shall see later, term-by-term integration of infinite series also is often permissible.) Thus by differentiating Equations 5.24 and 5.25 with respect to r, we find that (for $n \geq 2$)

$$S'_n = a + 2ar + 3ar^2 + 4ar^3 + \ldots + (n - 1)ar^{n-2} = \frac{\mathrm{d}S_n}{\mathrm{d}r}$$

$$= a\frac{\mathrm{d}}{\mathrm{d}r}\left(\frac{1 - r^n}{1 - r}\right) = a\frac{1 - nr^{n-1} + (n - 1)r^n}{(1 - r)^2} \tag{5.28}$$

and further sums of series may be obtained by repeated differentiation.

We notice that in Equations 5.25 and 5.28, if the modulus $|r|$ of r is less than 1 and n is sufficiently large, then the term $-r^n$ in the numerator of Equation 5.25, and the corresponding terms $-nr^{n-1}$ and $(n-1)r^n$ in the numerator of Equation 5.28 may be omitted. This is formally stated by saying that the series 5.24 has a 'sum to infinity' of $a/(1-r)$ if $|r|<1$; the series S'_n in Equation 5.28 likewise has a 'sum to infinity' $a/(1-r)^2$. If however $|r|$ equals or exceeds 1, no terms can be omitted from Equations 5.25 and 5.28, and S_n, S_n' do not tend to limits as n tends to infinity. A series having a 'sum to infinity' is called 'convergent'; a series which is not convergent is called 'divergent'. Some authors use the word 'divergent' to imply that the sum of n terms of the series increases without limit as n increases, so that they use another word 'oscillatory' for a series like

$$1 - 1 + 1 - 1 + 1 - 1 + \dots \text{ to } n \text{ terms} = \tfrac{1}{2}\{1 - (-1)^n\}$$

(5.29)

whose sum to n terms does not tend to a limit as n tends to infinity but, nevertheless, does not increase without limit. (Series 5.29 is of course a special case of series 5.24 with $a = 1$ and $r = -1$.) Here, however, we shall use the word 'divergent' in the broader sense of 'not convergent', because from the point of view of an engineer, a divergent series is useless. Mathematicians are at liberty to explore with delight and enjoyment the finer points of difference between various kinds of divergence, but their conclusions are of little assistance to engineers because the borderline cases which give rise to these finer points seldom occur in practice and, when they do, special methods to extract the information of practical value can usually be applied.

For engineering purposes, we need the smallest possible number of simple tests which will show us when a series is convergent (it will be an advantage if rapid convergence is clearly exhibited). We also need computation tricks for an adequate evaluation of the sum (to infinity) of a convergent series. Convergence is no guarantee that there is an explicit formula for the sum to n terms, as in Equation 5.25.

For series having only positive terms, there are only two tests of convergence important from the practical point of view, namely:

(i) The 'comparison' test: if u_n is the nth term of the series we wish to use, and $u_n \leqslant v_n$ for all n greater than some value n_0, then the series

$$U_n = u_1 + u_2 + u_3 + \ldots + u_n \tag{5.30}$$

is convergent if the series

$$V_n = v_1 + v_2 + v_3 + \ldots + v_n \tag{5.31}$$

is convergent.

(ii) The 'ratio test': if in Equation 5.30

$$\lim_{n \to \infty} \frac{u_{n+1}}{u_n} = l \ (l < 1) \tag{5.32}$$

then the series U_n is convergent. Note that this test fails if $l = 1$; if $l > 1$ then the series is definitely divergent. Rapid convergence is usually associated with small l.

In order to use the comparison test, we need to know a few useful convergent series. Foremost among these is the geometric series, Equation 5.24, when $|r| < 1$. Using the comparison test with the geometric series as the series of known convergence whose terms are respectively greater than those of the given series, however, is equivalent to using the ratio test. But now consider the series

$$W_n = 1 + \frac{1}{2^p} + \frac{1}{3^p} + \frac{1}{4^p} + \ldots + \frac{1}{n^p} \tag{5.33}$$

for which the ratio test fails. If $p = 1$, the series 5.33 is divergent, but if p is any greater number than 1, whether an integer or not, the series is well known to be convergent. If p is an even integer, Jolley[8] gives an explicit formula for the sum to infinity. Hence the series 5.33 may prove useful in showing the convergence of series for which the ratio test fails, but the convergence of such series is likely to be inconveniently slow.

For series having terms of either sign, or complex terms, the most important convergence test is that of 'absolute convergence'. If the series

$$X_n = |u_1| + |u_2| + |u_3| + \ldots + |u_n| \tag{5.34}$$

is convergent, where the vertical bars denote absolute or modulus values, then the series 5.30 is called absolutely convergent. An

absolutely convergent series is not only convergent; it is a very
'safe' sort of series, for which the derivative (or integral) of the sum
to infinity may be obtained by adding the derivatives (or integrals) of
the separate terms. Also, any rearrangement of the order of the
terms of an absolutely convergent series is permissible: it does not
affect the sum to infinity. It is, however, possible to alter the sum
to infinity by rearranging the order of the terms of other series.
Grouping terms, without rearranging their order, is always permissible. Thus the series

$$Y_n = 1 - \frac{1}{2} + \frac{1}{3} - \frac{1}{4} + \frac{1}{5} - \ldots + \frac{(-1)^{n+1}}{n} \qquad (5.35)$$

is not absolutely convergent, because if the signs are all made
positive, we obtain the series 5.33 with $p = 1$. It is nevertheless
convergent because, if we group the terms in pairs, we have

$$Y_{2n} = \left(1 - \frac{1}{2}\right) + \left(\frac{1}{3} - \frac{1}{4}\right) + \left(\frac{1}{5} - \frac{1}{6}\right)$$

$$+ \ldots + \left(\frac{1}{2n-1} - \frac{1}{2n}\right)$$

$$= \frac{1}{1 \cdot 2} + \frac{1}{3 \cdot 4} + \frac{1}{5 \cdot 6} + \ldots + \frac{1}{2n(2n-1)} \qquad (5.36)$$

and the nth term of the grouped series is less than, say, $1/(2n^2)$, so
that we can apply the comparison test with series 5.33 having
$p = 2$ to prove convergence. We must, of course, not overlook the
fact that Y_{2n+1} ought also to be considered, but Y_{2n+1} differs from
Y_{2n} only by a single term $1/(2n + 1)$ at the end, and this term tends
to zero as n tends to infinity. Actually, the sum of the series Y_2
to infinity is $\log_e 2$. On the other hand, the series

$$Z_n = x - \frac{x^3}{3} + \frac{x^5}{5} - \ldots + (-1)^{n+1} \frac{x^{2n+1}}{2n+1} \qquad (5.37)$$

is absolutely convergent for $|x| < 1$, since if in the series 5.37 we
make all the signs positive, we obtain in this case a series satisfying
the conditions of the ratio test. The sum to infinity can be obtained
explicitly, for

$$\frac{dZ_n}{dx} = 1 - x^2 + x^4 - \ldots + (-1)^{n+1} x^{2n} \qquad (5.38a)$$

Now the right-hand side of Equation 5.38a is a special case of Equation 5.24 with $a = 1$ and $r = -x^2$, so that applying Equation 5.25, we have

$$\frac{dZ_n}{dx} = \frac{1 - (-x^2)^n}{1 + x^2} \tag{5.38b}$$

and if $|x| < 1$, Equation 5.38b reduces to

$$\lim_{n \to \infty} \frac{dZ_n}{dx} = \frac{1}{1 + x^2} \tag{5.38c}$$

Since the series 5.37 is absolutely convergent for $|x| < 1$, and the terms of the series 5.37 are obtained by integrating the corresponding terms of the series 5.38a, the sum to infinity of the series 5.37 is given by integrating 5.38c, that is

$$\lim_{n \to \infty} Z_n = \tan^{-1} x \tag{5.39}$$

In fact, 5.39 is true if $|x| = 1$ as well as for $|x| < 1$. Since $\tan^{-1} 1 = \pi/4$ the series 5.37 could be used to calculate π, but its convergence would be very slow, even if the terms were grouped like those of the series 5.36. There is, however, what might be described as a trick identity which enables π to be calculated much more rapidly by means of the series 5.37. We have

$$\tan^{-1} a + \tan^{-1} b = \tan^{-1} \frac{a + b}{1 - ab} \tag{5.40}$$

Using this identity with $a = b = \frac{1}{5}$ gives

$$2 \tan^{-1} \frac{1}{5} = \tan^{-1} \frac{5}{12} \tag{5.41}$$

Using the identity 5.40 again with $a = b = 5/12$ gives

$$4 \tan^{-1} \frac{1}{5} = 2 \tan^{-1} \frac{5}{12} = \tan^{-1} \frac{120}{119} \tag{5.42}$$

and finally using the identity 5.40 with $a = 1$, $b = 1/239$ gives

$$\tan^{-1} 1 + \tan^{-1} \frac{1}{239} = \tan^{-1} \frac{120}{119} \tag{5.43}$$

From these results we have

$$\frac{\pi}{4} = \tan^{-1} 1 = 4 \tan^{-1} \frac{1}{5} - \tan^{-1} \frac{1}{239} \qquad (5.44)$$

Now the series 5.37 is very rapidly convergent if $x = 1/5$ or $x = 1/239$, so that the manipulation involved in Equations 5.40 to 5.44 would save an appreciable amount of time if accurate calculation of π to say 20 decimal places was required. It may well be argued that this is a mathematician's job and not an engineer's; the example merely illustrates the power of algebraic and other manipulations to change a mathematical expression into a form much more suitable for the particular task in hand.

A power series

$$P_n = a_0 + a_1 z + a_2 z^2 + \ldots + a_n z^n \qquad (5.45)$$

usually has a 'radius of convergence'; that is to say, there is a number R such that the series is absolutely convergent when $|z| < R$. For a given power series, R is usually determined easily by replacing z by $|z|$ in the series 5.45, and applying the ratio test. It is possible for R to be infinite, as in the case of the exponential series, or zero, as in the case where a_n in the series 5.45 is $n!$. Normally, however, R is finite, so that the power series can be used freely for $|z| < R$, and differentiated and integrated term by term also for $|z| < R$.

Having established the convergence (or, if possible, absolute convergence) of a series, we have to consider obtaining an adequate approximation to the sum to infinity in the general case when neither the sum to n terms nor the sum to infinity are known or obtainable from such a source as Jolley[8].

We have already seen, in connection with the series 5.35 and 5.36, that grouping the terms, provided that their order is not altered, may transform the given series into one which converges more rapidly. The same kind of improvement can be made if we wish to sum a series which is similar to, but not identical with, one whose sum is known. If, for instance, we wish to sum the series 5.30 when

$$u_n = 1/(n^2 + 1) \qquad (5.46)$$

we can consider the difference between the series 5.46 and the series 5.33 whose sum to infinity is known to be $\pi^2/6$ when $p = 2$. We have

$$(1/n^2) - u_n = (1/n^2) - 1/(n^2 + 1) = 1/\{n^2(n^2 + 1)\} \qquad (5.47)$$

7

Now the series associated with the last member of 5.47 is much more rapidly convergent than that represented by Equation 5.46; probably it is sufficient merely to add up a reasonably small number of terms in this case. If we wish, however, we can repeat the process and say

$$u_n - (1/n^2) + (1/n^4) = 1/\{n^4(n^2 + 1)\} \qquad (5.48)$$

and the series whose general term is the last member of 5.48 will be still more rapidly convergent; the series 5.33 when $p = 4$ has the known sum $\pi^4/90$.

Sometimes a series having terms of the same absolute value as those of the given series has a known sum, but there are discrepancies of sign, or the given series may have terms missing from those of a series with known sum or, more generally, the nth term of the given series can be broken up into a combination of terms each of which is associated with a known series. The techniques available in such circumstances are well illustrated in terms of the series

$$A_n = \frac{1}{2^2} - \frac{2}{3^2} + \frac{3}{4^2} - \ldots + (-1)^{n+1} \frac{n}{(n+1)^2} \qquad (5.49)$$

The sum to infinity is given[8] as $(\pi^2/12) - \log_e 2$, and we seek to derive this result using only series already mentioned above.

First of all, the nth term of the series 5.49 can be written

$$(-1)^{n+1} \frac{n}{(n+1)^2} = (-1)^{n+1} \frac{(n+1) - 1}{(n+1)^2}$$

$$= (-1)^{n+1} \left[\frac{1}{n+1} - \frac{1}{(n+1)^2} \right] \qquad (5.50)$$

The first part of 5.50 gives us the series

$$\frac{1}{2} - \frac{1}{3} + \frac{1}{4} - \frac{1}{5} + \ldots \qquad (5.51)$$

and this is the series 5.36 with the signs reversed and the first term missing. The sum to infinity of 5.51 is therefore $1 - \log_e 2$. The second part of 5.50 gives the series

$$-\frac{1}{2^2} + \frac{1}{3^2} - \frac{1}{4^2} + \ldots \qquad (5.52)$$

which is like the series 5.33 with $p = 2$ except that the first term is missing, and the signs are alternate instead of all positive.   We can rearrange 5.52 in the form

$$(-1) + 1 + \frac{1}{2^2} + \frac{1}{3^2} + \frac{1}{4^2} + \cdots$$

$$-\frac{2}{2^2} \qquad -\frac{2}{4^2} - \cdots \qquad (5.53)$$

and the sum of the top row of 5.53 is now clearly seen to be $(\pi^2/6) - 1$, while the terms of the bottom row can be taken respectively as

$$-\frac{1}{2} \cdot \frac{1}{1^2}, \; -\frac{1}{2} \cdot \frac{1}{2^2} \quad \text{etc.}$$

so that their total contribution is $-\dfrac{1}{2} \cdot (\pi^2/6)$ or $-\pi^2/12$.

Hence the sum to infinity of the series 5.45 is

$$(1 - \log_e 2) + \left(\frac{1}{6}\pi^2 - 1\right) - \left(\frac{1}{12}\pi^2\right) = \frac{1}{12}\pi^2 - \log_e 2$$

in agreement with Jolley[8].

The above remarks are intended merely to outline the ways in which series can be manipulated to give results useful to the engineer. The subject of series has rightly received a great deal of attention from mathematicians, and cases of difficulty should be quickly brought to their notice.   Here we have merely tried to show that engineers need not be frightened of series.

Chapter 6

DIFFERENTIATION AND INTEGRATION

Frequently we need to differentiate an expression such as a function of time. A number of useful tricks which help in practical cases are discussed in this chapter, together with the reverse process of integration. A few remarks are also included about partial differentiation and differential equations, but these are intended to prevent engineers from being put off by partial-differentiation signs on sight rather than to deal with the subject systematically. As always in this book, we are primarily concerned with the use that can be made of established mathematical results, rather than with proofs of their validity.

The fundamental starting-point to which we always have to return when exploring any new differential ground is

$$f'(x) \text{ or } \frac{\mathrm{d}f(x)}{\mathrm{d}x} = \lim_{h \to 0} \frac{f(x+h) - f(x)}{h} \tag{6.1}$$

and although this equation appears somewhat formidable in symbols, its significance is quite clear in terms of the geometry of Fig. 6.1.

In Fig. 6.1, the curve is $y = f(x)$. A is a typical point on the curve, whose co-ordinates are $OL = x_A$ and $AL = y_A = f(x_A)$. B is a neighbouring point on the same curve, whose co-ordinates are

$$OM = x_B = OL + LM = x_A + h$$

and

$$MB = y_B = f(x_B) = f(x_A + h)$$

It follows that the gradient or slope of the chord AB of the curve is

$$\frac{BN}{AN} = \frac{BM - AL}{LM} = \frac{f(x_A + h) - f(x_A)}{h} \tag{6.2}$$

so that Equation 6.1 merely expresses that the slope of the tangent (at A) to the curve is the limit of the slope of the chord AB as the point B moves towards A along the curve.

Although Fig. 6.1 is helpful in making clear the meaning of Equation 6.1, this equation, once established, may be freely used without reference to Fig. 6.1. Thus if $f(x) = x^2$, Equation 6.1 gives the well-known result

$$
\begin{aligned}
f'(x) &= \lim_{h \to 0} \frac{(x + h)^2 - x^2}{h} \\
&= \lim_{h \to 0} \frac{2xh + h^2}{h} \\
&= \lim_{h \to 0} (2x + h) = 2x
\end{aligned}
\tag{6.3}
$$

and it is important to note that we can only cancel the h to reduce $(2xh + h^2)/h$ to $(2x + h)$ provided that h is different from zero,

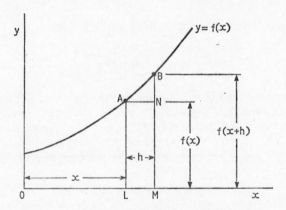

Fig. 6.1. Geometrical significance of Equation 6.1

however small; that is why we have to talk about 'taking the limit when h tends to zero' instead of merely putting h equal to zero.

More generally, Equation 6.1 gives us that if $f(x) = x^n$, then $f'(x) = nx^{n-1}$. We only have to assume the 'Binomial Theorem' discussed in Chapter 5. This theorem tells us that when h is sufficiently small,

$$\frac{(x+h)^n - x^n}{h} = \frac{1}{h}\left\{x^n\left[1 + \frac{nh}{x} + \frac{n(n-1)}{2}\left(\frac{h}{x}\right)^2 + \ldots\right] - x^n\right\}$$

$$= nx^{n-1} + \frac{n(n-1)}{2}x^{n-2}h + \ldots \tag{6.4}$$

and the result follows, since all terms of 6.4 on the right-hand side except the first contain positive powers of h.

TRIGONOMETRICAL DIFFERENTIATION

Again, Equation 6.1 enables us to deal with trigonometrical differentiation. For if x is in radians, and we assume the formula for $\sin (A + B)$ given in Equation 8.23

$$\frac{\sin (x+h) - \sin x}{h} = \frac{\sin x \cos h + \cos x \sin h - \sin x}{h}$$

$$= \cos x \cdot \frac{\sin h}{h} - \sin x \frac{1 - \cos h}{h} \tag{6.5}$$

and we can reasonably accept from Fig. 6.2 that

$$\lim_{h \to 0} \frac{\sin h}{h} = 1, \; \lim_{h \to 0} \frac{1 - \cos h}{h} = 0 \tag{6.6}$$

for if the circle in Fig. 6.2 has unit radius, the chord PQ has length $2 \sin h$ and the arc PQ has length $2h$; for sufficiently small h chord and arc are indistinguishable. $(1 - \cos h)$ is represented by the length NR, and there is a well-known geometrical theorem that since PNQ and ANR are chords of the circle meeting at N,

$$AN \times NR = PN \times NQ = PN^2 \tag{6.7}$$

and this gives

$$\frac{1 - \cos h}{h} = \frac{NR}{h} = \frac{PN^2}{h \cdot AN} = \frac{\sin^2 h}{h(1 + \cos h)}$$

$$\approx \frac{1}{2} \cdot \frac{\sin h}{h} \cdot \sin h \quad \text{for small } h \tag{6.8}$$

Now we have already seen that sin h/h is nearly unity for small h; Equation 6.8 shows that $(1 - \cos h)/h$ is small for small h and therefore that the last term of Equation 6.5 is small. It follows that if $f(x) = \sin x$,

$$f'(x) = \frac{d(\sin x)}{dx} = \cos x = \sin\left(x + \frac{\pi}{2}\right) \qquad (6.9)$$

The last member of Equation 6.9 has a usefulness that will become more obvious later. The other important simple, elementary case in which we need to know $f'(x)$ is when $f(x) = e^x$. The result in this case is

$$f'(x) = \frac{de^x}{dx} = e^x \qquad (6.10)$$

For engineering purposes, it is best to assume that Equation 6.10 is valid where e = 2.718281828 ... although, from the point of view of mathematicians, the orderly development of this part of the

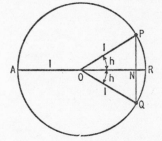

Fig. 6.2. Relation between sin h, $1 - \cos h$ and h

calculus is a matter of some importance for which several different approaches are possible. We shall also assume the 'exponential theorem', namely that

$$e^x = 1 + x + \frac{x^2}{2!} + \frac{x^3}{3!} + \cdots \qquad (6.11)$$

the infinite series on the right being convergent for all values of x.

The above remarks cover the differentiation once of powers of x, trigonometrical functions and exponentials, but we now need to consider general rules for differentiating which greatly extend the range of functions covered.

'INDIRECT' DIFFERENTIATION

If, for example, we want to differentiate

$$y = (a^2 - x^2)^{1/2} \qquad (6.12)$$

with respect to x, the procedure which gives us the greatest understanding is to square both sides of Equation 6.12 giving

$$y^2 = a^2 - x^2 \qquad (6.13)$$

and then differentiate both sides of Equation 6.13 with respect to x. We have no difficulty with the right-hand side; on the left-hand side we would prefer to differentiate with respect to y. The general rule which is useful in this sort of situation is

$$\frac{d(y^2)}{dx} = \frac{d(y^2)}{dy} \times \frac{dy}{dx} \qquad (6.14)$$

and in Equation 6.14, y^2 could be replaced by any function of y. We thus find that the result of differentiating both sides of Equation 6.13 with respect to x is

$$2y \cdot \frac{dy}{dx} = -2x \qquad (6.15)$$

so that

$$\frac{dy}{dx} = \frac{d(\{a^2 - x^2\}^{1/2})}{dx}$$

$$= -\frac{x}{y}$$

$$= -\frac{x}{(a^2 - x^2)^{1/2}} \qquad (6.16)$$

Most cases in which we have to differentiate what appears to be a complicated expression can be handled by giving names, like y in Equation 6.12, to the complicated parts, and then differentiating with respect to x, using Equation 6.14 every time we would find it easier to differentiate with respect to some variable other than x.

THE 'PRODUCT' RULE

The other important aid to differentiation is the 'product rule', namely that if $y = uv$, then

$$\frac{dy}{dx} = u\frac{dv}{dx} + v\frac{du}{dx} \qquad (6.17)$$

This rule applies in all cases, and is easy to remember because of its symmetry. There is a similar rule for finding the derivative of a quotient, say u/w, but this is less important because it can be deduced from Equation 6.17 by putting $v = 1/w$ and applying Equation 6.14 with $(1/w)$ instead of y^2 and w instead of y; there is then no danger of getting a sign wrong.

Most of the functions relevant to engineering are made up of powers, trigonometrical functions, and exponentials, so that the above remarks cover all the ground essential to enable us to differentiate such functions once. We may, however, often need to differentiate several times, and this we consider next. Differentiating x^n r times is straightforward enough; the result is

$$\frac{d^r(x^n)}{dx^r} = n(n-1)(n-2)\ldots(n-r+1)\,x^{n-r} \qquad (6.18)$$

Equation 6.18 tells us that if n and r are both integers, and r exceeds n, then one of the factors on the right-hand side will be zero and therefore the whole right-hand side will be zero. For trigonometrical expressions, the last member of Equation 6.9 comes into its own if differentiating several times is involved, thus

$$\frac{d^r}{dx^r}(\sin x) = \sin(x + \tfrac{1}{2}r\pi) \qquad (6.19)$$

and, by applying Equation 6.14 we could also obtain

$$\frac{d^r}{dx^r}\{\cos(ax+b)\} = a^r\cos(ax+b+\tfrac{1}{2}r\pi) \qquad (6.20)$$

and we thus have no worry about signs; after r differentiations we have the same trigonometrical ratio that we started with, but the argument is increased by $\tfrac{1}{2}r\pi$ and there is a multiplying factor a^r. In the case of exponentials, it is clear from Equation 6.10 that repeated differentiation presents no problem. When we seek to generalise Equation 6.14 to apply to any number of differentiations, the situation becomes more difficult; we can only apply Equation 6.14 repeatedly, with the help of Equation 6.17. We shall, however, see later that Equation 6.17 can be explicitly extended to n differentiations—a result known as Leibnitz' Theorem.

Suppose therefore that we want to differentiate y defined by Equation 6.12 three times with respect to x; that is to say, we require to determine $\dfrac{\mathrm{d}^3 y}{\mathrm{d}x^3}$ in terms of x. Differentiating both sides of Equation 6.13 once (Equation 6.13 is much more convenient than Equation 6.12) gives us Equation 6.15, and Equation 6.16 then gives us $\dfrac{\mathrm{d}y}{\mathrm{d}x}$ in terms of x, but we are ill-advised to worry about the fact that Equation 6.15 has both x and y in it too early. It is better to differentiate both sides of Equation 6.15 as it stands (after dividing through by 2) with respect to x. Again, the right-hand side presents no difficulty. For the left-hand side we have

$$\frac{\mathrm{d}}{\mathrm{d}x}\!\left(y\frac{\mathrm{d}y}{\mathrm{d}x}\right) = \left(\frac{\mathrm{d}y}{\mathrm{d}x}\right)^2 + y\frac{\mathrm{d}^2 y}{\mathrm{d}x^2} \qquad (6.21)$$

from Equation 6.17 with u replaced by y and v by $\dfrac{\mathrm{d}y}{\mathrm{d}x}$. Thus at this stage Equation 6.15 differentiated once gives

$$\left(\frac{\mathrm{d}y}{\mathrm{d}x}\right)^2 + y\frac{\mathrm{d}^2 y}{\mathrm{d}x^2} = -1 \qquad (6.22)$$

If we now differentiate both sides of Equation 6.22 with respect to x, we find

$$\frac{\mathrm{d}}{\mathrm{d}x}\!\left\{\left(\frac{\mathrm{d}y}{\mathrm{d}x}\right) \times \left(\frac{\mathrm{d}y}{\mathrm{d}x}\right)\right\} = \frac{\mathrm{d}^2 y}{\mathrm{d}x^2}\frac{\mathrm{d}y}{\mathrm{d}x} + \frac{\mathrm{d}y}{\mathrm{d}x}\frac{\mathrm{d}^2 y}{\mathrm{d}x^2} = \frac{2\mathrm{d}y}{\mathrm{d}x}\frac{\mathrm{d}^2 y}{\mathrm{d}x^2} \qquad (6.23)$$

from Equation 6.17 with $u = v = \dfrac{\mathrm{d}y}{\mathrm{d}x}$, and

$$\frac{\mathrm{d}}{\mathrm{d}x}\!\left\{y\frac{\mathrm{d}^2 y}{\mathrm{d}x^2}\right\} = y\frac{\mathrm{d}^3 y}{\mathrm{d}x^3} + \frac{\mathrm{d}y}{\mathrm{d}x}\frac{\mathrm{d}^2 y}{\mathrm{d}x^2} \qquad (6.24)$$

from Equation 6.17 with $u = y$, $v = \dfrac{\mathrm{d}^2 y}{\mathrm{d}x^2}$, and therefore

$$3\frac{\mathrm{d}y}{\mathrm{d}x}\frac{\mathrm{d}^2 y}{\mathrm{d}x^2} + y\frac{\mathrm{d}^3 y}{\mathrm{d}x^3} = 0 \qquad (6.25)$$

Equation 6.25 gives us the essential information about $\dfrac{d^3y}{dx^3}$, since $\dfrac{d^2y}{dx^2}$ is known from Equation 6.21 in terms of y and $\dfrac{dy}{dx}$; $\dfrac{dy}{dx}$ can be expressed by means of Equation 6.15 in terms of x and y, and finally y can be eliminated by means of Equation 6.12. We can therefore deduce $\dfrac{d^3y}{dx^3}$ in terms of x if we wish by a series of eliminations of the unwanted quantities $\dfrac{d^2y}{dx^2}$, $\dfrac{dy}{dx}$ and y which are known. This elimination is somewhat tedious but quite straightforward. It must be emphasized at this point that the elimination may be unnecessary. If for example we require $\dfrac{d^3y}{dx^3}$ only for a particular value of x such as $a \cos \theta$, Equation 6.12 tells us that $y = a \sin \theta$, Equation 6.15 that $\dfrac{dy}{dx} = - \cot \theta$, and Equation 6.22 that $\dfrac{d^2y}{dx^2}$ is $- 1/(a \sin^3 \theta)$. Substitution into Equation 6.25 gives

$$\frac{d^3y}{dx^3} = - \frac{3 \cos \theta}{a^2 \sin^5 \theta} \tag{6.26}$$

and this result is just as useful as, and easier to obtain than, a result only involving x.

REPEATED DIFFERENTIATION: LEIBNITZ' THEOREM

As already mentioned, Equation 6.17 can be explicitly extended to n differentiations. Differentiating both sides once, we obtain

$$\frac{d^2y}{dx^2} = \frac{d^2(uv)}{dx^2} = \frac{du}{dx}\frac{dv}{dx} + u\frac{d^2v}{dx^2} + \frac{dv}{dx}\frac{du}{dx} + v\frac{d^2u}{dx^2} \tag{6.27}$$

the first pair of terms coming from Equation 6.17 with u unaltered and v replaced by dv/dx, and the second pair from the same equation with u replaced by v and v by du/dx. Equation 6.27 simplifies to

$$\frac{d^2(uv)}{dx^2} = u\frac{d^2v}{dx^2} + 2\frac{du}{dx}\frac{dv}{dx} + \frac{d^2u}{dx^2}v \tag{6.28}$$

Repeating the differentiation with respect to x, we find similarly, after a little rearrangement,

$$\frac{\mathrm{d}^3(uv)}{\mathrm{d}x^3} = u\frac{\mathrm{d}^3v}{\mathrm{d}x^3} + 3\frac{\mathrm{d}u}{\mathrm{d}x}\frac{\mathrm{d}^2v}{\mathrm{d}x^2} + 3\frac{\mathrm{d}^2u}{\mathrm{d}x^2}\frac{\mathrm{d}v}{\mathrm{d}x} + \frac{\mathrm{d}^3u}{\mathrm{d}x^3}v \qquad (6.29)$$

and, at this stage, the resemblance to the Binomial Theorem (for a positive integral index) discussed in Chapter 5 becomes clear. The result of n differentiations can be written in the form known as Leibnitz' Theorem, namely

$$\frac{\mathrm{d}^n(uv)}{\mathrm{d}x^n} = u\frac{\mathrm{d}^nv}{\mathrm{d}x^n} + \frac{n}{1}\frac{\mathrm{d}u}{\mathrm{d}x}\frac{\mathrm{d}^{n-1}v}{\mathrm{d}x^{n-1}} + \frac{n(n-1)}{1.2}\frac{\mathrm{d}^2u}{\mathrm{d}x^2}\frac{\mathrm{d}^{n-2}v}{\mathrm{d}x^{n-2}} +$$

$$+ \ldots + \frac{n(n-1)\ldots(n-r+1)}{1.2\ldots r}\frac{\mathrm{d}^ru}{\mathrm{d}x^r}\frac{\mathrm{d}^{n-r}v}{\mathrm{d}x^{n-r}} +$$

$$+ \ldots + \frac{\mathrm{d}^nu}{\mathrm{d}x^n}v \qquad (6.30)$$

so that any expression can be differentiated n times immediately if it consists of terms each of which is the product of pairs of functions each of which can be differentiated n times. In particular, if u is x^k (k integer > 0) the right-hand side of Equation 6.30 has only $(k+1)$ terms.

PARTIAL DIFFERENTIATION

So far we have only considered functions of one variable, and procedures required for finding their rates of change with respect to that variable. We must also consider the variations of functions of more than one variable, whether these variables are independent or not. The case of two variables is sufficiently typical to be the only one we need consider.

We have to form an equation analogous to Equation 6.1, and note that

$$\triangle f = f(x+h, y+k) - f(x, y) \qquad (6.31)$$

which is the change in $f(x, y)$ when x is increased to $x + h$ and y is simultaneously increased to $y + k$, can also be written

$$\Delta f = h\left[\frac{f(x + h,\, y + k) - f(x,\, y + k)}{h}\right] +$$

$$+ k\left[\frac{f(x,\, y + k) - f(x,\, y)}{k}\right] \qquad (6.32)$$

and the expressions within large square brackets are very similar in form to those which occur in Equation 6.1. In each of them, only the variation of one variable is under consideration. If $(y + k)$ could be regarded as a number, and h as sufficiently small, we could follow Equation 6.1 and write the first term on the right-hand side of Equation 6.32 as $hf'(x)$ or $h\frac{df(x)}{dx}$, but we need a special sign to indicate that $(y + k)$ is held constant during the process. This sign is ∂ instead of d; it indicates, wherever it occurs, that any variable other than that which immediately follows the (lower) ∂ is to be regarded as held constant while the process of differentiation is going on. Thus we write

$$\lim_{h \to 0} \frac{f(x + h,\, y + k) - f(x,\, y + k)}{h} = \frac{\partial f(x,\, y + k)}{\partial x} \qquad (6.33)$$

and similarly

$$\lim_{k \to 0} \frac{f(x,\, y + k) - f(x,\, y)}{k} = \frac{\partial f(x,\, y)}{\partial y} \qquad (6.34)$$

Assuming that $\frac{\partial f(x,\, y)}{\partial x}$ and $\frac{\partial f(x,\, y)}{\partial y}$ are continuous functions of both x and y, as they are in all genuine physical situations, we can substitute back into Equation 6.32 and say that, for sufficiently small h and k,

$$\Delta f \approx h\frac{\partial f(x,\, y)}{\partial x} + k\frac{\partial f(x,\, y)}{\partial y} \qquad (6.35)$$

and a similar equation holds if f depends on several variables instead of only two.

If x and y are both functions of some other variable, say t, so that $x = \phi(t)$ and $y = \psi(t)$, and, at time $t + t_0$, x becomes $x + h$ and y becomes $y + k$, we have

$$x + h = \phi(t + t_0); \quad y + k = \psi(t + t_0) \qquad (6.36)$$

and it follows that, for sufficiently small t_0

$$\frac{h}{t_0} = \frac{\phi(t + t_0) - \phi(t)}{t_0} \approx \frac{\mathrm{d}\phi(t)}{\mathrm{d}t} \text{ or } \frac{\mathrm{d}x}{\mathrm{d}t} \qquad (6.37)$$

and

$$\frac{k}{t_0} = \frac{\psi(t + t_0) - \psi(t)}{t_0} \approx \frac{\mathrm{d}\psi(t)}{\mathrm{d}t} \text{ or } \frac{\mathrm{d}y}{\mathrm{d}t} \qquad (6.38)$$

If we now divide through Equation 6.35 by t_0, and substitute for h/t_0 and k/t_0 from Equations 6.37 and 6.38, $\triangle f$ is simply the change in f associated with increasing t to $t + t_0$. Equation 6.35 therefore reduces, for sufficiently small t_0, to

$$\frac{\mathrm{d}f}{\mathrm{d}t} = \frac{\partial f(x, y)}{\partial x} \frac{\mathrm{d}x}{\mathrm{d}t} + \frac{\partial f(x, y)}{\partial y} \frac{\mathrm{d}y}{\mathrm{d}t} \qquad (6.39)$$

In writing down Equation 6.39 we have assumed that all limits exist and that if two terms are multiplied together, the limit of the product is the same as the product of the limits. Now a textbook intended mainly for pure mathematicians would devote considerable space to points of this nature, but we do not intend to do so. Although a mathematician can easily invent functions which can bring into being all kinds of difficulties connected with Equations 6.35 or 6.39, they are not relevant to the study of natural phenomena, where such functions do not in fact occur. If they appear to occur, it is most likely that the formulation of the problem is wrong. Time is much better spent in finding a more appropriate formulation than in studying the precise properties of awkward functions. In general, functions which can properly be associated with natural phenomena can be regarded as continuous and differentiable any number of times, and limiting processes, as in Equation 6.39, can be carried out in any order. Isolated infinities (simple poles) and finite step-discontinuities can usually be handled without much difficulty, and expressions containing these need not therefore be ruled out straightway, but any more complicated discontinuities (except possibly 'at infinity', as with e^x) should be regarded as associated with a wrong formulation of the problem.

The above discussion enables us to differentiate most of the expressions likely to be associated with practical, physical problems, and to determine the way in which a function of two variables varies when small changes, related or unrelated, are made in either or both of the variables; a function of three or more variables behaves in a very similar manner.

INTEGRATION

It remains to consider the opposite process of integration, which is also associated with finding areas under, or enclosed by, curves.

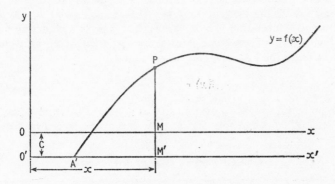

Fig. 6.3.   Derivation of $f(x)$ given $f'(x)$

Now the first point we have to notice is that whereas when we are given $f(x)$, $df(x)/dx$ is uniquely determined from Equation 6.1, if $df(x)/dx$ is given, $f(x)$ is not uniquely determined; the addition of any constant C to $f(x)$ will not affect $f'(x)$.   If therefore we first differentiate $f(x)$ and derive $f'(x)$, and then integrate $f'(x)$, we shall finish up with $f(x) + C$ and not necessarily with $f(x)$.   In other words, the processes of integration and differentiation are not completely reversible unless we can take steps to ensure that C is always zero. This matter is important in connection with Heaviside's operational calculus, briefly discussed in Chapter 9 and more fully elsewhere[7]. [This has the disadvantage that in an operation involving a series of integrations and differentiations, the order in which the integrations and differentiations are performed will matter.   For some purposes (such as the solution of differential equations) it is very desirable to ensure that integration is so performed that these arbitrary 'constants of integration' are taken as zero, so that the processes of integration and differentiation are completely reversible.]   The geometrical significance of C is clear from Fig. 6.3, and for the time being we shall assume that it is best to accept the fact that $f(x)$ is not unique when $f'(x)$ is given.

In Fig. 6.3 we suppose that the curve drawn is $y = f(x)$; we are given the slope $f'(x)$ of the tangent at every point (of which P is typical, at a distance $x = OM$ to the right of Oy). But this slope will be unaltered if we replace the original x-axis Ox by $O'x'$ parallel to Ox and a distance C below it, the y-axis being unaltered so that the new origin is O'. The complete specification of $f(x)$ therefore requires an additional item of information besides the value of the slope $f'(x)$ of the tangent to $y = f(x)$ at each point P. If this additional information is lacking, we must simply include the term $+C$ with $f(x)$. Thus, if we know only that $f'(x) = x^2$, all we can deduce (with the help of Table 6.1) is that

$$f(x) = \tfrac{1}{3} x^3 + C \tag{6.40}$$

If, however, we also know that $f(0) = 3$, we deduce from Equation 6.40 that $C = 3$ and thus $f(x)$ is now completely specified for all

Table 6.1. SIMPLE CASES OF INTEGRATION

$f'(x)$	$x^n, (n \neq -1)$	$\cos(kx + \alpha)$	$\exp(ax)$
$f(x)$	$x^{n+1}/(n+1) + C$	$\dfrac{1}{k} \cos\left(kx + \alpha - \dfrac{\pi}{2}\right) + C$	$\dfrac{1}{a} e^{ax} + C$

other relevant values of x. Alternatively, the additional information might be given in the form that $f(x)$ was zero for some value α of x. In this case, putting α for x in Equation 6.40 tells us that

$$C = -\tfrac{1}{3}\alpha^3$$

so that
$$f(x) = \tfrac{1}{3}(x^3 - \alpha^3) \tag{6.41}$$

From the previous section, we can draw up Table 6.1 showing the corresponding values of $f(x)$ when $f'(x)$ is given.

To these must be added another (which is in fact deducible from the last entry in Table 6.1), namely:

if
$$f'(x) = 1/x$$

then
$$f(x) = \log_e x + C \tag{6.42}$$

INTEGRATION AND AREA

Now the notation 'if $f'(x)$ is given, then $f(x)$ has a certain value' which we have so far used is cumbersome even if comprehensible, and we need an explicit notation for integration. But this notation will be clearer if we first consider Fig. 6.4. Suppose that $A(x)$ is the shaded area bounded on the left by the ordinate AM at $x = \alpha$, on the right by the ordinate PK where $x = OK$, below by the axis of x and above by the curve $y = \phi(x)$. Then it can be shown that

$$A'(x) = \phi(x) \tag{6.43}$$

so that the process of integration, which we first regarded as the opposite or inverse of differentiation is, in fact, also related to finding the area under a given curve. (Fig. 6.4 has been drawn for the simplest case when K is to the right of O, and x and $\phi(x)$ are positive. As is usually the case when functions formulated mathematically are illustrated geometrically, the 'signs take care of themselves' in other cases provided that any shaded area below Ox is counted negative.)

From Table 6.1 it therefore follows that if $\phi(x) = x^2$, then

$$A(x) = \tfrac{1}{3} x^3 + C \tag{6.44}$$

and since $A(x)$ is zero when $x = \alpha$, we have $C = -\tfrac{1}{3}\alpha^3$ and therefore

$$A(x) = \tfrac{1}{3} (x^3 - \alpha^3) \tag{6.45}$$

Thus the case considered in Equations 6.41 and 6.45 is one which arises naturally when we wish to deal with areas bounded on the left by a particular ordinate like AM in Fig. 6.4. The notation for integration takes this into account. We write

$$f(x) = \int f'(x)dx + C; \quad A(\beta) = \int_a^\beta \phi(x) \, dx \tag{6.46}$$

The sign $\int$ is called the 'sign of integration', and the expression dx can be regarded simply as a short-hand for 'with respect to x'. (We shall see later that there is a simple rule for dealing with dx if we wish to simplify the integration by changing the variable x into say y.) Thus the first of Equations 6.46 reads '$f(x)$ is the integral of $f'(x)$ with respect to x'; the constant C of integration is often omitted though its presence is always implied. The second of Equations 6.46 reads 'The area $A(\beta)$ (bounded by the ordinates AM, BN,

8

the axis of x and the curve $y = \phi(x)$ in Fig. 6.4) is obtained by integrating $\phi(x)$ with respect to x from α to β'. This means that we have to determine $I(x)$ where

$$I(x) = \int \phi(x) \, dx + C \tag{6.47}$$

and we may allow C to have any value we please; $A(\beta)$ is defined to mean $I(\beta) - I(\alpha)$. The quantities α and β are called the lower and upper limits of the 'definite' integral $A(\beta)$, and it should be noted that $A(\beta)$ depends only upon these limits, not upon the variable (x) with respect to which the integration was performed. When there are no limits and an arbitrary constant of integration, as in Equation 6.47, the integral $I(x)$ is said to be 'indefinite'. The process of evaluating the definite integral (second of Equations 6.46) can be summed up

$$A(\beta) = \int_{\alpha}^{\beta} \phi(x) \, dx$$

$$= \Big[I(x) \Big]_{\alpha}^{\beta} = I(\beta) - I(\alpha) \tag{6.48}$$

the square brackets in the third member of Equation 6.48 indicating that the result of substituting α for x in $I(x)$ is to be subtracted from the result of substituting β for x. Thus if $\phi(x) = x^2$, Equation 6.48 becomes

$$A(\beta) = \int_{\alpha}^{\beta} x^2 \, dx$$

$$= \left[\frac{x^3}{3} \right]_{\alpha}^{\beta} = \tfrac{1}{3} (\beta^3 - \alpha^3) \tag{6.49}$$

Now it is an unfortunate fact that while we can nearly always formulate explicitly the gradient $f'(x)$ of a given function $f(x)$ it is not by any means always possible to integrate a function explicitly. We are therefore fortunate if we can express the function we wish to integrate as a combination of functions whose integrals are known from, say, Table 6.1. We shall next consider a few simple cases in which this can be done, and thereafter the process of changing the variable, which in effect enables us to add greatly to the list of functions which could be included in Table 6.1.

Now from Table 6.1 (omitting the constant of integration)

$$\int \cos \theta \, d\theta = \sin \theta; \quad \int \cos 3\theta \, d\theta = \tfrac{1}{3} \sin 3\theta \qquad (6.50$$

But it is well known (from Equation 8.32) that

$$\cos 3\theta = 4 \cos^3 \theta - 3 \cos \theta \qquad (6.51)$$

so that combining Equations 6.50 and 6.51 we can evaluate

$$\int \cos^3 \theta \, d\theta = \int \tfrac{1}{4} (3 \cos \theta + \cos 3\theta) \, d\theta$$

$$= \tfrac{1}{4} (3 \sin \theta + \tfrac{1}{3} \sin 3\theta) \qquad (6.52)$$

which is not in the original list. There are many trigonometrical identities which can be used in the same sort of way as Equation

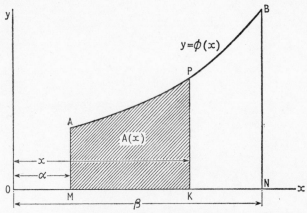

Fig. 6.4. *Integration and area*

6.51 to transform a trigonometrical integrand into a form more amenable to integration.

Now consider three integrals

$$\int_a^b x (c^2 - x^2) \, dx ; \quad \int_a^b \frac{x \, dx}{(c^2 - x^2)^2} ; \quad \int_a^b \frac{dx}{(c^2 - x^2)^{1/2}} \qquad (6.53)$$

where $0 < a < b < c$.

The first of these is straightforward from Table 6.1; we have

$$\int (c^2x - x^3)\, dx = \tfrac{1}{2} c^2 x^2 - \tfrac{1}{4} x^4$$

$$= \tfrac{1}{4} [c^4 - (c^2 - x^2)^2]$$

so that the integral reduces to

$$[\tfrac{1}{2}c^2x^2 - \tfrac{1}{4}x^4]_a^b = \tfrac{1}{2}c^2 (b^2 - a^2) - \tfrac{1}{4}(b^4 - a^4)$$

$$= \tfrac{1}{4}(b^2 - a^2)(2c^2 - a^2 - b^2) \qquad (6.54)$$

A clue to the second integral is obtained by differentiating $(c^2 - x^2)^{-1} = y$ for if y has this value

$$(c^2 - x^2)\, y = 1 \qquad (6.55)$$

and differentiating both sides of Equation 6.55 with respect to x as in Equation 6.15

$$(c^2 - x^2)\frac{dy}{dx} - 2\,xy = 0 \qquad (6.56)$$

so that

$$\frac{dy}{dx} = \frac{2xy}{(c^2 - x^2)} = \frac{2x}{(c^2 - x^2)^2} = \text{twice integrand} \qquad (6.57)$$

Hence

$$\int \frac{x\, dx}{(c^2 - x^2)^2} = \frac{1}{2\,(c^2 - x^2)} + C\,;$$

$$\text{integral} = \left[\frac{1}{2(c^2 - x^2)}\right]_a^b = \tfrac{1}{2}\left[\frac{1}{c^2 - b^2} - \frac{1}{c^2 - a^2}\right] \qquad (6.58)$$

INTEGRATION BY SUBSTITUTION

But there does not seem to be any satisfactory way of finding any expression which when differentiated gives the integrand of the third of the integrals 6.53, and we were clearly somewhat fortunate that the differentiation of Equation 6.53 gave us a method of doing the second. A more general method of attack is needed, and this is provided by the method of changing the variable. Not even this is infallible; it is, however, worth trying and sometimes spectacularly successful.

In the integrals 6.53 let $x = c \sin \theta \; (- \pi/2 < \theta < \pi/2)$ and consider the last integral first as we have failed hitherto to do it at all. We have

$$\frac{\mathrm{d}x}{\mathrm{d}\theta} = c \cos \theta \qquad (6.59)$$

and the rule for dealing with $\mathrm{d}x$ in this situation is

Replace $\mathrm{d}x$ by $\dfrac{\mathrm{d}x}{\mathrm{d}\theta} \, \mathrm{d}\theta$

so that
$$\int_{x=a}^{x=b} \frac{\mathrm{d}x}{(c^2 - x^2)^{1/2}} = \int_{\theta = \sin^{-1}(a/c)}^{\theta = \sin^{-1}(b/c)} \frac{c \cos \theta \, \mathrm{d}\theta}{c \cos \theta}$$

$$= \int_{\theta = \sin^{-1}(a/c)}^{\theta = \sin^{-1}(b/c)} 1 \, \mathrm{d}\theta = \sin^{-1}(b/c) - \sin^{-1}(a/c) \qquad (6.60)$$

Hence the substitution technique has been successful; the basis of its success was that when we made a change of variable designed to simplify $(c^2 - x^2)^{1/2}$ (which was the most awkward expression involved in the integrand), the factor $\left(\dfrac{\mathrm{d}x}{\mathrm{d}\theta}\right)$ associated with the rule for replacing $\mathrm{d}x$ introduced something into the θ-integrand, namely $c \cos \theta$, which was also simple and fitted in conveniently. There is no guarantee that the factor $\left(\dfrac{\mathrm{d}x}{\mathrm{d}\theta}\right)$ may not introduce something more complicated into the integrand. Applying the same technique to the second of the integrals 6.53, it reduces to

$$\frac{1}{c^2} \int_{\sin^{-1}(a/c)}^{\sin^{-1}(b/c)} \frac{\sin \theta \, \mathrm{d}\theta}{\cos^3 \theta} \qquad (6.61)$$

and in this case a second substitution $\cos \theta = y$ is the easiest way to evaluate the integral in terms of y, because differentiating this with respect to y gives

$$- \sin \theta \frac{\mathrm{d}\theta}{\mathrm{d}y} = 1 \qquad (6.62)$$

so that, replacing $\mathrm{d}\theta$ by $\left(\dfrac{\mathrm{d}\theta}{\mathrm{d}y}\right) \mathrm{d}y$ we have that the integral reduces to

$$\frac{1}{c^2} \int_a^\beta -\frac{1}{y^3} \, \mathrm{d}y = \frac{1}{2c^2}\left(\frac{1}{\beta^2} - \frac{1}{\alpha^2}\right) \tag{6.63}$$

where $\alpha = \cos\theta$ when $\sin\theta$ is a/c. It follows that $\alpha = \{1 - (a^2/c^2)\}^{\frac{1}{2}}$ and similarly $\beta = \{1 - (b^2/c^2)\}^{1/2}$.

It is easily seen that Equations 6.58 and 6.63 give the same result, and wisdom after the event suggests that the integral could have been done in one step by substituting $y = (1 - x^2/c^2)^{\frac{1}{2}}$. In this kind of situation, however, it is often very much easier to see and understand by taking two reasonably obvious steps rather than to make a great effort to replace these by one more difficult step.

The first of the integrals 6.53 could also have been done by means of the substitution $x = c \sin\theta$ but, in this case, direct integration with respect to x is obviously the correct method.

A few general guides to the sort of substitution that is worth trying are given in Table 6.2 and briefly discussed below. In each case, the form of the integrand in terms of the new variable is also given. It is often necessary, as in Equation 6.63, to make a second substitution. This is a case of a general principle of mathematics and physics, that one should not 'weary of well doing'.

The list is not complete, because, as already mentioned, not every function can be integrated explicitly in terms of elementary functions; for example, any integral of the form

$$\int \frac{\mathrm{d}x}{(\text{cubic or quartic in } x)^{1/2}} \tag{6.64}$$

is an 'elliptic integral'. Nowadays many such integrals are tabulated, so that the disadvantage of having to deal with a function not having an explicit integral is less than it used to be. Nevertheless, here we are only concerned with cases where explicit integrals can be found in a reasonably straightforward manner. Cases where explicit integrals cannot be found, if not reducible to a tabulated form, can be dealt with by means of an approximation such as 'Simpson's Rule' to be described.

The general idea in substitution is to make a change of variable which simplifies the worst feature of the integrand, as in Equation 6.60.

In all the above integrals we have expressed results in terms of the new variable after substitution. Officially, one is supposed to substitute back in terms of the original variable after an integral not 'between limits' is completed. This is an unnecessary infliction,

Table 6.2

Initial	Form of Integrand	Substitution	Resulting Form of Integrand
A.	$\displaystyle\int xF(x^2)\,dx$	$x^2 = y$	$\displaystyle\frac{1}{2}\int F(y)\,dy$
B.	$\displaystyle\int \frac{1}{F(x)}\cdot\frac{dF(x)}{dx}\,dx$	$F(x) = u$	Integral reduces to $\log_e u$
C.	$\displaystyle\int f(F(x))\frac{dF(x)}{dx}\,dx$	$F(x) = u$	$\displaystyle\int f(u)\,du$
D.	$\displaystyle\int \sin\theta\,F(\cos\theta)\,d\theta$	$\cos\theta = u$ (special case of C)	$\displaystyle-\int F(u)\,du$
E.	$\displaystyle\int \cos\theta\,F(\sin\theta)\,d\theta$	$\sin\theta = u$ (special case of C)	$\displaystyle\int F(u)\,du$
F.	$\displaystyle\int \frac{\alpha+\beta\sin\theta+\gamma\cos\theta}{a+b\sin\theta+c\cos\theta}\,d\theta$	$\tan\tfrac{1}{2}\theta = t$	Of form $\displaystyle\int \frac{A+Bt+Ct^2}{(1+t^2)(D+Et+Ft^2)}\,dt$ (Discussed below; use partial fractions)
G.	$\displaystyle\int \frac{dx}{a^2+x^2}$	$x = a\tan\theta$	Integral is θ/a
H.	$\displaystyle\int \frac{dx}{x^2-a^2}$	Use partial fractions	Integral is $\dfrac{1}{2a}\log_e\dfrac{x-a}{x+a}$
I.	$\displaystyle\int \frac{dx}{(a^2-x^2)^{1/2}}$ or $\displaystyle\int (a^2-x^2)^{1/2}\,dx$	$x = a\sin\theta$	Integral is θ or $\frac{1}{4}a^2(2\theta + \sin 2\theta)$
J.	$\displaystyle\int \frac{dx}{(a^2+x^2)^{1/2}}$ or $\displaystyle\int (a^2+x^2)^{1/2}\,dx$	$x = a\sinh\theta$	Integral is θ or $\frac{1}{4}a^2(2\theta + \sinh 2\theta)$
K.	$\displaystyle\int \frac{dx}{(x^2-a^2)^{1/2}}$ or $\displaystyle\int (x^2-a^2)^{1/2}\,dx$	$x = a\cosh\theta$	Integral is θ or $\frac{1}{4}a^2(\cosh 2\theta - 2\theta)$
L.	$\displaystyle\int \frac{dx}{(ax^2+bx+c)^{1/2}}$ or $\displaystyle\int (ax^2+bx+c)^{1/2}\,dx$	$x = -(b/2a) + y$	Reduces to form B, I, J or K
M.	$\displaystyle\int \frac{dx}{\{(x-a)(b-x)\}^{1/2}}$ or $\displaystyle\int \{(x-a)(b-x)\}^{1/2}\,dx$	$x = a\cos^2\theta + b\sin^2\theta$ $(b > a > 0)$	Integral is 2θ or $\frac{1}{16}(b-a)^2\{4\theta - \sin 4\theta\}$
N.	$\displaystyle\int \frac{dx}{ax^2+bx+c}$	$x = -\dfrac{b}{2a} + y$	Reduces to G or H

since in practice one normally wishes to use integrals between limits, and then one can just as easily work with the new variable as the old, using the equation of the substitution to determine the limits of integration for the new variable.

Little comment is required on the above list; not all the substitutions complete the integration, but they do reduce the complexity of the integrand. In the case of F, the integrand can be reduced by the 'partial fraction' technique discussed in Chapter 5, and combining complex conjugate terms, to the form

$$\int \left[\frac{P + 2Qt}{1 + t^2} + \frac{R(2Ft + E) + S}{D + Et + Ft^2} \right] \, dt \qquad (6.65)$$

The P-term in the integral 6.65 is of type G, the Q-term is of type B, the R-term is also of type B and the S-term of type N in Table 6.2, so that integrals of the form F can always be done explicitly.

INFINITIES IN INTEGRATION

Finally, we have to consider the situation if either the integrand or one of the limits becomes infinite. In the last of the integrals 6.53, for example, if $b = c$ the integrand becomes infinite when $x = b = c$. But Equation 6.60 is still correct; even if $b = c$, it merely means than $\sin^{-1} (b/c)$ can be replaced by $\pi/2$. Now the general rule for dealing with this sort of situation is to examine the situation carefully if the critical value likely to cause difficulty is closely approached. The substitution of $c \sin \theta$ for x shows that in this case no difficulty occurs. As a rough general guide it my be mentioned that if

$$I = \int_{\alpha}^{\beta} \frac{dx}{x^n} \qquad (6.66)$$

then if $n < 1$, there is no difficulty when α, β are on opposite sides of zero and if $n > 1$ there is no difficulty when $\alpha \to - \infty$, $\beta < 0$ or when $\alpha > 0$, $\beta \to \infty$. If the integrand is $\phi(x)$, and we suspect a difficulty because $\phi(x)$ tends to infinity when $x = 0$, then if $x^n \phi(x)$ is small for x sufficiently small and n greater than n_0 (n_0 being less than but *not* equal to 1) we can ignore the fact that $\phi(x)$ tends to infinity. Again, if $x^n \phi(x)$ is small for x sufficiently large, n being greater than n_1 where n_1 is greater than but *not* equal to 1, we need not treat an infinite upper limit in any special way different from that appropriate to a finite limit. In this connection it should be noted that e^{-ax} can be regarded as decaying very rapidly to zero as x tends to infinity when a is positive, because $x^n e^{-ax}$ tends to zero as x tends to infinity however large n may be and however small a may be, provided that n is finite and a is not actually equal to zero.

We have thus found that there are cases when integration can be easily performed because we can recognise the integrand as the derivative of a known function or a combination of known functions, and that a change of variable may reduce the integral to this condition when originally it was not obvious. If the integrand or the limits become infinite, there are a large number of cases in which no special difficulties are introduced; sometimes integration is possible even when the restrictions just mentioned are not satisfied, but such cases are a mathematician's job rather than an engineer's.

INTEGRATION BY PARTS

We now consider a general process, known as 'integration by parts,' which sometimes permits us to integrate an expression which cannot be easily integrated otherwise, and approximate methods for dealing with more difficult cases where the integral is either very complicated or not explicitly obtainable at all.

The general idea behind such methods is to replace the given integrand, say $F(x)$, by some other function $G(x)$ which can be integrated and which is a good approximation to $F(x)$ for at any rate some part of the range of integration; it may be necessary to use different approximations for different parts of the range of integration. The method of 'integration by parts' is really another way of looking at Equation 6.17 with y replaced by uv where u and v and both functions of x.

Now integrate both sides of Equation 6.17 between the limits a and b; after rearrangement, we find

$$\int_a^b u\frac{\mathrm{d}v}{\mathrm{d}x}\,\mathrm{d}x = u(b)v(b) - u(a)v(a) - \int_a^b v\frac{\mathrm{d}u}{\mathrm{d}x}\,\mathrm{d}x \qquad (6.67)$$

Equation 6.67 is the formula for 'integration by parts'. It assumes that we have to integrate the product of two functions, one of which is given as u and the other as $\dfrac{\mathrm{d}v}{\mathrm{d}x}$. It is therefore essential that we should be able to integrate the function chosen as $\dfrac{\mathrm{d}v}{\mathrm{d}x}$ explicitly; any value we please may be taken for the constant of this integration, because this constant cancels out of the right-hand side of Equation 6.67. Equation 6.67 thus reduces the integral on the left-hand side with which we started to a different integral, specified by the last term on the right-hand side. Unfortunately there is no guarantee that this second integral may not be more intractable than the first, but the process is well worth trying if u is x or an integral power of x. The process may have to be applied more than once to achieve the desired result. Consider for example

$$I_1 = \int_0^1 x^2 \cos(\pi x)\, dx \qquad (6.68)$$

Here the first step is to apply Equation 6.67 with u as x^2 and $\dfrac{dv}{dx}$ as $\cos \pi x$, so that v can be taken as $\{\sin(\pi x)\}/\pi$. We thus find

$$I_1 = -\int_0^1 \left\{\frac{1}{\pi}\sin(\pi x)\right\}. 2x\, dx \qquad (6.69)$$

Equation 6.69 is better than Equation 6.68, but we have to apply Equation 6.67 a second time before we can evaluate I_1 explicitly. This time we take the constant factor $(2/\pi)$ outside the integral, and put $u = x$ and $\dfrac{dv}{dx} = \sin(\pi x)$ so that v can be taken as $-\{\cos(\pi x)\}/\pi$. We thus find

$$I_1 = -\frac{2}{\pi}\left[-\frac{\cos \pi}{\pi} + \int_0^1 \frac{\cos \pi x}{\pi}\, dx\right] \qquad (6.70a)$$
$$= -(2/\pi^2) \qquad (6.70b)$$

since the term remaining to be integrated in Equation 6.70a is one which can be integrated directly by means of Table 6.1.

Another case in which 'integration by parts' is successful is

$$I_2 = \int_0^1 e^{-x} \cos \pi x\, dx \qquad (6.71)$$

and the same technique would work for the integrand $e^{-x} \cos(\beta x + \gamma)$. Putting $u = e^{-x}$ and $v = \{\sin(\pi x)\}/\pi$ in Equation 6.67, we find

$$I_2 = \frac{1}{\pi}\int_0^1 e^{-x} \sin \pi x\, dx \qquad (6.72)$$

Again, at this stage Equation 6.72 does not appear to be any improvement on Equation 6.71, but, as in the previous example, success depends upon being ready to apply Equation 6.67 more than once. Applying Equation 6.67 for the second time with $u = e^{-x}$ as before but $\dfrac{dv}{dx} = \sin(\pi x)$ so that v can be taken as $- \{\cos(\pi x)\}/\pi$, we find

$$I_2 = \frac{1}{\pi^2}(1 + e^{-1}) - \frac{1}{\pi^2} I_2 \text{ or } I_2 = \frac{1 + e^{-1}}{1 + \pi^2} \qquad (6.73)$$

and, in this case, success was due to the fact that after two 'integrations by parts', the integration remaining to be performed happened to be not a known integral but a multiple of the original integral I_2 required.

INTEGRATION BY SERIES EXPANSION

Next consider the integral

$$\int_0^1 \cosh\{(0 \cdot 1x + 0 \cdot 05)^{1/2}\} \, dx \qquad (6.74)$$

Here the fact that the argument is $(0 \cdot 1x + 0 \cdot 05)^{1/2}$ inhibits direct integration, but the fact that this argument never exceeds $0 \cdot 15$ numerically suggests strongly that the correct procedure is to replace the integrand 6.74 by a series expansion

$$1 + \frac{0 \cdot 1x + 0 \cdot 05}{2!} + \frac{(0 \cdot 1x + 0 \cdot 05)^2}{4!} + \dots \qquad (6.75)$$

Substituting only the first two terms of the series 6.75 into the integral 6.74, it reduces to $1 \cdot 05$. The next term contributes $10(0 \cdot 15^3 - 0 \cdot 05^3)/72$, which is about $0 \cdot 00045$, so that it just fails to affect the third decimal place.

Now the series 6.75 happens to be a very 'safe' series, because it is convergent for all values of x.

We have already discussed series approximations sufficiently in Chapter 5, and they are frequently very useful for integrations.

In general, a series of positive powers of y, say

$$S(y) = a_0 + a_1 y + a_2 y^2 + \qquad (6.76)$$

has a 'radius of converence' R. This means that if the modulus of

y (which may be complex) is less than R, the series is safely convergent, and the technique used above of substituting the first few terms of the series (which are easy to integrate) for the sum is permissible. This technique must not be used if the modulus of y is equal to R and, if the modulus of y is greater than R, the series is divergent. If the modulus of y is near R but less than R, convergence will be slow. R is usually found from the equation

$$\lim_{n \to \infty} \left| \frac{a_{n+1}R}{a_n} \right| = 1 \qquad (6.77)$$

which is, in effect, applying the 'ratio test' Equation 5.32, to the series derived from Equation 6.76 by replacing y by R and considering only absolute values. In the case of the series expression 6.75, R is infinite, so that this series is particularly easy to handle. Again, a short-range expansion of an otherwise unwieldy expression is often possible. Consider for example

$$I_3 = \int_{\pi/3}^{\pi/2} \cos (3 \cos \theta) \, d\theta \qquad (6.78)$$

and first put $\theta = \phi - (5\pi/12)$, so that the integral I_3 reduces to

$$I_3 = \int_{-\pi/12}^{\pi/12} \cos \{3 \cos[\phi - (5\pi/12)]\} \, d\phi \qquad (6.79)$$

Now ϕ never numerically exceeds $\pi/12$, and therefore if we can neglect $\frac{1}{2}(\pi/12)^2$, we can write (using Equation 8.17)

$$\cos \{\phi - (5\pi/12)\} = \cos (5\pi/12) \cos \phi + \sin (5\pi/12) \sin \phi \qquad (6.80a)$$

$$\approx \cos (5\pi/12) + \phi \sin (5\pi/12) \qquad (6.80b)$$

and substitution from Equation 6.80b into Equation 6.79 reduces the latter to an integration which we can evaluate explicity, and shall call I_{31}.

When this kind of approximation is made, it is advisable to have a rough idea of the size of the principal error made. In the case of I_3 (Equation 6.79) we replaced $\cos \phi$ by 1 when we should have replaced it by $1 - \frac{1}{2}\phi^2$; replacing $\sin \phi$ by ϕ instead of $\phi - \frac{1}{6}\phi^3$ was also an error, but of higher order. (We have here assumed the series for $\sin \phi$ and $\cos \phi$ (ϕ in radians) obtained by means of Taylor's Theorem (*see* p. 144), namely $\sin \phi = \phi - (\phi^3/3!) + (\phi^5/5!) \ldots$; $\cos \phi = 1 - (\phi^2/2!) + (\phi^4/4!) \ldots$) The principal error is thus neglecting the term $(1 - \frac{1}{2}\phi^2)$ which should have multiplied cos $(5\pi/12)$ in Equation 6.80b. Now when ϕ has the extreme value $\pm(\pi/12)$, $\frac{1}{2}\phi^2$ is about 0·034, and if in Equation 6.79 we had replaced cos $[\phi - (5\pi/12)]$ by

$$(1 - 0·034) \cos (5\pi/12) + \phi \sin (5\pi/12) \qquad (6.80c)$$

we could have evaluated the integral I_3 explicitly, obtaining a result I_{32} say. I_3 will then lie between I_{31} and I_{32}, and the difference

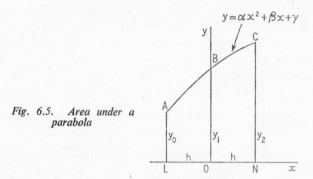

Fig. 6.5. Area under a parabola

between these two quantities will indicate the error adequately; in such cases we usually only require to know its order of magnitude. It should be noted that this error involves ϕ^2, so that reducing the range over which the approximation 6.80b was applied would more than proportionately reduce the error; if the limits of integration in Equation 6.79 were $-\pi/24$ to $+\pi/24$, the error would be greatly reduced.

INTEGRATION BY SIMPSON'S RULE

Another kind of approximation which is very useful in dealing with awkward integrals (between finite limits) is known as Simpson's Rule. This is by no means the only such approximation available, but it has a simple idea behind it and is very generally applicable where the integrand does not oscillate too rapidly over the range of integration.

Consider first the area $LABCN$ in Fig. 6.5, if we are given that the curve ABC is a parabola with a vertical axis so that its equation is of the form

$$y = \alpha x^2 + \beta x + \gamma \qquad (6.81)$$

Although we know that the *form* of the equation of the curve ABC

is as in Equation 6.81, we are not given the values of α, β and γ; we merely know that the parabola passes through the points $A(-h, y_0)$, $B(0, y_1)$ and $C(h, y_2)$. This tells us immediately that $\gamma = y_1$ and we can solve the simultaneous equations

$$y_0 = \alpha h^2 - \beta h + y_1$$

$$y_2 = \alpha h^2 + \beta h + y_1 \qquad (6.82)$$

to give

$$\beta = \frac{1}{2h}(y_2 - y_0); \quad \alpha = \frac{1}{2h^2}(y_0 - 2y_1 + y_2) \qquad (6.83)$$

It is also clear that

$$\text{Area } LABCN = \int_{-h}^{h} y \, dx \qquad (6.84)$$

and by substitution from Equation 6.83 into Equation 6.81 and simplifying, we obtain

$$\text{Area } LABCN = \frac{1}{3} h (y_0 + 4y_1 + y_2) \qquad (6.85)$$

Now Equation 6.85, though equivalent to Equation 6.84, is much more useful, because it is expressed in terms of the quantities which are given in Fig. 6.5. Once Equation 6.85 has been obtained, we can forget the particular position of the axes used in Fig. 6.5; the validity of Equation 6.85 depends only upon the fact that the curve ABC was a parabola whose axis was perpendicular to LN.

Now if the points A, B, C are on some other curve, say $y = f(x)$ with the axes used in Fig. 6.5, and h is sufficiently small, the curve $y = f(x)$ will not in general differ greatly from the parabola unless $f(x)$ oscillates very rapidly. The idea behind Simpson's Rule is to divide up the area $L_1A_1B_1C_1B_2C_2B_3C_3 \ldots QM$ in Fig. 6.6 into a collection of areas $L_1A_1B_1C_1N_1$, $N_1C_1B_2C_2N_2$ etc., such that each of these areas can be regarded as like Fig. 6.5. We then have

$$\text{Area } LA_1B_1C_1N_1 = \tfrac{1}{3}h(y_0 + 4y_1 + y_2)$$

$$\text{Area } N_1C_1B_2C_2N_2 = \tfrac{1}{3}h(y_2 + 4y_3 + y_4) \qquad (6.86)$$

and so on. Adding these, and assuming that $L_1M = 2nh$, we find total area $L_1A_1B_1C_1 \ldots QM$

$$= \tfrac{1}{3}h[(y_0 + y_{2n}) + 4(y_1 + y_3 + y_5 + \ldots + y_{2n-1}) + \\ + 2(y_2 + y_4 + y_6 + \ldots + y_{2n-2})] \qquad (6.87)$$

Equation 6.87 is what is generally known as Simpson's Rule. In order to use it, we require only to calculate a suitable number of values of the integrand. For a given range if integration, taking a

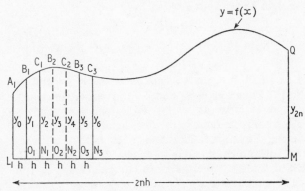

Fig. 6.6. Simpson's rule

small value of h increases the accuracy but also increases the number of ordinates which have to be calculated.

Perhaps the best way to illustrate the accuracy obtainable with Simpson's Rule is to apply it to the integration of

$$I_4 = \int_0^\pi \sin kx \, dx \qquad (6.88)$$

The exact value is in this case easily obtainable and is

$$I_4 = (1 - \cos k\pi)/k \qquad (6.89)$$

If we take h to be $\pi/12$, Equation 6.87 gives

$$I_4 = \frac{\pi}{36}\left[\sin k\pi + 4\sum_{r=0}^{5} \sin \frac{(2r+1)k\pi}{12} + 2\sum_{r=1}^{5} \sin \frac{rk\pi}{6}\right] \qquad (6.90)$$

Now Equation 6.90 can be simplified by means of two trigonometrical identities which will be considered more fully in Chapter 8, namely

$$\sin \alpha + \sin \beta = 2 \sin \tfrac{1}{2}(\alpha + \beta) \cos \tfrac{1}{2}(\alpha - \beta)$$

$$\cos \alpha + \cos \beta = 2 \cos \tfrac{1}{2}(\alpha + \beta) \cos \tfrac{1}{2}(\alpha - \beta) \qquad (6.91)$$

I_4 reduces to

$$I_4 = \frac{\pi}{36}\Bigg[\sin k\pi + 2 \sin \tfrac{1}{2} k\pi +$$

$$+ 8 \sin \tfrac{1}{2}k\pi \cos \tfrac{1}{4}k\pi\left(1 + \cos \frac{k\pi}{12} + 2 \cos \frac{k\pi}{6}\right)\Bigg] \qquad (6.92)$$

If $k\pi$ is so small that $\sin k\pi$ can be taken as $k\pi$ and $\cos k\pi$ as $1 - \tfrac{1}{2}(k\pi)^2$, Equations 6.89 and 6.92 are in complete agreement. Even if k is as large as unity, Equations 6.89 and 6.92 give results which only disagree in the fifth significant figure. If k is any even integer, Equations 6.89 and 6.92 both necessarily agree, but this is fortuitous: it is due to a cancellation associated with the symmetry of $\sin kx$. We therefore tabulate (Table 6.3) the values obtained from Equations 6.89 and 6.92 when k takes certain odd-integral values:

Table 6.3

k	1	3	5	7	9
Equation 6.89	2	0·66667	0·4	0·28571	0·22222
Equation 6.92	2·0001	0·66817	0·40816	0·31461	0·31912

Thus it appears that Simpson's Rule is very satisfactory for k up to about 5, but that when k exceeds 5, the replacement of $\sin kx$ by a parabolic arc (as in Fig. 6.5) over successive intervals of $\pi/6$ for x rapidly deteriorates in accuracy. This suggests as a rough general rule that, in the notation of Fig. 6.5 and 6.6, h should be so chosen that the interval $2h$ does not include more than about half a cycle of the highest frequency contained in the integrand.

Chapter 7

LABOUR-SAVING DEVICES AND GENERAL TECHNIQUES

A number of loosely related topics will be discussed in this chapter; the early part of the chapter is concerned with computational procedures, including algebraic division, which can save labour in repetitive calculations. Unfortunately there is an almost unavoidable tendency to make silly mistakes, especially over signs, and any rearrangement which increases the extent to which a calculation can be done mechanically (without the necessity for thought except about the immediate next step once the calculation is under way) is of very great value. Mistakes are almost bound to occur, and thus an arrangement of the work which 'shows them up' before they have wrecked much subsequent work, is also most helpful. The latter part of the chapter deals with interpolation, extrapolation and the derivation of smooth curves from experimental data.

From the point of view of the practical engineer, numerical computation is often at best a bore and, at worst, a severe hindrance. Unfortunately, effective progress in practical work is usually impossible for long without it. We may need it in order to apply a well-understood general formula to a particular case, or to obtain a general understanding of the behaviour of certain quantities in relation to each other. Labour-saving tricks of computation can be applied widely; they do not depend for their effectiveness on the nature of the particular problem in question.

COMPUTATION TRICKS

If we wish to evaluate an expression of the form

$$y = x_1 x_2^2 x_3 / x_4^3 \tag{7.1}$$

a slide rule is quite adequate if accuracy to two or three significant

9   121

figures is required, but a slide rule is of less use in computations where additions or subtractions are combined with multiplications or divisions; if the result required is a difference between two nearly-equal quantities, special care is required. Suppose, for example, we need to evaluate

$$y = (1,000 + x)^{1/3} - (1,000 - x)^{1/3} \qquad (7.2)$$

for x of the order 10. A slide rule will give $(1,000 + x)^{1/3}$ to 3 significant figures so, as this number is slightly over 10, the first decimal place will be doubtful. Similarly, $(1,000 - x)^{1/3}$ will be a number just under 10 for which the first decimal place will be doubtful. The difference will be a decimal which may well be less than 0.1 so that we shall, in effect, have no reliable information at all about its value. In this particular case, the obvious way out is to use the binomial theorem (Equation 5.2).

Applying this to the determination of y, we have

$$y = 10\left(1 + \frac{x}{1,000}\right)^{1/3} - 10\left(1 - \frac{x}{1,00}\right)^{1/3}$$

$$= \frac{x}{150} + \frac{x^3}{81 \times 10^7} + \cdots \qquad (7.3)$$

so that $x/150$ is a very good approximation to y when x is small compared to 1,000. A less obvious way out is to use the fact that

$$\alpha - \beta = (\alpha^3 - \beta^3)/(\alpha^2 + \alpha\beta + \beta^2) \qquad (7.4)$$

which gives, when $\alpha = (1,000 + x)^{1/3}$, $\beta = (1,000 - x)^{1/3}$,

$$y = \frac{(1,000 + x) - (1,000 - x)}{(1,000 + x)^{2/3} + (1,000 + x)^{1/3}(1,000 - x)^{1/3} + (1,000 - x)^{2/3}}$$

$$(7.5)$$

The numerator now simplifies to $2x$ and, in the denominator, the terms are added instead of subtracted so that, roughly speaking, the whole denominator will be obtained to three-figure accuracy if each individual term is obtained to that accuracy. The last equation for y could be used, whatever the value of x might be, whereas the binomial series would converge slowly if x were, say, 973; if x were numerically greater than 1,000, y would have to be rearranged to give a series of descending instead of ascending powers of x.

DIVISION AND THE REMAINDER THEOREM

It is often necessary to evaluate a polynomial, or the sum of the first few terms of a series. If, for example,

$$y = 153 - 82x + 14x^2 - 7x^3 + x^4 \qquad (7.6)$$

direct substitution is straightforward if x is any integer between 1 and 10 multiplied by a positive or negative power of 10, such as 2 or 30 or 400 or 0·07. If x has a value like 1·2347, such substitution is still a possible method, but may be laborious if the polynomial has high degree or if high accuracy is required. Alternatively, we can evaluate y by means of algebraic division by $x - 1·2347$. The 'remainder theorem' states that if a polynomial $f(x)$ is divided by $x - a$, the remainder is $f(a)$; that is, the value of the polynomial when x is replaced by a. Thus, in doing the division, we are not interested in the quotient, but only in the remainder. Even when the value of y is required for a complex value of x, it can be found in a similar manner. Thus, if we require y when $x = 2 + 3j$, we note first that

$$(x - 2 - 3j)(x - 2 + 3j) = x^2 - 4x + 13 \qquad (7.7)$$

and divide y by $x^2 - 4x + 13$. Again, we are not concerned with the quotient, but only with the remainder, which is

$$y_R = -87x + 296 \qquad (7.8)$$

y_R will have the same value as y when $x = 2 + 3j$, since $y - y_R$ is necessarily a multiple of $(x^2 - 4x + 13)$ and, therefore, zero when $x = 2 + 3j$. We therefore substitute $(2 + 3j)$ for x in y_R instead of in y, and obtain

$$y = 122 - 261j$$

when $\qquad\qquad x = 2 + 3j \qquad\qquad\qquad (7.9)$

Sometimes we are concerned with the inverse problem: What is the value of x when y is given? In the case we have just been considering, we can find this out by solving an algebraic equation; this has been discussed in Chapters 3 and 4 and need not be considered further here. In the case where y is a tabulated function of x, such as $\sin x$ or e^x, we can find x given y by 'inverse interpolation', or using the tables 'backwards'.

NEWTON'S APPROXIMATIONS

If, however, y is a function of x, which is not a polynomial, and is either not tabulated or only sparsely tabulated, we can often obtain y satisfactorily by Newton's method, which uses the fact that in general, if a is an approximation to a root of the equation

$$f(x) = 0 \tag{7.10}$$

then $a - f(a)/f'(a)$ is a better approximation, $f'(x)$ being the derivative of $f(x)$ (which can be any function which possesses a derivative for values of x near a). Consider, for example, the real positive root of the equation

$$f(x) = \sin x - \tfrac{1}{2}x^2 = 0 \tag{7.11}$$

(x being in radians). A rough graph makes it clear that x is somewhat less than $\tfrac{1}{2}\pi$. We also know that $\sin x$ changes very slowly when x is near $\tfrac{1}{2}\pi$, and is nearly 1; this suggests that $x \approx \sqrt{2}$. We therefore start with $x = 1\cdot4$. Then $f(1\cdot4) = 0\cdot00545$; $f'(1\cdot4) = \cos 1\cdot4 - 1\cdot4 = -1\cdot23003$, so the next approximation is

$$1\cdot4 + \frac{0\cdot00545}{1\cdot23003} = 1\cdot4044 \tag{7.12}$$

and we find $f(1.4044) = 0\cdot00002$. Newton's method is unsatisfactory if $f'(x)$ is small in the neighbourhood considered; this is the case when two or more roots of $f(x) = 0$ are close together. A straightforward approximate equation of the form

$$(x')^n \approx A \tag{7.13}$$

can then usually be obtained as indicated in Chapter 4.

TABULATION

Another computation which is frequently required is one in which we wish to tabulate and plot a function. If, for example,

$$y = \frac{(x^4 - 2x^2 + 3)^{1/2}}{x^2 + 7} + \frac{1}{100}\, x^2 \tag{7.14}$$

and we are interested in values of x from 0 to 10, the first point to notice is that only even powers of x occur.   It therefore saves labour to choose values of x^2, not x, as round numbers; there is no need for the values of x tabulated to be equally spaced, though it is usually desirable that they should be approximately so.   We shall therefore take x^2 as 1, 5, 10, 20, 30, 40, 60, 80 and 100.   The details of the calculation are given in Table 7.1.

Here, the most important step is the initial one of deciding what quantities shall be computed in order to obtain y with as little thought during the process of computation as possible.   For, where hard thinking is required during the process of computation, one is likely to make a systematic error.   An isolated error, such as an error of addition, is likely to show because one of the values computed will give rise to a point which obviously does not lie on a smooth curve with the remainder, but a systematic error may mean that we have the wrong curve.   We first complete Column B with the chosen values of x^2; Column A, the corresponding values of x, can be left till last because it is only required to enable us to plot y against x, not in order to help with the calculation.   Column C is simply Column B × 0·01, but it is worth putting in unless one is completely confident of being able to manage without it.   Column D is obtained by squaring Column B and adding 3; we then subtract twice Column B to obtain Column E, the square root of this being Column F.   The quantity in this column has to be divided by the quantity in Column G (seven more than that in Column B) to obtain the first term of y, recorded in Column H, and then Column C has to be added to obtain y itself.

It saves a surprising amount of effort to work vertically, not horizontally.   When working out Column C, we concentrate entirely on dividing by 100; we can forget why we have to do so, and the required values are then soon written down.   In Column D, all we need to think of is squaring Column B and adding 3; this can be recorded as $B^2 + 3$ before we start if necessary.   In Column E, we only have to think of subtracting twice Column B, which is easy because we chose the entries in Column B to be round numbers.   Similar remarks apply to the remaining columns.   The point is that while doing any one column we only have to think of one simple process—squaring, addition, subtraction, or looking up square roots (with tables or slide rule), etc.   Should we find we need extra points, it may be necessary to work horizontally, but then we have the easily-calculated points already in Table 7.1 as a guide.

Thus, we see that the process of computation is not so difficult as it seems initially to those unaccustomed to it.   It pays to break it up into a number of steps each of which is elementary and easy, and the process required at each step is worth recording. It is better to have too many steps than too few, because the time wasted in chasing mistakes when there are too few steps is usually large compared with the time required to do the extra steps. Time spent in preliminary algebraic manipulation of an expression to get it

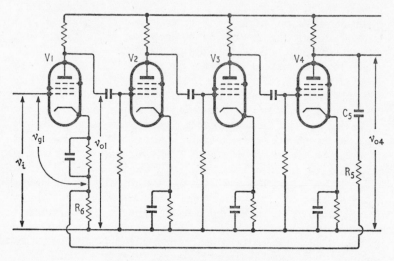

Fig. 7.1. Four-stage feedback amplifier

into the form most suitable for numerical computation is seldom wasted.

There are occasions when laziness is enlightened. Sometimes useful discoveries have been made simply because the discoverer could not be bothered to do a job by the hard ways previously available, and was therefore obliged to invent a new and better way. Before undertaking a computation, it is worth examining the problem briefly to see if it can be tackled in an indirect way not initially obvious, especially if we wish to consider the effect of variations in one quantity upon those of a related quantity.

'WORKING BACKWARDS'

We now consider two particular examples in which the mathematical techniques and ideas involved are very generally applicable. In devising or using such techniques, a mathematician might be

Table 7.1. VALUES OF y

A x	B x^2	C $0.01x^2$	D $x^4 + 3$	E $D - 2B$	F $E^{1/2}$	G $x^2 + 7$	H F/G	I $C+H=y$
0	0	0	3	3	1·7321	7	0·2474	0·2474
1	1	0·01	4	2	1·4142	8	0·1768	0·1868
2·2361	5	0·05	28	18	4·2426	12	0·3536	0·4036
3·1623	10	0·1	103	83	9·1104	17	0·5359	0·6359
4·4721	20	0·2	403	363	19·053	27	0·7057	0·9057
5·4772	30	0·3	903	843	29·034	37	0·7847	1·0847
6·3246	40	0·4	1603	1523	39·025	47	0·8303	1·2303
7·7460	60	0·6	3603	3483	59·017	67	0·8809	1·4809
8·9443	80	0·8	6403	6243	79·013	87	0·9082	1·7082
10	100	1	10003	9803	99·01	107	0·9253	1·9253

said to be exercising his privilege of 'working backwards' when necessary.

The first example is associated with the four-stage feedback amplifier of Fig. 7.1 whose stability can be shown to be closely bound up with the equation

$$A_0 = \frac{A_L}{(1 + pC_1R_1)(1 + pC_2R_2)(1 + pC_3R_3)(1 + pC_4R_4) + A_L\beta}$$
(7.15)

where p is the Heaviside operator equivalent to d/dt (discussed in Chapter 9 and elsewhere[7]), A_0 is the overall gain, A_L is the gain at low frequencies, and the R and C elements are respectively the values of anode a.c. resistance and coupling resistance in parallel, and of total shunt capacitance, for each stage of the amplifier. β has the value $R_6/(R_5 + R_6)$ (see Fig. 7.1). For the amplifier to be stable, A_L/A_0 in Equation 7.15 must be zero for four values of p, none of which has a positive real part. In Chapter 13 we shall consider 'stability criteria' systematically; the point here is that there is another way of looking at Equation 7.15 (and, as we shall see later, Equation 7.32), so that we can find out all that is worth knowing about the roots, and the effect on those roots of varying certain quantities connected with the corresponding elements, without having actually to calculate anything more difficult than the roots of a quadratic equation. For simplicity we shall suppose that

$$C_1R_1 = C_2R_2 = C_3R_3 = \alpha; \quad C_4R_4 = 20\alpha; \quad A_L\beta = \beta' \quad (7.16)$$

The denominator of the right-hand side of Equation 7.15 then reduces to

$$D = (1 + \alpha p)^3 (1 + 20\alpha p) + \beta' \quad (7.17)$$

It must be possible to express D in the form of two real quadratic factors, so that

$$D = 20(\alpha^2 p^2 + \lambda \cdot \alpha p + \mu)(\alpha^2 p^2 + \nu \cdot \alpha p + \rho) \qquad (7.18)$$

and we here consider how to determine the variation of λ, μ, ν and ρ for a given variation in β'. For it is the quantities λ, μ, ν, ρ which give the most important information about the behaviour of the amplifier. If λ is much less than $2\sqrt{\mu}$, for instance, the first factor in Equation 7.18 will give rise to a lightly-damped oscillation, whereas, if $\lambda = 2\sqrt{\mu}$, the damping will be critical, and if λ exceeds $2\sqrt{\mu}$ there will be no oscillation due to this first factor in Equation 7.18. Similar considerations apply independently to the second factor in Equation 7.18. If λ or ν is negative, Equation 7.18 will be associated with an oscillation which grows exponentially; that is to say, there will be instability.

If D is given by Equation 7.17 and has the factors given by Equation 7.18, the following relations between λ, μ, ν, ρ and β' can be obtained by equating coefficients of p^3, p^2, p and the constant term respectively:

$$\lambda + \nu = 3 \cdot 05 \qquad (7.19)$$

$$\mu + \rho + \lambda\nu = 3 \cdot 15 \qquad (7.20)$$

$$\lambda\rho + \mu\nu = 1 \cdot 15 \qquad (7.21)$$

$$\mu\rho = 0 \cdot 05 \, (1 + \beta') \qquad (7.22)$$

Now in fact we are given β' and required to determine λ, μ, ν and ρ. It is perfectly possible to attack the problem directly, and factorise the right-hand side of Equation 7.17, as shown in Chapters 3 and 4. What we wish to emphasise here, however, is that this is not necessary; it is preferable, for a general exploration of the way in which λ, μ, ν, ρ vary with β', to proceed as if λ was given and not β'. For if λ is given, ν follows immediately from Equation 7.19, and Equations 7.20 and 7.21 then become linear simultaneous equations for μ and ρ; finally, substitution into Equation 7.22 gives β' immediately. If we choose a number of values of λ and deduce the corresponding values of β', μ, ν, and ρ in this way, it is perfectly possible afterwards to plot λ and μ against β' as in Fig. 7.2, and ρ against β' as in Fig. 7.3. The curious behaviour of μ in the neighbourhood of $\beta' = 0$ is not of practical importance; it is associated with the fact that in Equation 7.17 there is a factor

$(1 + \alpha p)^3$ on the right-hand side. ν is of course deducible from λ by means of Equation 7.19, so that ν has not been included in Fig. 7.2.

Once Figs. 7.2 and 7.3 have been obtained, we can in effect factorise (to graphical accuracy) the right-hand side of Equation 7.17 at sight; it therefore seems worth while to extend Figs. 7.2 and 7.3 to cover all values of β', and not merely those between -1 and 19·91 for which the amplifier is stable. If β' is less than -1, stability breaks down because μ becomes negative; if β' exceeds 19·91, stability breaks down because λ becomes negative. For large λ, we have approximately from Equations 7.19–7.22

$$\nu \approx -\lambda; \quad \mu \approx \rho \approx \tfrac{1}{2}\lambda^2; \quad \beta' \approx 5\lambda^4 \tag{7.23}$$

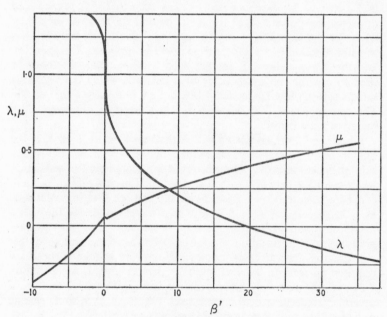

Fig. 7.2. Plot of λ and μ against the feedback parameter β' so that D has the factors 7.18

Our second example is concerned with the practical realisation of a network whose group-delay shall be 'quartically flat'. Suppose that we have a network whose transfer function is $1/f(p)$ where

$$f(p) = 1 + x_0(p/\omega_0) + Kx_0^2(p/\omega_0)^2$$
$$+ (K - \tfrac{1}{3})x_0^3(p/\omega_0)^3 + \tfrac{1}{3}(K - 0{\cdot}4)x_0^4(p/\omega_0)^4 \tag{7.24}$$

Then the group delay G, which is the real part of $f'(p)/f(p)$, with p^2 replaced by $-\omega^2$ at frequency $\omega/2\pi$, is given by

$$G = \frac{x_0}{\omega_0} \; \frac{1 + a_2\xi^2 + a_4\xi^4 + a_6\xi^6}{1 + a_2\xi^2 + a_4\xi^4 + b_6\xi^6 + b_8\xi^8} \tag{7.25a}$$

where

$$
\begin{aligned}
a_2 &= 1 - 2K & b_6 &= \tfrac{1}{3}K^2 - 0.4K + \tfrac{1}{9} \\
a_4 &= \tfrac{1}{15}(15K^2 - 20K + 6) & b_8 &= \tfrac{1}{9}(K - 0.4)^2 \\
a_6 &= \tfrac{1}{3}(K - \tfrac{1}{3})(K - 0.4)
\end{aligned} \tag{7.25b}
$$

where $\xi = x_0\omega/\omega_0$. Gouriet[9] discovered that if $f(p)$ was given by Equation 7.24, the group delay G was such that if G is expanded in ascending powers of ξ^2 (or ω^2), there is no term in ω^2 or ω^4 whatever the values of x_0 and K may be. If a lattice network has transfer function $f(-p)/f(p)$, the gain will be unity at all frequencies, and the group delay $2G$, so that such a lattice can sometimes be used to correct the group delay of a network which is reasonably satisfactory at low frequencies, but not at frequencies near $\omega_0/2\pi$. The way in which G varies with K is discussed by Gouriet. x_0 is merely a scale factor.

Equation 7.24 is associated with a realisable network if $K > 0.4$ but, in order to realise it, we require the factors of the right-hand side of Equation 7.24; Gouriet gives the technique for realisation when a lattice network with transfer function $\phi(-p)/\phi(p)$ is used, $\phi(p)$ being quadratic. If K is between 0.4 and 3/7, G always decreases as ω increases; for $K > 3/7$, G at first increases, passes through a maximum, and thereafter steadily decreases. The rise is very gradual for K up to about 0.45, but steep for K exceeding say 0.5.

From the general behaviour of the network whose group-delay requires correction, we can suppose that K and x_0 in Equation 7.24 are approximately known (or the values of each K and x_0 if several correcting lattices are needed). We then have to determine a, b and b' so that Equation 7.24 can also be written

$$f(p) = \left(1 + a\frac{px_0}{\omega_0} + b\frac{p^2x_0^2}{\omega_0^2}\right)\left(1 + [1 - a]\frac{px_0}{\omega_0} + b'\frac{p^2x_0^2}{\omega_0^2}\right) \tag{7.26}$$

As in the amplifier example above, we are in fact given K and require a, b and b' but, as we wish to explore the variation of a, b and b' for a wide variation of K, it is better to proceed as if a was given, and the other quantities required. By equating coefficients of p^2, p^3 and p^4 in Equations 7.24 and 7.25, we obtain

$$b + b' + a(1 - a) = K \qquad (7.27)$$

$$ab' + (1 - a)b = K - \tfrac{1}{3} \qquad (7.28)$$

$$bb' = \tfrac{1}{3}(K - 0 \cdot 4) \qquad (7.29)$$

and if a is regarded as given, Equations 7.27 and 7.28 become linear simultaneous equations for b and b' in terms of a, K. Their solution is easily found to be

$$(1 - 2a)b = K(1 - a) + a^2(1 - a) - \tfrac{1}{3} \qquad (7.30)$$

$$(1 - 2a)b' = \tfrac{1}{3} - aK - a(1 - a)^2 \qquad (7.31)$$

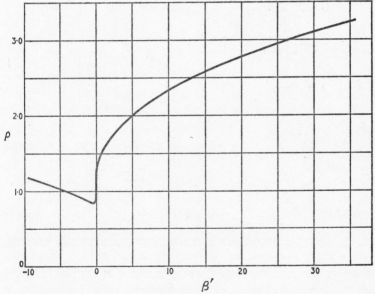

Fig. 7.3. Plot of ρ against the feedback parameter β' so that D has the factors 7.18

Multiplying Equations 7.30 and 7.31, and substituting for bb' from Equation 7.29, we obtain a relation between K and a which is only quadratic in K, and reduces to

$$CK^2 - \tfrac{1}{3}CK(1 + 6C) + [C^3 + 0 \cdot 2C - (1/45)] = 0 \qquad (7.32)$$

where $C = a(1 - a)$; the solution of Equation 7.32 is

$$K = C + \tfrac{1}{6}\left\{1 \pm \left[(1 - 4C)\left(\frac{0\cdot8}{C} - 3\right)\right]^{1/2}\right\} \qquad (7.33)$$

Thus, given a, we immediately deduce C; K is then derived from Equation 7.33 and finally b and b' from Equations 7.30 and 7.31

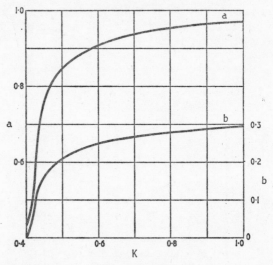

Fig. 7.4.   *Values of a and b in equation 7.26 required to factorise Equation 7.24 for given K*

and, in order to obtain a set of corresponding values of a, b, b' and K, the most difficult operation required has been the solution of the quadratic equation 7.33. The minus sign in this equation is only relevant for values of K lying between 0·4 and 5/12 since, if $K < 0\cdot4$, the network given by Equation 7.24 is unrealisable. For $K = 0\cdot4$, a is 0·43055 and C is 0·24518. a and b are plotted against K in Fig. 7.4, and b' is plotted against K in Fig. 7.5. In this example, there seems little point in allowing K to vary outside the limits 0·4 to 1; K tends to infinity as a tends to 1, so that if $(1 - a)$ is denoted by ϵ and ϵ is small (say less than 0·01)

$$K \approx \tfrac{1}{6}\left\{\left(\frac{0\cdot8}{\epsilon}\right)^{1/2} + 1 - 3\cdot375(0\cdot8\epsilon)^{1/2}\right\} + \epsilon \qquad (7.34)$$

the first term neglected being of order $\epsilon^{3/2}$.

Now Equation 7.32 is a very useful result, easily obtained by the present method of attack. Not only does it give the relation between K and a explicitly, but it incorporates the fact that if, in Equation 7.25, a is replaced by $(1 - a)$ and b is replaced by b' and vice versa, the same factors are present and only the order is reversed. If we had factorised the right-hand side of Equation 7.24 directly, not only would we have taken longer to obtain each set of associated values of K, a, b and b', but we would have been most unlikely to derive the true relation between a and K; we would probably have become aware of the fact that replacing a by $(1 - a)$ left K unchanged, but no more.

It is always worth bearing in mind that an indirect attack on a problem involving computation, by regarding as independent a

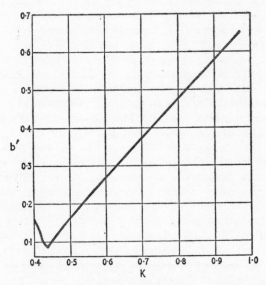

Fig. 7.5. Values of b' in Equation 7.26 required to factorise Equation 7.24 for given K

variable different from that which is independent in the practical problem, is worth considering. In the case of the amplifier example, this method has enabled us to see clearly how variations in feedback affect damping, and the way in which instability arises (λ becomes negative if β' exceeds 19·91 and μ becomes negative if β' is less than -1). In the case of the group-delay correcting network, the method has given us easily and explicitly a rather complicated relation (Equation 7.32) between the quantities K and a.

CHANGE OF VARIABLE

Another trick that is widely useful is to make quite a simple change of variable; for example, if we wish to consider the expression

$$f_0(x) = x^6 - 3x^5 + 9x^4 - 27x^3 + 40x^2 - 60x + 100 \qquad (7.35)$$

for several values of x in the immediate neighbourhood of 2, there is much to be said for writing

$$y = x - 2 \qquad (7.36)$$

and trying to express $f_0(x)$ in terms of y. As in the neighbourhood of 2, y is small, the terms of high degree in y will contribute little, whereas all the x-terms of the original Equation 7.35 contribute comparable amounts when x is near 2. The obvious way of turning Equation 7.35 into a y-equation is to express x as $(y + 2)$ from Equation 7.36, substitute $(y + 2)$ for x in each term of Equation 7.35, and use the Binomial Theorem (Chapter 5). There is another possible way also; this is mentioned not because it is necessarily a better way, but because in numerical work it is an excellent idea to have more than one way of carrying out any process. If the same answer is obtained by two processes involving radically different numerical operations (although algebraically the processes may be equivalent) there is a very high probability that the answer is correct; if different answers are obtained, the existence of an error is brought to one's notice in good time and there may be also a useful indication as to which part of the calculation is suspect. The alternative method is to divide $f_0(x)$ by $(x - 2)$ and note the quotient $Q_0(x)$ and the remainder R_0; then divide $Q_0(x)$ by $(x - 2)$ and note the quotient $Q_1(x)$ and remainder R_1 and so on. The y-language version of $f_0(x)$ is then given by

$$f_0(x) = R_0 + R_1 y + R_2 y^2 + \ldots + R_5 y^5 + y^6 \qquad (7.37)$$

The actual expressions $Q_0(x)$, $Q_1(x)$ etc. are given in Table 7.2 below, and Equation 7.37 thus agrees with the Binomial Theorem version.

Hitherto in this chapter our basic objective might be said to be to evaluate some expression $f(x)$ for several different values of x. We also considered the possibility of proceeding as if some variable other than x was given, and working 'backwards' to find the required value or behaviour of $f(x)$ in terms of x. In Chapters 3 and 4, however, we had the most straightforward example of the opposite idea, that we want to choose x so that $f(x)$ shall have a given value such as zero. We next consider a further case in which our aim is to choose quantities under our control in such a way that a result

Table 7.2

$Q_0(x) = f_0(x) \div (x-2)$	$x^5 - x^4 + 7x^3 - 13x^2 + 14x - 32$	$R_0(x) = 36$
$Q_1(x) = Q_0(x) \div (x-2)$	$x^4 + x^3 + 9x^2 + 5x + 24$	$R_1(x) = 16$
$Q_2(x) = Q_1(x) \div (x-2)$	$x^3 + 3x^2 + 15x + 35$	$R_2(x) = 94$
$Q_3(x) = Q_2(x) \div (x-2)$	$x^2 + 5x + 25$	$R_3(x) = 85$
$Q_4(x) = Q_3(x) \div (x-2)$	$x + 7$	$R_4(x) = 39$
$Q_5(x) = Q_4(x) \div (x-2)$	1	$R_5(x) = 9$

we consider desirable is achieved, namely that the overall gain of the circuit of Fig. 7.6 shall be 'maximally flat', that is, vary as little as possible at low frequencies.

CANCEL WITH CARE

Fig. 7.6 shows an equivalent circuit for a transformer which has unity ratio, at frequencies sufficiently high for the shunting effect of the primary and secondary inductances to be negligible. Leakage inductance is represented by L and the primary and secondary capacitances by C_1 and C_2; these represent internal as well as external capacitances. The resistances R_1 and R_2 are mainly the source and load resistances, but can be taken to include also shunt losses in the transformer.

A constant current I is supplied, and the resulting secondary voltage V_0 at frequency $\omega/2\pi$ is easily obtained in the form

$$\left. \begin{array}{c} \dfrac{IR}{V_0} = 1 - \omega^2 T_1{}^2(1+b)d + j\omega T_1 \left(\dfrac{1+ab}{1+a} + d - \omega^2 T_1{}^2 bd \right) \\[2mm] \text{where} \\[2mm] R = \dfrac{R_1 R_2}{R_1 + R_2},\ T_1 = C_1 R_1,\ a = R_1/R_2 \\[2mm] b = C_2 R_2 / C_1 R_1,\ d = L/C_1 R_1(R_1 + R_2) \end{array} \right\} \quad (7.38)$$

The magnitude of IR/V_0, say $1/G$, is therefore given by

$$\frac{1}{G^2} = 1 + \omega^2 T_1^2 \{(x + d)^2 - 2d(1 + b)\}$$
$$+ \omega^4 T_1^4 \{d^2(1 + b)^2 - 2bd(x + d)\} + \omega^6 T_1^6 b^2 d^2$$

$$(7.39)$$

where

$$x = \frac{1 + ab}{1 + a} \tag{7.40}$$

For maximal flatness we require the coefficients of $\omega^2 T_1^2$ and $\omega^4 T_1^4$ to be zero, so that

$$(x + d)^2 = 2d(1 + b) \tag{7.41}$$

$$d^2(1 + b)^2 = 2bd(x + d) \tag{7.42}$$

Now if $b = d = x = 1$ it is easily verified that Equations 7.41 and 7.42 are both true, but when $b = 1$, 7.40 tells us that x must be 1 whatever the value of a may be. Physically, $b = 1$ means that the time constants $C_1 R_1$ and $C_2 R_2$ are equal. In a practical case we might have $R_1 = 20$ kΩ, $R_2 = 5$ kΩ, $C_1 = 100$ pF, $C_2 = 400$ pF and $L = 50$ mH; a then has the value 4 and $b = d = 1$, the time constants $C_1 R_1$ and $C_2 R_2$ being 2 μsec.

Now let us consider the general case. In Equations 7.41 and 7.42 the quantities b, d and x are all real, positive and finite. The obvious way to proceed is to eliminate x (or rather $(x + d)$) by

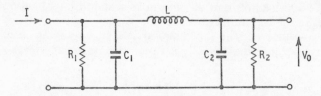

Fig. 7.6.   An equivalent circuit for a unity-ratio transformer at high frequencies

squaring both sides of Equation 7.42 and substituting from Equation 7.41; this gives

$$(1 + b)^4 d^4 = 4b^2 d^2 \cdot 2d(1 + b) \tag{7.43}$$

At this point we must note carefully that Equation 7.43 could not only be obtained from Equations 7.41 and 7.42 as they stand, but would also be obtained if Equation 7.42 had been

$$d^2(1 + b)^2 = - 2bd\,(x + d) \tag{7.44}$$

Equation 7.44 is fortunately irrelevant to our present investigation, because b, d and x are positive, but when squaring has to be done in order to solve equations, it is most important that all solutions obtained are checked in the original equations, because a solution of Equation 7.43 could have been a solution of Equations 7.41 and 7.44 instead of a wanted solution of Equations 7.41 and 7.42.

Returning to Equation 7.43, we can be quite sure that $(1 + b)$ and d^3 are different from zero, and therefore may be cancelled to give

$$d = \frac{8b^2}{(1 + b)^3} \tag{7.45}$$

Substituting from Equation 7.45 to 7.41, we may also safely cancel a d and divide through by b to obtain

$$x = \frac{(1 + b)^2 d}{2b} - d = \frac{4b(1 + b^2)}{(1 + b)^3} \tag{7.46}$$

and we can easily verify that these values of x and d satisfy the original Equations 7.41 and 7.42, whatever the value of b may be. We have, however, already seen that although Equation 7.40 is apparently a relation between x and a, it reduces to $x = 1$ (which is independent of a) when $b = 1$. Let us therefore try and express a in terms of x from Equation 7.40 and see how the result is affected by putting $b = 1$.

Multiplying through Equation 7.40 by the safely positive quantity $(1 + a)$, we have

$$(1 + a)x = 1 + ab$$
$$\therefore a(x - b) = 1 - x \tag{7.47}$$

Now provided that x is not equal to b, we can deduce from Equation 7.47

$$a = \frac{1 - x}{x - b} \tag{7.48}$$

Substituting from Equation 7.46 for x, we can safely multiply numerator and denominator by $(1 + b)^3$ to clear cumbersome fractions, and we thus obtain

$$a = \frac{(1 + b)^3 - 4b(1 + b^2)}{4b(1 + b^2) - b(1 + b)^3}$$

$$= \frac{1 - b + 3b^2 - 3b^3}{b\{3 - 3b + b^2 - b^3\}}$$

$$= \frac{(1 - b)(1 + 3b^2)}{b(1 - b)(3 + b^2)} \qquad (7.49)$$

Provided that b is not equal to 1, Equation 7.49 yields

$$a = \frac{1 + 3b^2}{b(3 + b^2)} \qquad (7.50)$$

by cancelling the factor $(1 - b)$. If, however, b is equal to 1, we have already seen that x has the required value 1 whatever the value of a may be.

We have also noted that Equation 7.48 is not valid when $x = b$; Equation 7.47 in this special case tells us that $x = 1$. There is thus only one special case, when both x and b are equal to 1.

In order to understand the peculiarities of the special case, let us consider first what happens for a general value of b if we are content to allow a small tolerance in the value of x, so that we accept x_1 as sufficiently near the required value of x given by Equation 7.46, where

$$x_1 = \frac{4b(1 + b^2)}{(1 + b)^3}(1 + \lambda) \qquad (7.51)$$

If we think of λ as 0·01, this means that we are prepared to tolerate a 1% excess in x; if λ is −0·01, we are prepared to tolerate a 1% deficiency. When we allow x to be replaced by x_1, we must correspondingly replace a by a_1 where

$$x_1 = \frac{1 + a_1 b}{1 + a_1} \qquad (7.52)$$

Multiplying through Equation 7.52 by $(1 + a_1)$ (which is positive in cases of practical interest) and rearranging, we have

$$a_1(x_1 - b) = 1 - x_1 \qquad (7.53)$$

In order to obtain a usable value of a_1 from Equation 7.53, we must adjust λ so that x_1 is between b and 1 (if $b = 1$, Equation 7.53 simply tells us that $x_1 = 1$ since a_1 cannot usefully be -1, and Equation 7.51 then tells us that λ is necessarily zero. No tolerance is thus required, and a_1 reduces to a, which, as we have already seen, can have any value in this case). If b exceeds 1, $(1 - x_1)$ and $(x_1 - b)$ will both be negative, so that a useful, positive value of a_1 is obtained; if b is less than 1, $x_1 - b$ and $(1 - x_1)$ will both be positive, so that again a useful value of a_1 is obtained. In either case we can find an explicit formula for a_1 from Equation 7.53 by dividing through by $(x_1 - b)$. If we then substitute for x_1 from Equation 7.51, we have

$$a_1 = \frac{1 - x_1}{x_1 - b}$$

$$= \frac{(1 - b)(1 + 3b^2) - 4\lambda b(1 + b^2)}{b(1 - b)(3 + b^2) + 4\lambda b(1 + b^2)} \tag{7.54}$$

The position we have now reached is that if we require exact maximal flatness in the general case ($b \neq 1$) we must make R_1/R_2 have the value a given by Equation 7.50. Nevertheless, if we are prepared to tolerate a slight departure from maximal flatness (measured by the quantity λ defined in Equation 7.51) we can allow R_1/R_2 to have instead the value a_1 given by Equation 7.54. λ must necessarily be small, or the variation of G with frequency (Equation 7.39) will be excessive. If therefore $(1 - b)$ is not small, whether it is positive or negative, a_1 will not be very different from a. On the other hand, if $(1 - b)$ is comparable with λ, a_1 can be very different from a. Suppose, for example, that $b = 0.99$. Then Equation 7.54 reduces to

$$a_1 = \frac{0.0394 - 7.8412\lambda}{0.0394 + 7.8412\lambda} \tag{7.55}$$

and therefore if λ is just below $+0.005$, a_1 is small and positive, while if λ is just above (i.e. nearer zero than) -0.005, a_1 is very large. Hence although the value of a for maximal flatness is in this case very close to unity (from Equation 7.50 with $b = 0.99$ or Equation 7.55 with $\lambda = 0$) λ will not numerically exceed 0.005 for *any* value of R_1/R_2, so that the error in x will not exceed $\frac{1}{2}\%$ and there will be very little change of G with frequency whatever the value of R_1/R_2

may be.   Correspondingly, if we put $(1 - \epsilon)$ for b in Equation 7.54 and neglect ϵ^2 and $\epsilon\lambda$, Equation 7.54 reduces to

$$a_1 = \frac{\epsilon - 2\lambda}{\epsilon + 2\lambda} \tag{7.56}$$

and, therefore, although the correct value for maximal flatness is found from Equation 7.50 to be unity, λ will only lie between $+\frac{1}{2}\epsilon\,[R_1 \ll R_2, a_1$ small$]$ and $-\frac{1}{2}\epsilon\,[R_1 \gg R_2, a_1$ large$]$ whatever the value of a_1 may be.

If $\frac{1}{2}\epsilon$ numerically exceeds the greatest value of $|\lambda|$ that can be tolerated, say λ_0, then Equation 7.56 shows that a_1 can only be varied between finite limits which include the value given by Equation 7.50; in fact

$$\frac{|\epsilon| - 2\lambda_0}{|\epsilon| + 2\lambda_0} < a_1 < \frac{|\epsilon| + 2\lambda_0}{|\epsilon| - 2\lambda_0} \tag{7.57}$$

and, as we have already noted, if $|\epsilon|$ is large compared to λ_0 (though still sufficiently small to justify the neglect of ϵ^2 and $\epsilon\lambda$ in deriving Equation 7.56) a_1 differs little from the value unity obtained for a in Equation 7.50 neglecting ϵ^2. If ϵ^2 cannot be neglected, we must, of course, use Equation 7.54 instead of Equation 7.56, but the result is still essentially the same—a_1 does not differ appreciably from a if the error in x is to be kept within the prescribed tolerance.

Thus the apparently anomalous case when $b = 1$ is now seen in its proper perspective as a limiting case.   The value a_0 of a obtained from Equation 7.50 after the factor $(1 - b)$ is cancelled always gives maximal flatness, and if $(1 - b)$ is not small (whether positive or negative) we cannot vary a appreciably from a_0 without seriously disturbing the constancy of G with respect to frequency.   If $(1 - b)$ is small, but of the same order of magnitude as the maximum relative discrepancy in x that can be tolerated, a_0 is still the correct value of a for maximal flatness, but considerable variation of a can be permitted without seriously disturbing the constancy of G.   When $(1 - b)$ is very small, even the variation of a from 0 to ∞ will have so little effect on the value of x, that the maximal flatness is virtually independent of a.   When b is actually 1, we simply proceed to the limit so that the maximal flatness is completely independent of the value of a, and no tolerance in the value of x is required.

The remainder of this chapter is devoted to the questions of interpolation, extrapolation and 'smoothing'—so important in connection with the use of tables and the analysis of experimental results.

INTERPOLATION

Recently, especially since the invention of electronic computers, there has been a great increase in the number of functions which are tabulated, and the question frequently arises: How are we to obtain, to a satisfactory degree of accuracy, the value of the function for an argument which is not tabulated?

Suppose therefore that we know from the table, which is at intervals α of the argument t for the function $f(t)$, that

$$f(t_0 - \alpha) = f_{-1}; \; f(t_0) = f_0; \; f(t_0 + \alpha) = f_1; \; f(t_0 + 2\alpha) = f_2$$

$$(7.58)$$

so that f_{-1}, f_0, f_1 and f_2 are simply numbers read out from the table. Then if we require the value of $f(t)$ for any value $(t_0 + k\alpha)$ of t between t_0 and $t_0 + \alpha$ (so that $0 < k < 1$), we can obtain it by means of Bessel's (quadratic) interpolation formula

$$f(t_0 + k\alpha) = f_0 + k[f_1 - f_0] - \frac{k(1-k)}{4}[(f_2 - f_1) - (f_0 - f_{-1})]$$

$$(7.59)$$

We notice that Equation 7.59 is quadratic in k and necessarily gives $f(t_0)$ correctly as f_0 when $k = 0$; it also gives $f(t_0 + \alpha)$ correctly as f_1 when $k = 1$.

It is not obvious that Equation 7.59 is the best quadratic interpolation formula for obtaining $f(t)$ when t is between t_0 and $t_0 + \alpha$, but we shall assume that this is so for the purposes of this chapter and see what follows from that assumption. A discussion of the relative merits of Equation 7.59 and other well-known interpolation formulae is outside the scope of this book.

Consider first a numerical example—the derivation of tan 80° 3′ and tan 80° 5′ from a table giving tan θ at intervals of 6′ for θ, so that tan 79° 54′, tan 80°, tan 80° 6′ and tan 80° 12′ are tabulated. This example is chosen because some books of tables merely remark that 'differences' in this region of the tangent table are untrustworthy, and because it illustrates the full power of Equation 7.59. There are many cases in which the contribution of the last term on the right-hand side of Equation 7.59 is negligible for all values of k between 0 and 1, but we shall consider the simplification then possible later.

For using Equation 7.59, the tabulated values and their differences should be arranged as in Table 7.3. Some sets of tables

Table 7.3

θ	$\tan \theta$	First Differences	Second Differences
79° 54′	5·6140		
		0·0573	
80° 0′	5·6713		0·0011
		0·0584	
80° 6′	5·7297		0·0013
		0·0597	
80° 12′	5·7894		

include first, second and even higher-order differences which are obtained similarly.

In this table, the second, or tan θ, column is obtained direct from the tabulated values. The column 'First Differences' is obtained as the difference between two consecutive tabular entries; as tan θ increases with θ, these differences are all positive, but the sign of the differences is important. The first difference 0·0573, which is 5·6713 − 5·6140 or tan 80° 0′ − tan 79° 54′, is conveniently placed half-way between the line 79° 54′ and the line 80° 0′, and similarly with the remaining first differences. Each entry in the second-difference column is likewise obtained as the difference between the two first-differences between which it lies, thus the second-difference entry 0·0011 is obtained as 0·0584 − 0·0573, and is placed on a level half-way between these two first-differences; that is, on the 80° 0′ level. Again, the sign of the second-differences matters; it is positive here because not only does tan θ increase with θ, but {tan $(\theta + 6')$ − tan θ} also increases with θ in the range of θ under consideration.

We are now ready to apply Equation 7.59. t_0 is 80°, α is 6′, f_{-1} is tan 79° 54′ or 5·6140, f_0 is tan 80° or 5·6713, f_1 is tan 80° 6′ or 5·7297 and f_2 is tan 80° 12′ or 5.7894. Hence the coefficient of k in Equation 7.59 is merely 0·0584, the middle entry in the first difference column. The coefficient of $\frac{1}{4}k(1 - k)$ in the last term of Equation 7.59 is $(f_2 - f_1) - (f_0 - f_{-1})$, that is, the difference between the lowest entry in the first-differences column and the highest entry in the first-differences column; this is the sum of the two entries in the second-differences column. Thus Bessel's interpolation formula applied to the range of tan θ under consideration becomes

$$\tan (80° 6k') = 5·6713 + 0·0584k - \tfrac{1}{4}k(1 - k) . 0·0024 \quad (7.60)$$

Notice that as the tabular interval is 6', k is $\frac{1}{2}$ when we seek tan 80° 3' and $\frac{5}{6}$ when we seek tan 80° 5'. Also, the sign of the last term of Equation 7.60 needs watching; it is negative when the second-differences are positive as here. Putting $k = \frac{1}{2}$ and $k = \frac{5}{6}$ in Equation 7.60, we obtain

$$\tan 80° 3' = 5\cdot7003(5); \quad \tan 80° 5' = 5\cdot7199 \qquad (7.61)$$

and these agree with tabulated values of tan 80° 3' and tan 80° 5'.

Thus we are able by means of the general interpolation formula, Equation 7.59, to obtain tan 80° 3' to the same degree of accuracy as the tabular entries in the tangent table in spite of the very rapid increase of tan θ in this neighbourhood. If we try to determine tan θ for values of θ very near 90°, we might find that Equation 7.59 was not sufficiently accurate for tabulations at 6' intervals. There are two obvious remedies: the interval of tabulation can be made smaller, say 1', for such values of θ, or we can use a more general formula than Equation 7.59 which is of higher degree in k and involves higher-order differences. We shall not consider this further here, because for the accuracy required in practical engineering problems, Equation 7.59 is usually quite adequate. It remains to consider the easier case (which is fortunately the usual one) where the second-differences are so small that the last term of Equation 7.59 can be neglected. Now in the case of the tangent table just considered, where Equation 7.59 reduces to Equation 7.60, the maximum value of $\frac{1}{4}k(1 - k)$ is $\frac{1}{16}$ (when $k = \frac{1}{2}$), so that the last term of Equation 7.60 is only just worth retaining. It would not have been worth retaining if the sum of the two second-differences in Table 7.3 had been less than 0·0008. This happens, for example, if we are concerned with tan 72° 3'. The table corresponding to Table 7.3 is then Table 7.4, so that Equation 7.58 becomes

$$\tan (72° 6k') = 3\cdot0777 + 0\cdot0184k - \tfrac{1}{4}k(1 - k)\,.\,0\cdot0003 \qquad (7.62)$$

and the last term is never numerically greater than 0·00001875. When this happens, linear interpolation is sufficient, that is, for θ between 72° 0' and 72° 6' we can regard tan θ as increasing uniformly with respect to θ or k. However, the difference between tan 72° 6' and tan 72° 0' is 0·0184 whereas the difference between tan 73° and tan 72° 54' is 0·0203. Hence between 72° 0' and 72° 6' we can regard tan θ as increasing by $\frac{1}{6}$ of 0·0184 per minute of increase in θ, whereas between 72° 54' and 73° we must regard the increase as $\frac{1}{6}$ of

Table 7.4

θ	$\tan \theta$	First Differences	Second Differences
71° 54′	3·0595		
		0·0182	
72° 0′	3·0777		0·0002
		0·0184	
72° 6′	3·0961		0·0001
		0·0185	
72° 12′	3·1146		

0·0203 per minute in θ, which is appreciably more. To obtain five-figure accuracy, therefore, we must subtract tan 72° 0′ from tan 72° 6′ to find the rate of increase for values of θ between 72° 0′ and 72° 6′, and we must subtract tan 72° 54′ from tan 73° to find the rate of increase for values of θ between 72° 54′ and 73°. We cannot use the same rate of increase for all values of θ between 72° and 73°. For values of θ between 62° and 63°, however, this can be done without serious error. For the difference between tan 62° 6′ (1·8887) and tan 62° 0′ (1.8807) is 0·0080, and the difference between tan 62° 54′ (1·9542) and tan 63° (1·9626) is 0·0084, so a mean rate of increase of 0·0082 per 6′ interval in the range 62°–63° is sufficiently accurate. To the nearest 0·0001, $\frac{1}{6}$ of 0·0082 is 0·0014, $\frac{1}{3}$ of 0·0082 is 0·0027, $\frac{1}{2}$ of 0·0082 is 0·0041, $\frac{2}{3}$ of 0·0082 is 0·0055, and $\frac{5}{6}$ of 0·0082 is 0·0068. Thus we obtain the entries 14, 27, 41, 55 and 68 which are found in the 'mean differences' or 'mean proportional parts' columns of five-figure tangent tables in the 62° row; these mean differences apply to any angle between 62° and 63°. Where 'mean differences' are given, therefore, in any tables, the compiler of the tables has in effect done the interpolation for us; he knows that the second differences are so small that the last term of Equation 7.59 does not contribute, and that the first differences are changing so slowly that a satisfactory 'mean' rate of increase can be used, and we are spared the trouble of having to find the difference between the two tabulated entries surrounding the point we require, and dividing that difference into suitable proportional parts.

TAYLOR'S THEOREM

It can also happen that at a given moment (say $t = t_0$) we know (theoretically or experimentally) the values of some function of time and of a number of its derivatives, and that we want to find a simple expression $F(t)$ which is indistinguishable from that function for values of t not too far removed from t_0. The function may be a very complicated expression, or it may not even be explicitly known; $F(t)$ will be effectively a polynomial in t, perhaps only a quadratic or even linear, but it may occasionally be worth allowing $F(t)$ to be a polynomial of higher degree. The formula which covers this situation is known as Taylor's Theorem. This can be stated by means of a single equation

$$F(t) = F(t_0 + h) = f(t_0) + \frac{h}{1!} f'(t_0) + \frac{h^2}{2!} f''(t_0)$$

$$+ \ldots + \frac{h^{r-1}}{(r-1)!} f^{(r-1)}(t_0) + \frac{h^r}{r!} f^{(r)}(t_0 + \theta h) \qquad (7.63)$$

but that equation requires considerable explanation, as follows. We require $F(t)$ when t is near t_0, say equal to $t_0 + h$; t_0 may have any size, but h may have to be small (though of either sign). $f(t_0)$, $f'(t_0)$, $\ldots f^{(r-1)}(t_0)$ are the known values of the function under consideration and its first $(r-1)$ derivatives when $t = t_0$. We assume that the function has an rth derivative, which we will call $f^{(r)}(t)$, for values of t sufficiently near t_0. For all functions relevant to practical engineering, this rth derivative will be finite. θ is an unknown quantity between 0 and 1. In using Equation 7.63 we need to ensure that the last term of the right-hand side is negligible, so that its precise value need not be determined. If we can arrange this, Equation 7.63 reduces, without the last term, to a polynomial of degree $(r-1)$ in h or $(t - t_0)$, and we can regard the function under consideration as effectively represented by $F(t)$ when t is sufficiently near t_0, or h is sufficiently small.

We can see the reasonableness of Equation 7.63 by means of a simple example. By straightforward multiplication, or by the Binomial Theorem (Chapter 5), it is clear that

$$(t_0 + h)^4 = t_0^4 + 4t_0^3 h + 6t_0^2 h^2 + 4t_0 h^3 + h^4 \qquad (7.64)$$

$$= t_0^4 + (4t_0^3) \cdot \frac{h}{1!} + (12t_0^2) \cdot \frac{h^2}{2!} + (24t_0) \frac{h^3}{3!} + (24) \frac{h^4}{4!} \qquad (7.65)$$

and t_0^4, $4t_0^3$, $12t_0^2$, $24t_0$ and 24 are precisely the values of t^4 and its successive derivatives when $t = t_0$; all higher derivatives of t^4 are zero for all values of t including t_0. Thus, if the function under discussion happened to be t^4, the representation of it by means of Equation 7.63 would have been completely correct for all values of t so long as r was 5 or more, and the last term of Equation 7.63 would be zero. It can similarly be shown that if the function under discussion is any polynomial of degree $(r - 1)$, Equation 7.63 will represent it correctly for *all* values of t with the last term omitted. If however h is sufficiently small, say numerically less than $0.01t_0$, $(t_0 + h)^4$ is indistinguishable from $t_0^4 + 4t_0^3h$; if h is less than about $0.05t_0$, $(t_0 + h)^4$ differs from the first three terms of Equation 7.65 by less than $0.0005t_0^4$, and not until h is about $0.2\,t_0$ is there an appreciable contribution from the last term of Equation 7.65. In the general case, the last term of Equation 7.63 is not identically zero as above, but it can be made as small as we please, for a given value of r, by taking h sufficiently small. There will therefore be a limited range of h for which we can regard $F(t)$ as adequately represented by the first two terms on the right-hand side of Equation 7.63, a somewhat wider range of h for which the first three terms of the right-hand side of Equation 7.63 are adequate, and so on.

If the function under discussion is $A \sin (\omega t + \phi)$, its rth derivative is $A\omega^r \sin (\omega t + \phi + \frac{1}{2}r\pi)$, which is numerically less than or equal to $A\omega^r$. Hence the last term in Equation 7.63 cannot numerically exceed $A\omega^r h^r/r!$. If the function has a number of sinusoidal components, the last term in Equation 7.63 similarly cannot exceed $(h^r/r!)$ times the sum of the values of $A\omega^r$ for each of the components, and only high-frequency components will contribute appreciably if r is moderate or large. It is therefore reasonably easy to set an upper limit to the value of h which can safely be used when a given number of terms of Equation 7.63 is taken to approximate to a function which is oscillating but has no components at frequencies above a given value say $\omega/2\pi$. The main usefulness of Equation 7.63, however, is in cases where the first two or three terms are an adequate representation of the function under discussion over a relatively short range. When representation is required over a relatively wide range, it is more satisfactory to tabulate (or determine experimentally) a sufficient number of equally-spaced values of the function under discussion, and interpolate between them as explained above.

FITTING LINES OR CURVES BY LEAST SQUARES

We frequently have to try to draw conclusions from results subject to experimental error, in the form of several pairs of corresponding values of an independent variable (which we shall here call x) and a dependent variable (which we shall here call y). It often happens that we have some idea of the general nature of the relation between

x and y (e.g., that they are linearly related) but we require to find a specific formula for it.

Consider first the rather trivial case in which we know two pairs (x_1, y_1) and (x_2, y_2) of corresponding values of the variables, and that x and y are linearly related.   Since x and y are linearly related, we must have

$$y = ax + b \qquad (7.66)$$

where a and b are constants which we have to determine.   Since (x_1, y_1) and (x_2, y_2) are corresponding pairs, we must have

$$y_1 = ax_1 + b \qquad (7.67)$$

$$y_2 = ax_2 + b \qquad (7.68)$$

and these are ordinary linear simultaneous equations for a and b, which have a unique solution.   We can safely and easily find a and b by solving Equation 7.67 and 7.68 in the ordinary way but the solution in this case can be written down by a trick which we shall find useful when we come to consider more general relations.   The required line (Equation 7.66) is in fact

$$y = y_1 \frac{x - x_2}{x_1 - x_2} + y_2 \frac{x - x_1}{x_2 - x_1} \qquad (7.69)$$

because if in Equation 7.69 we put x_1 for x, the first term of the right-hand side reduces to y_1 and the second to zero, while if we put x_2 for x, the first term reduces to zero and the second to y_2; Equation 7.69 is obviously linear in x and y, so it necessarily represents a line, and therefore *the* line, joining the points (x_1, y_1) and (x_2, y_2). By comparing Equations 7.69 and 7.66, or by solving Equations 7.67 and 7.68, we find

$$a = (y_2 - y_1)/(x_2 - x_1)$$

and

$$b = (x_2 y_1 - x_1 y_2)/(x_2 - x_1).$$

We next have to consider what to do if there are more than two pairs, say n pairs of corresponding values of x and y available. It must be remembered that our data are experimental so that a line is unlikely to pass through all the points.   We can still write down n equations expressing that the line specified by Equation 7.66 goes through the various points representing corresponding values of the variables but, as we now have more than two of these equations, we can no longer solve them as they stand. Each pair of points may be joined by a somewhat different line from each other pair and what we want to do is to find the best approximation to a line through them all. What we have to do is to derive, from the n equations like Equation 7.67, a single pair which involve the various pairs of observations symmetrically, and which can be solved to give a and b. The trick for doing this is to multiply each of the n equations by the coefficient of a and add, so that we obtain

$$\sum_{r=1}^{n} y_r x_r = a \sum_{r=1}^{n} x_r^2 + b \sum_{r=1}^{n} x_r \qquad (7.70)$$

and then we multiply each of the n equations by the coefficient of b and add; that is, we just add them all up. This gives

$$\sum_{r=1}^{n} y_r = a \sum_{r=1}^{n} x_r + n \cdot b \qquad (7.71)$$

Solving Equations 7.70 and 7.71 gives the required values of a and b.

Example

Suppose, for example, we are given the following pairs of values of corresponding points:

x	-10	-5	0	10	20
y	$1 \cdot 4$	$1 \cdot 1$	$0 \cdot 5$	$-0 \cdot 5$	$-1 \cdot 3$

Equations 7.70 and 7.71 become

$$-50 \cdot 5 = 625a + 15b$$

$$1 \cdot 2 = 15a + 5b$$

whence $a = -\dfrac{54 \cdot 1}{580} = -0 \cdot 0933$, $b = 0 \cdot 520$, so the line is

$$y = 0 \cdot 520 - 0 \cdot 0933x.$$

This is plotted in Fig. 7.7.

Now suppose that we are given the same set of points displaced as a whole. The straight line that best fits must be similarly displaced, but the equations to be solved for it may be simplified or made more complicated by the displacment. Suppose first that each x is reduced by 3 and each y by 0·24, so that the mean x and the mean y are both reduced to zero. The tabulated values now become

x	−13	− 8	−3	7	17
y	1·16	0·86	0·26	−0·74	−1·54

Equation 7.70 now reduces to

$$-54 \cdot 1 = 580a$$

and Equation 7.71 becomes

$$b = 0$$

so that the line is

$$y = -0 \cdot 0933x$$

and goes through the new origin, which means that with the original data, the line goes through the point where $x = 3$, $y = 0·24$, marked A in Fig. 7.7. This point is the 'centre of mass' of the observed

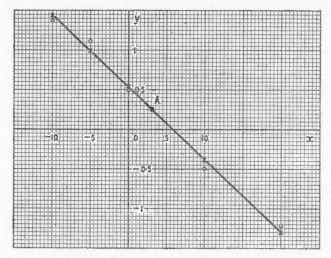

Fig. 7.7. Plot of 'least-squares' line among experimental points

points. Hence, making the mean value of x and y zero has greatly simplified the determination of the line.

If, on the other hand, all the x are severely displaced in the positive direction, large numbers occur in the equations for a, b:

x	40	45	50	60	70
y	1·4	1·1	0·5	−0·5	−1·3

$$9·5 = 14,625a + 265b$$

$$1·3 = 265a + 5b$$

We still find $a = -0·0933$; b is now 5·1849, but much larger numbers enter into the equations.

If, as in Fig. 7.7, we plot the line l, derived from Equation 7.66 with the values of a and b derived from Equations 7.70 and 7.71, it will be found to lie evenly among the points representing the observed values. If all the n points lay exactly on a line, l would be that line and, in general, the line l has the property that the sum of the squares of the distances of the various points (measured in the y-direction) from l is a minimum for varying a and b. For this reason, the Equations 7.70 and 7.71 are usually known as 'least-squares equations'.

It greatly simplifies Equations 7.70 and 7.71 if a round number approximately equal to the mean x_r is subtracted from each x_r and a round number approximately equal to the mean y_r is subtracted from each y_r before Equations 7.70 and 7.71 are written down; otherwise the coefficients of Equations 7.70 and 7.71 tend to be inconveniently large and loss of accuracy due to the subtraction of nearly equal quantities may result. Geometrically, this means we should take the origin of co-ordinates in the (x, y) plane to be near the centre of gravity of the points (x_r, y_r); this centre of gravity, from Equation 7.71, always lies on the line l.

NON-LINEAR RELATIONS

The question now arises as to whether we can deal in a similar manner with a known relation which does not happen to be linear. It may be possible to replace y by some other variable Y which is a function of x and y, and x by some other variable X which is a function of x and y, in such a way that Y and X are linearly related even if y and x are not. For example, if we expect y to be exponentially related to x, $\log y$ will be linearly related to x.   Again, if x and y are related by a power law, $\log x$ and $\log y$ are linearly related. By using logarithmic, probability, and other types of paper, we can, in suitable cases, find corresponding pairs of values of the variables X and Y which are linearly related merely by measuring distances along this special paper instead of by calculation.   Such a change of variable, however, is not always available.   We may be obliged to express the relation sought by means of a curve of higher degree. We shall therefore consider the case in which the relation is expected to be of the form

$$y = A + Bx + Cx^2 \tag{7.72}$$

but, in fact, a similar procedure can be applied to curves of any degree.   The complication, however, increases severely as the degree increases.   It may happen, too, that a curve of high degree appears to fit the observed points more closely, but it may contain oscillations which are unlikely to correspond to any practically significant variation, as they are associated rather with unavoidable experimental uncertainties.

If we have three points (x_1, y_1), (x_2, y_2) and (x_3, y_3) representing corresponding pairs of values, there is just one curve of the form 7.72 which goes through them exactly.   We can obtain it by solving for A, B, C the simultaneous equations

$$\left. \begin{array}{l} y_1 = A + Bx_1 + Cx_1{}^2 \\ y_2 = A + Bx_2 + Cx_2{}^2 \\ y_3 = A + Bx_3 + Cx_3{}^2 \end{array} \right\} \tag{7.73}$$

or we can write it down; the required equation is analogous to Equation 7.69 and is

$$y = y_1 \frac{(x - x_2)(x - x_3)}{(x_1 - x_2)(x_1 - x_3)} + y_2 \frac{(x - x_3)(x - x_1)}{(x_2 - x_3)(x_2 - x_1)} +$$

$$+ y_3 \frac{(x - x_1)(x - x_2)}{(x_3 - x_1)(x_3 - x_2)} \tag{7.74}$$

but, when there are more than three pairs of corresponding points, say n pairs, we have to find simultaneous equations analogous to

Equations 7.70 and 7.71 for A, B, C; these are obtained by

(a) adding up Equations 7.73:

$$\sum_{r=1}^{n} y_r = nA + B \sum_{r=1}^{n} x_r + C \sum_{r=1}^{n} x_r^2 \qquad (7.75)$$

(b) multiplying each of Equations 7.73 by the coefficient of B and adding:

$$\sum_{r=1}^{n} x_r y_r = A \sum_{r=1}^{n} x_r + B \sum_{r=1}^{n} x_r^2 + C \sum_{r=1}^{n} x_r^3 \qquad (7.76)$$

(c) multiplying each of Equations 7.73 by the coefficient of C and adding:

$$\sum_{r=1}^{n} x_r^2 y_r = A \sum_{r=1}^{n} x_r^2 + B \sum_{r=1}^{n} x_r^3 + C \sum_{r=1}^{n} x_r^4 \qquad (7.77)$$

and these simultaneous equations are then solved for A, B, C. They are greatly simplified, as in the case of Equations 7.70 and 7.71, if the origin of co-ordinates is shifted to the centre of gravity of the points (x_1, y_1), (x_2, y_2), etc.

The values of A, B, C obtained from Equations 7.73, 7.75–7.77 determine the curve (Equation 7.72) which has the best 'least-squares fit' to the experimental results, but the solution of Equations 7.75, 7.76 and 7.77 is somewhat tedious. A possible way of obtaining a rough-and-ready result is to draw by eye a smooth curve among the points, choose three key well-spaced (but not necessarily equally-spaced) points on it, and apply Equation 7.74, taking (x_1, y_1), (x_2, y_2) and (x_3, y_3) to be the co-ordinates of the chosen points. By plotting the curve (Equation 7.74) thus obtained, we can soon see if our key points were chosen unsuitably. If we are in doubt we must, of course, solve Equations 7.75, 7.76 and 7.77 which are only theoretically-defensible equations, but they require excessive labour of calculation when only a rough result is required.

In general, it is not worth while to try to fit a curve of the form Equation 7.72 to points representing observed results. Equation

7.72 will always fit better than Equation 7.67, but it does not usually fit very much better.   In a small minority of cases, however, a curve given by Equation 7.72, or even a curve of higher degree, may be the most satisfactory way available for representing the experimental data.

Chapter 8

VERSORS, VECTORS AND TRIGONOMETRY

So far, we have considered mainly algebraic operations applied to real or complex numbers, such as evaluating some function $f(x)$ of x when x is a given real or complex number, or solving equations to find x so that $f(x)$ shall have a prescribed value. A real number is fully specified in terms of its magnitude, except insofar as the possibility that it could be positive or negative must be considered. A complex number, on the other hand, needs two quantities—its real part, say x and imaginary part, say y—to be determined before it is fully specified, and this remains true even if we prefer to specify the complex number in terms of its magnitude R and direction θ measured anti-clockwise relative to the real axis according to the formula

$$x + jy = R(\cos \theta + j \sin \theta) = R\,e^{j\theta} \tag{8.1}$$

where

$$R = (x^2 + y^2)^{1/2} \quad \cos \theta = x/R \quad \sin \theta = y/R \tag{8.2}$$

In this chapter we shall use the term 'versor' to denote a complex number in the form $Re^{j\theta}$, which requires the determination of a magnitude R and a direction θ for adequate specification. For there are other quantities, commonly called vectors, for which the same is true. Displacements, velocities, accelerations, forces, and so on are all vectors, and they can be handled by means of an algebra similar in some respects, to that of complex numbers, but not identical with it. It is therefore very important to be clear whether we are discussing versors or vectors, so that we do not use the wrong algebra. When the right algebra for the situation being considered is fully exploited, it can greatly increase understanding.

Both versors and vectors are subject to the same 'parallelogram'

154

law of addition, but the laws of multiplication are different—indeed, there are two quite distinct sorts of vector multiplication, and both are different from the law of versor multiplication.

Now a mathematician would be quite prepared initially to consider any laws of addition and multiplication for versors, vectors and other such quantities, and the definitions given below are essentially arbitrary. But results obtained with these definitions have a relevance to the practical situations where they are applied; this is the sole reason why versor and vector algebra based on these definitions continue to be studied. A mathematician who used other definitions might enjoy himself for a time, but ultimately he would find that his algebra might be an amusing game (like chess) with little relevance to reality.

VERSOR AND VECTOR ADDITION AND MULTIPLICATION

Fig. 8.1 explains the basis of the law of addition which is common to versors and vectors. In its simplest form, this law states that to add $x_1 + jy_1$ and $x_2 + jy_2$, we add x_1 and x_2 to get the real part or x-component, and add y_1 and y_2 to get the imaginary or j-part or y-component. In this context the symbol j simply means that any number following is measured in the upward or y-direction, whereas a number not followed by j is measured to the right or in the x-direction. If we are given the magnitudes R_1, R_2 and directions θ_1, θ_2 of the two versors (or vectors) to be added, we can use Equations 8.2 to find the corresponding quantities x_1, x_2, y_1 and y_2, or we can set the given vectors (or versors) end to end as in Fig. 8.1 and join OQ; OQ is the correct sum-versor (or vector) in magnitude and direction. In Fig. 8.1, θ_1 and θ_2 have both been taken as acute angles but Equations 8.2 apply whatever the signs and relative sizes of x_1 x_2 y_1 y_2 θ_1 and θ_2 (R_1 and R_2 are always taken to be positive) and the same is true of all formulae to be derived in this chapter. It is easiest to see and understand the results obtained with Fig. 8.1 etc. as drawn, as long as a mental note is made that for example Q could be below and/or to the left of P or even O.

The reason why this law of addition is often called the 'parallelogram law' is that it arises at an early stage in mechanics when the effect of two forces in different directions on a particle, say at O in Fig. 8.1, is considered. If OS is drawn equal and parallel to PQ in Fig. 8.1, the quadrilateral $OPQS$ is a parallelogram and SQ is also equal and parallel to OP. OS thus has the same magnitude and direction as PQ. Now a force does not have the same effect as an equal and parallel force, because rotational effects have to be considered, but displacements, velocities, accelerations and many other quantities correctly specified by vectors are not subject to this disadvantage; these quantities do not have a 'line of action' but only a magnitude and direction.   We shall assume that all vectors discussed below are not changed by being shifted without change in magnitude or direction unless the contrary is explicitly stated.

The laws for multiplication of versors and vectors are different, and will be stated first, both in terms of magnitude and direction

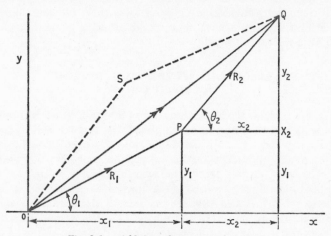

Fig. 8.1.   Addition of versors and vectors

and in terms of x and y components as indicated in Fig. 8.1 and specified in Equations 8.2, and subsequently discussed separately.

For versors:

$$(x_1 + jy_1)(x_2 + jy_2) = (x_1x_2 - y_1y_2) + j(x_1y_2 + x_2y_1) \quad (8.3)$$

$$\{R_1\,e^{j\theta_1}\}\,\{R_2\,e^{j\theta_2}\} = R_1R_2\,e^{j(\theta_1+\theta_2)} \quad (8.4)$$

For vectors there are two separate multiplication laws.   The 'scalar' or 'inner product' is a number defined by

$$R_1 \,.\, R_2 = R_1R_2 \cos(\theta_2 - \theta_1) \quad (8.5)$$

or if R_1 has components

$$x_1 = R_1 \cos \theta_1 \text{ in the } x\text{-direction}$$

$$y_1 = R_1 \sin \theta_1 \text{ in the } y\text{-direction}$$

as in Equation 8.2 and similarly for R_2, the scalar product is given by

$$R_1 . R_2 = x_1 x_2 + y_1 y_2 \qquad (8.6)$$

On the other hand the 'vector' or 'outer' product is given by

$$R_1 \times R_2 = \text{a vector of magnitude } R_1 R_2 \sin (\theta_2 - \theta_1) \left.\begin{array}{l}\\ \\ \\\end{array}\right\} \qquad (8.7)$$
perpendicular to the plane of R_1 and R_2 in the 'right-handed screw' sense

which in terms of the components of R_1 and R_2 reduces to

$$R_1 \times R_2 = \text{vector of magnitude } (x_1 y_2 - x_2 y_1) \text{ (per-} \left.\begin{array}{l}\\ \\ \\\end{array}\right\} \qquad (8.8)$$
pendicular to the plane of R_1 and R_2 as above)

Equations 8.3 and 8.4 are familiar and need little further discussion; complex algebra is not essentially different from real algebra except insofar as j^2 and -1 can be regarded as freely interchangeable. Again, Equations 8.7 and 8.8 need not concern us very much here. They are included mainly for the sake of completeness, and because they are closely related to the fundamentals of

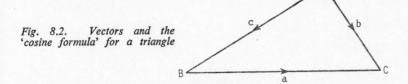

Fig. 8.2. Vectors and the 'cosine formula' for a triangle

electromagnetic theory. If a field H is produced at a point having a displacement r from a charged particle moving with velocity V, the Biot-Savart formula can be expressed in the form

$$H = \frac{eV \times r}{4\pi r^3} \qquad (8.9)$$

with full allowance for the relative directions of V r and H. In Equation 8.9 the multiplication sign means vector multiplication in the sense of Equation 8.7, and r means the magnitude of r without reference to its direction.

On the other hand, Equations 8.5 and 8.6 can be used to give much useful information about geometrical and trigonometrical relations, mainly by using the fact, deducible from Equation 8.5 when $R_1 = R_2$, that

$$R_1{}^2 = R_1{}^2 \tag{8.10}$$

For example, if ABC is any triangle, and the sides are vectors a, b and c specified according to Fig. 8.2, we have

$$b^2 = b^2 = (c + a)^2$$
$$= c^2 + 2c \cdot a + a^2$$

Hence

$$b^2 = c^2 + a^2 - 2ca \cos B \tag{8.11}$$

since the angle between the forward directions of c and a is not B but $\pi - B$. Now Equation 8.11 is a formula which in itself has nothing necessarily to do with vectors at all, and can be proved by more elementary methods. Nevertheless, Equation 8.11 shows how much can be deduced from simple applications of Equations 8.5 and 8.6.

Again, the well known formula for the distance between two points (x_1, y_1) and (x_2, y_2) can be obtained at once from Fig. 8.3. For the line joining O to $P(x_1, y_1)$ can be regarded as the sum of a vector x_1 of magnitude x_1 and direction Ox and a vector y_1 of magnitude

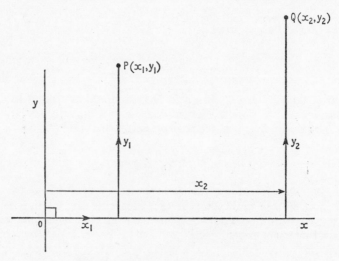

Fig. 8.3. The distance between two points

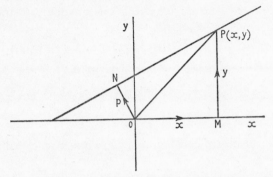

Fig. 8.4. The equation of a straight line

y_1 and direction Oy, and similarly for the line OQ. Hence the vector PQ is given by

$$PQ = (x_2 + y_2) - (x_1 + y_1)$$

Hence

$$PQ^2 = PQ^2 = \{x_2 - x_1 + y_2 - y_1\}^2$$
$$= (x_2 - x_1)^2 + (y_2 - y_1)^2 +$$
$$+ 2(x_2 - x_1)(y_2 - y_1) \cos \frac{\pi}{2}$$

$$\therefore \qquad PQ^2 = (x_2 - x_1)^2 + (y_2 - y_1)^2 \qquad (8.12)$$

EQUATIONS OF STRAIGHT LINE AND CIRCLE

Again, the condition for the point $P(x, y)$ to lie on a straight line or circle can be found from Figs. 8.4 and 8.5. If p is the vector from the origin perpendicular to the line, and $P(x, y)$ is any point of the line, as in Fig. 8.4, so that the vector OP is $x + y$, then we have

$$NP = x + y - p$$

and the directions of NP and p are perpendicular, so that

$$p . (x + y - p) = 0$$

or, if p makes an angle θ with Ox (which may be of any size from 0 to 2π)

$$xp \cos \theta + yp \sin \theta - p^2 = 0$$

or

$$x \cos \theta + y \sin \theta = p \qquad (8.13)$$

which is one of the standard forms of the equation of a straight line.
   In Fig. 8.5, correspondingly, we have

$$r^2 = CP^2 = (CO + OP)^2 = (-a - b + x + y)^2$$
$$= \{(x - a) + (y - b)\}^2$$

$$= (x - a)^2 + (y - b)^2 + 2(x - a)(y - b) \cos \frac{\pi}{2}$$

$$\therefore \qquad\qquad r^2 = (x - a)^2 + (y - b)^2 \qquad\qquad (8.14)$$

which is the standard equation to a circle centre. (a, b) and radius r.

FORMULAE FOR $\cos(A+B)$ AND $\sin(A+B)$

In Equations 8.2 and 8.5, there is no restriction on θ or θ_1, but
R and R_1 are necessarily positive.   In other words, if we start from
the origin and proceed along a vector of magnitude unity having
direction making an angle A with the positive direction of the
x-axis, we always arrive at the point A whose co-ordinates are
$(\cos A, \sin A)$, whatever the size of A may be, as in Fig. 8.6, and
similarly if we proceed along a unit vector having direction making

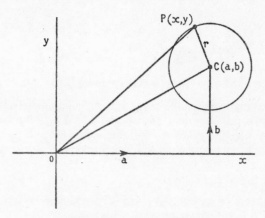

Fig. 8.5.   The equation of a circle

an angle B with the positive direction of the x-axis, we arrive at the
point B whose coordinates are $(\cos B, \sin B)$.   If we now apply
Equations 8.11 and 8.12 to Fig. 8.6, we obtain a general formula
for $\cos (A - B)$ in terms of the trigonometrical ratios of A and B
which is applicable whatever the relative sizes and signs of A and B.

We have, from Equation 8.11

$$AB^2 = 1^2 + 1^2 - 2 \cdot 1 \cdot 1 \cos (B - A) \qquad (8.15)$$

and from Equation 8.12

$$AB^2 = (\cos A - \cos B)^2 + (\sin A - \sin B)^2 \qquad (8.16)$$

whence

$$\cos (A - B) \text{ or } \cos (B - A) = \cos A \cos B + \sin A \sin B \quad (8.17)$$

and Equation 8.17 has been derived in such a way that there is no restriction on the signs and sizes of A and B.

Now in most textbooks on trigonometry, Equation 8.17, and similar equations for $\sin (A \pm B)$ are derived in a later chapter. We

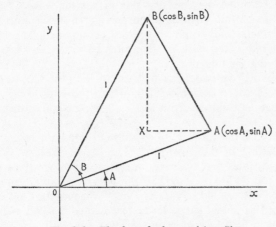

Fig. 8.6. The formula for $\cos (A - B)$

prefer here to derive most well-known and useful results as special cases of Equation 8.17, which we have proved whatever the sizes of the angles A and B may be.

First, put A equal to $\pi/2$ radians (or 90°) and we find from Equation 8.17

$$\cos (\pi/2 - B) = \sin B \qquad (8.18)$$

since $\cos \dfrac{\pi}{2} = 0$ and $\sin \dfrac{\pi}{2} = 1$.

Again, putting A equal to zero gives

$$\cos (-B) = \cos B \qquad (8.19)$$

and in a similar way all the well-known results about the trigonometrical ratios of angles differing from a given angle by multiples of
π may be derived. These results can be summarised by means of
the following mnemonics (the first of which is due to C. V. Durell)

		Subtract from π (180°)	Leave it alone	
S	A			(8.20)
T	C	Subtract π (180°)	Subtract from 2π (360°)	

The meaning of these mnemonics will be made clear by examples;
it should be noted that the first one makes the word CAST if we
start at the bottom right-hand corner and proceed anticlockwise.
The mnemonics only apply to the sine, cosine and tangent; if the
ratio required is, say, sec 127°, that must be written as 1/cos 127° before applying the mnemonics.

Now cos 127° is associated with an angle in the second (top left)
quadrant of the mnemonics 8.20, where the letter S appears and
the instruction 'Subtract from 180°'. The mnemonics therefore tell
us that cos 127° is $-$ cos (180° $-$ 127°) $=$ $-$ cos 53°; the sign is
minus because the ratio (cosine) required does not begin with the
letter S falling in the quadrant. The 'A' in the first (top right)
quadrant denotes that *all* trigonometrical ratios are there positive.
Similarly, tan 253° $=$ $+$ tan (253° $-$ 180°) $=$ $+$ tan 73° and sin 340°
$=$ $-$ sin (360° $-$ 340°) $=$ $-$ sin 20°. When letters are involved,
we proceed as if any single letter represented a small acute angle,
whether it in fact does so or not. Thus, sin (180° $-$ A) is treated
as in the second quadrant, and reduces to $+$ sin [180° $-$ (180° $-$ A)]
$=$ $+$ sin A. In the case of cos (270° $+$ B), the angle is treated as
in the fourth quadrant, and reduces to $+$ cos [360° $-$ (270° $+$ B)]
$=$ $+$ cos (90° $-$ B); this reduces to sin B as already seen in Equation 8.18.

Our safeguard in any of the above is that they can always be
derived by giving suitable values to A and B in Equation 8.17 but
the mnemonics (8.20) do the calculation for us instantaneously.

If in Fig. 8.7, AN is drawn perpendicular to BC meeting BC in N,
we have

$$c \sin B = AN = b \sin C \qquad (8.21)$$

In the form of Equation 8.21 the result is true even if B or C is an obtuse angle; it can be divided through by $\sin B \sin C$ to give

$$\frac{b}{\sin B} = \frac{c}{\sin C} = \frac{a}{\sin A} \qquad (8.22)$$

the last member of Equation 8.22 being added by symmetry (or by drawing CX perpendicular to AB). Equations 8.11 and 8.22 are those used to 'solve triangles', that is to say, to find all of a, b, c, A, B, C which are not known when enough is given to determine the triangle. Equation 8.11 is not always very convenient and alternatives are available, but we shall not discuss these here since solving triangles is not often necessary for electrical engineering. Any soluble triangle *can* be solved by means of these two equations.

There are a number of general results, similar to Equation 8.17 and derivable from it, which permit us to manipulate trigonometrical expressions into the form most suitable for a particular problem. These results are:

$$\left.\begin{aligned}
\cos (A + B) &= \cos A \cos B - \sin A \sin B \\
\sin (A + B) &= \sin A \cos B + \cos A \sin B \\
\sin (A - B) &= \sin A \cos B - \cos A \sin B
\end{aligned}\right\} \qquad (8.23)$$

The first of these is derived from Equation 8.17 by putting $- B$ instead of B, and the last of Equations 8.23 is similarly derived from the second. To obtain the second, replace A by $(\pi/2 - A)$ in Equation 8.17

So far, the obvious significance of Equations 8.17 and 8.23 is that they are 'addition formulae', giving the trigonometrical ratios of compound angles $A \pm B$ in terms of those of the component angles A and B. If now we add the first of Equations 8.23 to Equation 8.17, we obtain

$$2 \cos A \cos B = \cos (A - B) + \cos (A + B) \qquad (8.24)$$

and if we subtract the first of Equations 8.23 from Equation 8.17

$$2 \sin A \sin B = \cos (A - B) - \cos (A + B) \qquad (8.25)$$

By similarly manipulating the second and third of Equations 8.23 we derive

$$2 \sin A \cos B = \sin (A + B) + \sin (A - B) \qquad (8.26)$$

$$2 \cos A \sin B = \sin (A + B) - \sin (A - B) \qquad (8.27)$$

Equations 8.24 to 8.27 enable us to break up a product of two trigonometrical ratios into a sum; this is often advantageous in numerical work, because adding is easier than multiplying. Thus for example

$$\sin 33° \sin 27° = \tfrac{1}{2} (\cos 6° - \cos 60°)$$
$$= \tfrac{1}{2} (0·99452 - 0·5) = 0·24726$$

Conversely, we may sometimes find it desirable to factorise a trigonometrical expression given as the sum or difference of two terms. In this case we really need to use Equations 8.24 to 8.27 the other way round, with

$$A + B = \alpha, \quad A - B = \beta,$$
$$A = \tfrac{1}{2} (\alpha + \beta), \quad B = \tfrac{1}{2} (\alpha - \beta) \tag{8.28}$$

These formulae are given explicitly in Equations 8.59–8.62. Consider for example the expression

$$X = \sin x + \sin \left(x + \frac{2\pi}{3}\right) + \sin \left(x + \frac{4\pi}{3}\right) \tag{8.29}$$

Applying Equation 8.26 to the first and last terms, with

$$A + B = x + \frac{4\pi}{3}, \quad A - B = x$$

so that

$$A = x + \frac{2\pi}{3}, \quad B = \frac{2\pi}{3} \tag{8.30}$$

we find

$$X = 2 \sin \left(x + \frac{2\pi}{3}\right) \cos \frac{2\pi}{3} + \sin \left(x + \frac{2\pi}{3}\right)$$
$$= \sin \left(x + \frac{2\pi}{3}\right) \left\{1 + 2 \cos \frac{2\pi}{3}\right\} = 0 \tag{8.31}$$

since $\cos (2\pi/3) = - \cos (\pi/3) = - \tfrac{1}{2}$.

This is typical of the way in which trigonometrical expressions often contain astonishing possibilities of simplification within themselves. Very often, a process like that indicated in Equation 8.30 is begun simply because the given expression, here Equation 8.29, does not look as if it was in a convenient form, and any alternative is worth considering. When the process is complete, we have often not only simplified the given expression, but obtained a clue as to its significance; in Equation 8.29, if the middle term had the coefficient k instead of 1, Equation 8.31 would tell us that sin $(x + 2\pi/3)$ was a factor, which is not at all obvious from the form of Equation 8.29.

DE MOIVRE'S THEOREM

In Equation 8.1, we at the time assumed that if the versor $x + jy$ was expressed in terms of its magnitude R and direction θ, the versor could be represented correctly by the expression $Re^{j\theta}$ as well as by the more obvious form $R(\cos \theta + j \sin \theta)$. Historically, the fact that the expression $(\cos \theta + j \sin \theta)$ has an exponential nature was discovered in the form of 'De Moivre's Theorem', namely

$$(\cos \theta + j \sin \theta)^n = \cos n\theta + j \sin n\theta \qquad (8.32)$$

where n is not necessarily an integer. Equation 8.32, however, has a usefulness of its own, particularly because it enables us to obtain explicit formulae for cos $n\theta$ and sin $n\theta$ in terms of cos θ and sin θ for integral values of n. Thus when $n = 2$ we obtain

$$\cos 2\theta + j \sin 2\theta = (\cos \theta + j \sin \theta)^2$$

$$= (\cos^2\theta - \sin^2\theta) + j \,.\, 2 \sin \theta \cos \theta \qquad (8.33)$$

so that

$$\cos 2\theta = \cos^2\theta - \sin^2\theta; \; \sin 2\theta = 2 \sin \theta \cos \theta \qquad (8.34)$$

Equation 8.34 could also be obtained by putting $A = B = \theta$ in the first two of Equations 8.23. But n can have any value in Equation 8.32, and by using the Binomial Theorem (Chapter 5) we can obtain directly formulae for cos $n\theta$ and sin $n\theta$ in terms of cos θ and sin θ which would require repeated application of Equations 8.23. If cos θ is replaced by x and sin θ by $(1 - x^2)^{\frac{1}{2}}$, cos $n\theta$ and sin $n\theta$ can be expressed in terms of x, and become what are known as Tchebycheff polynomials and functions respectively Here, however, we merely wish to point out that the form of these expressions (easily obtained from Equation 8.32) with both cos θ (or x) and sin θ or $(1 - x^2)^{1/2}$ present, is often just as useful as the strict Tchebycheff form in which only x is allowed.

MISCELLANEOUS FORMULAE: TRIGONOMETRICAL EQUATIONS

Hitherto this chapter might be described as a short basic course on vector analysis and its applications to trigonometry. We shall now use the results already derived to obtain further labour-saving results not commonly given in textbooks, although they are easily deducible from the formulae discussed above.

First, we shall collect together, for easy reference, the results to be discussed:

$$\cos [\tan^{-1} A] = 1/(1 + A^2)^{1/2} \tag{8.35}$$

$$\sin [\tan^{-1} A] = A/(1 + A^2)^{1/2} \tag{8.36}$$

$$\cos [\sin^{-1} A] = (1 - A^2)^{1/2} \tag{8.37}$$

$$\tan [\sin^{-1} A] = A/(1 - A^2)^{1/2} \tag{8.38}$$

(Note that these results apply on the assumption that the angles $\tan^{-1}A$ and $\sin^{-1}A$ are between $-\pi/2$ and $+\pi/2$ and may require modifications of sign otherwise.)

If A is an angle between $-\pi/2$ and $+\pi/2$, then

$$\left. \begin{array}{l} \sin x = \sin A \text{ implies } x = A + 2n\pi \\ \text{or } x = (\pi - A) + 2n\pi \end{array} \right\} n \text{ integer} \tag{8.39}$$

$$\tan x = \tan A \text{ implies } x = A + n\pi \tag{8.40}$$

while if B is an angle between 0 and π

$$\cos x = \cos B \text{ implies } x = 2n\pi \pm B \tag{8.41}$$

If α is any angle whatsoever

$$1 + \cos \alpha = 2 \cos^2 \frac{\alpha}{2} \tag{8.42}$$

$$1 - \cos \alpha = 2 \sin^2 \frac{\alpha}{2} \tag{8.43}$$

and if α and β are likewise completely arbitrary angles and a is an arbitrary positive number while b is an arbitrary number, positive or negative,

$$a \cos \alpha + b \sin \alpha = (a^2 + b^2)^{1/2} \sin \left(\alpha + \tan^{-1} \frac{a}{b} \right) \tag{8.44}$$

$$a \cos \alpha + b \sin \alpha = (a^2 + b^2)^{1/2} \cos \left(\alpha - \tan^{-1} \frac{b}{a} \right) \tag{8.45}$$

$$a \sin \alpha + b \sin \beta = (a + b) \sin \frac{\alpha + \beta}{2} \cos \frac{\alpha - \beta}{2} +$$
$$+ (a - b) \cos \frac{\alpha + \beta}{2} \sin \frac{\alpha - \beta}{2} \tag{8.46}$$

$$a \cos \alpha + b \cos \beta = (a + b) \cos \frac{\alpha + \beta}{2} \cos \frac{\alpha - \beta}{2} +$$

$$+ (b - a) \sin \frac{\alpha + \beta}{2} \sin \frac{\alpha - \beta}{2} \tag{8.47}$$

where in Equations 8.44 and 8.48 the angles $\tan^{-1} (a/b)$ and $\tan^{-1} (b/a)$ are taken as lying between $-\pi/2$ and $+\pi/2$.

In dealing with Equations 8.35–8.38, we have first to be careful as to what we mean by $\tan^{-1} A$ and $\sin^{-1} A$. Given the angle A, its sine, cosine and tangent are perfectly definite, but when the sine, cosine or tangent of an angle is given, there is an infinite set of angles having that sine, cosine or tangent. Increasing an angle by any multiple of 2π has no effect on its sine, cosine or tangent, and it is always possible to find two angles in the range 0 to 2π whose sine, cosine or tangent have a given value; this becomes clear from a study of the mnemonics 8.20.

Before we use an expression like $\tan^{-1} x$, we have in some way to identify a particular and uniquely defined member of this infinite set of angles whose tangent is equal to x. This particular member is commonly called the 'principal value' of a many-valued expression like $\tan^{-1} x$, and it is better only to use the expression '$\tan^{-1} x$' to mean this principal value; if a general angle whose tangent is x is meant, this is best described as either 'Tan$^{-1} x$' or '$\tan^{-1} x + k\pi$, k any integer'. When x varies from $-\pi/2$ to $+\pi/2$, $\sin x$ and $\tan x$ pass through all possible values, so we can specify the 'principal value' in these cases as having to lie between $-\pi/2$ and $+\pi/2$ (inclusive). On the other hand, $\cos x$ is always positive for $-\pi/2 < x < \pi/2$, so that we must in this case specify that x lies between 0 and π (inclusive). We shall therefore hereafter use the expressions '$\sin^{-1} x$', '$\cos^{-1} x$' and '$\tan^{-1} x$' in the 'principal value' sense discussed above, namely:

'$\sin^{-1} x$' means the angle lying between $-\pi/2$ and $+\pi/2$ (inclusive) whose sine is equal to x,

'$\cos^{-1} x$' means the angle lying between 0 and π (inclusive) whose cosine is equal to x, and

'$\tan^{-1} x$' means the angle lying between $-\pi/2$ and $+\pi/2$ (inclusive) whose tangent is equal to x.

Equations 8.35 and 8.36 are now easily obtained from Fig. 8.8 (a) (A positive) and (b) (A negative), while Equations 8.37 and 8.38 follow similarly from Fig. 8.9 (a) (A positive) and (b) (A negative). In the case of Fig. 8.9 (a) and (b), A must necessarily be numerically less than unity, or the angle $\sin^{-1} A$ ceases to be real; the value of A, however, is unrestricted in Fig. 8.8 (a) and (b).

If $\angle POM$ is the angle $\tan^{-1} A$, then for $A > 0$ the point P will be in the first quadrant, and we can take $PM = A$ and $OM = 1$. OP is therefore $(1 + A^2)^{1/2}$ (by Pythagoras's theorem) and Equations 8.35 and 8.36 follow immediately. Geometrically, Fig. 8.8 (b)

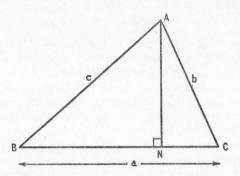

Fig. 8.7. The 'sine formula' for a triangle

when A is negative is the same; the only difference is that the triangle OPM is now necessarily in the fourth quadrant and the actual length of PM must be $-A$ since A is negative.

If $\angle POM$ is $\sin^{-1} A$ as in Fig. 8.9 (a), then again P will be in the first quadrant, but this time it is OP which we must take as having unit length instead of OM, so that OM has the length $(1 - A^2)^{1/2}$. Again, Equations 8.37 and 8.38 follow directly, and if A is negative, the only difference is, as before, that the triangle OPM is in the fourth quadrant instead of the first and PM is $(-A)$ instead of $(+A)$.

In the foregoing, we have assumed that $\sin^{-1} A$ and $\tan^{-1} A$ denoted principal values. Any failure to take sufficient care about this is likely to cause an error of sign. For example, if A is unity, $\tan^{-1} A$ means $\pi/4$ in the principal value sense and, while it is quite true that $\sin \pi/4$ and $\cos \pi/4$ are correctly given by Equations 8.35 and 8.36 as $1/\sqrt{2}$ in each case, if the angle $\tan^{-1} A$ is taken as $5\pi/4$, we have wrong signs for the sine and cosine from Equations 8.35 and 8.36. A similar error of sign occurs in Equations 8.35 and 8.36 if we take A as $\frac{1}{2}$ and $\sin^{-1} A$ as $5\pi/6$ instead of the correct principal value $\pi/6$.

It is very necessary to be clear as to just what we can deduce from a trigonometrical equation, otherwise genuine solutions of a problem may be disastrously overlooked.   Consider first the equation

$$\sin x = \sin A \qquad (8.48)$$

where A is given to be an angle between $-\pi/2$ and $\pi/2$ inclusive.
It is clear that one solution is

$$x = A \qquad (8.49)$$

and furthermore that $(A + 2n\pi)$ is equally a solution when n is any
integer, since adding multiples of 2π does not alter any of the trigonometrical ratios.   But from the mnemonics 8.20, we know that

$$\sin (\pi - A) = \sin A \qquad (8.50)$$

so that there is a second set of solutions $(\pi - A) + 2n\pi$.   Now
although we have been careful to express results so far obtained
only in terms of principal values, there is no reason why the solution
to a problem giving rise to an equation of the form 8.48 should
necessarily be an angle in the principal-value range.   We must
therefore take *all* the values $(A + 2n\pi)$ and $(\pi - A) + 2n\pi$ into
account and only reject those that do not fit the practical considerations associated with the particular problem;   mathematically all

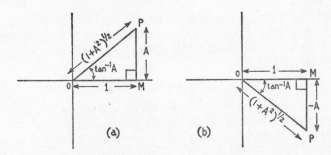

Fig. 8.8.   The angle $\tan^{-1}A$; (a) $A > 0$, (b) $A < 0$

these values are equally relevant, as specified in Equation 8.39.
Correspondingly, if

$$\tan x = \tan A \qquad (8.51)$$

where A is between $-\pi/2$ and $\pi/2$ as before, we have $A + 2n\pi$ as
one set of solutions.   When any manipulation of trigonometrical
ratios other than sines and cosines is required, it usually pays first

12

to express these other ratios first in terms of sines and cosines by means of the relations

$$\tan x = \frac{\sin x}{\cos x}; \ \sec x = \frac{1}{\cos x}; \ \operatorname{cosec} x = \frac{1}{\sin x}$$

$$\cot x = \frac{1}{\tan x} = \frac{\cos x}{\sin x} \tag{8.52}$$

From Equations 8.52, or from the mnemonics 8.20, we can deduce that increasing x by π negatives $\sin x$ and $\cos x$ but leaves $\tan x$

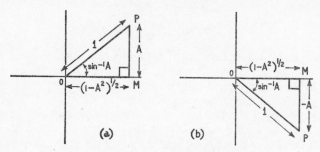

Fig. 8.9. The angle $\sin^{-1}A$; (a) $A > 0$, (b) $A < 0$

unchanged. Hence the second set of solutions is in this case $(\pi + A) + 2n\pi$, and these can be combined with the original set $(A + 2n\pi)$ into the single result given in Equation 8.40.

The remaining case,

$$\cos x = \cos B \tag{8.53}$$

is similar except that, this time, we are given that B is between 0 and π; as before, $x = B + 2n\pi$ is one set of solutions, but this time the other set is more obviously $(-B) + 2n\pi$ because $\cos x$ is an even function of x. These two sets of results can be combined into a single result, Equation 8.41. Text-books often combine the two results given in Equation 8.39 into the equivalent single form

$$x = n\pi + (-1)^n A \tag{8.54}$$

so that all three results, Equations 8.39–8.41, are given in single form, but the advantage of Equation 8.54 over Equation 8.39 is doubtful.

Equations 8.42 and 8.43 are easily proved but are so often overlooked that the writer's mathematical master found it necessary to have them permanently on the blackboard and always referred to them as 'the formulae on the board'.   Equation 8.34 was

$$\cos^2 \theta - \sin^2 \theta = \cos 2\theta \qquad (8.55)$$

while the fact that

$$\cos^2 \theta + \sin^2 \theta = 1 \qquad (8.56)$$

is merely a trigonometrical way of expressing 'Pythagoras's Theorem' about right-angled triangles.   Adding Equations 8.55 and 8.56 gives Equation 8.42;   subtracting Equation 8.55 from Equation 8.56 gives Equation 8.43 (if α is put equal to $\theta/2$).

Equation 8.44 follows from Equations 8.35 and 8.36 with A replaced by a/b.   If we denote $\tan^{-1} (a/b)$ by ϕ, we have

$$a \cos \alpha + b \sin \alpha = (a^2 + b^2)^{1/2} [\sin \phi \cos \alpha + \cos \phi \sin \alpha]$$
$$= (a^2 + b^2)^{1/2} \sin (\alpha + \phi) \qquad (8.57)$$

the last member being derived from the second of Equations 8.23. Equation 8.45 is derived similarly, except that in Equations 8.35 and 8.36 A is now replaced by b/a, and it is Equation 8.17 which simplifies the result instead of Equations 8.23.   The restriction that a must be positive is imposed so that we always deal with the principal value $\tan^{-1} (b/a)$ or $\tan^{-1} (a/b)$ as the case may be, and thus avoid any ambiguities of sign.

Finally, Equations 8.46 and 8.47 can be derived from Equations 8.24 to 8.27.   It is convenient to repeat these equations here in the equivalent form when $(A + B)$ is put equal to α and $(A - B)$ is put equal to β, so that

$$A = \frac{\alpha + \beta}{2}, \quad B = \frac{\alpha - \beta}{2} \qquad (8.58)$$

The equations then reduce to

$$\cos \alpha + \cos \beta = 2 \cos \tfrac{1}{2} (\alpha + \beta) \cos \tfrac{1}{2} (\alpha - \beta) \qquad (8.59)$$

$$-\cos \alpha + \cos \beta = 2 \sin \tfrac{1}{2} (\alpha + \beta) \sin \tfrac{1}{2} (\alpha - \beta) \qquad (8.60)$$

$$\sin \alpha + \sin \beta = 2 \sin \tfrac{1}{2} (\alpha + \beta) \cos \tfrac{1}{2} (\alpha - \beta) \qquad (8.61)$$

$$\sin \alpha - \sin \beta = 2 \cos \tfrac{1}{2} (\alpha + \beta) \sin \tfrac{1}{2} (\alpha - \beta) \qquad (8.62)$$

Equation 8.46 follows by multiplying Equation 8.61 by $\tfrac{1}{2} (a + b)$ and Equation 8.62 by $\tfrac{1}{2} (a - b)$ and adding; Equation 8.47 follows by multiplying Equation 8.59 by $\frac{1}{2}$ $(a + b)$ and Equation 8.60 by $\frac{1}{2}$ $(b - a)$ and adding.

Thus while the basic trigonometrical facts were given in Equations 8.11 and 8.17–8.34, the later equations of this chapter give these same essential facts in an alternative form which is often more directly applicable to practical problems.

Trigonometrical expressions can often take many equivalent forms which are very different in appearance, and changing such expressions from one form to another (as we have done several times in this chapter) is frequently not merely a mathematical manipulation but a source of practical understanding of the significant essentials of a problem.

Chapter 9

OPERATIONAL CALCULUS

Hitherto we have been discussing a number of mathematical techniques (such as solving algebraic equations) which may be required in almost any physical situation, in fields as apparently unrelated as astronomy, electrical engineering and atomic physics. For the remainder of this book, however, we shall be concerned with techniques somewhat more advanced than the foregoing, which have particular relevance to electrical engineering theory.

The first of these is operational calculus. In this book we shall only discuss the subject sufficiently to enable an engineer to solve a reasonably straightforward problem concerning lumped-element two-terminal networks. In Chapter 10 we shall discuss matrices, by means of which the techniques of operational calculus can be extended to similar networks having four (or even more) terminals. But a much fuller discussion of operational calculus will be given elsewhere[7], so that in what follows only the minimum of discussion, background material and proof to make the subject readily understood and self-consistent will be included.

Operational calculus of a kind has been studied by mathematicians since the middle of the last century, but Heaviside was the pioneer in applying it to the solution of practical problems in electrical engineering. Heaviside used this calculus with consummate skill himself, but could not be bothered to explain his methods sufficiently for others to be able to follow them. The historical result of this was that contemporary mathematicians regarded Heaviside's methods as unsound, and tried to achieve the same results otherwise, by techniques which have developed into present-day 'symbolic calculus', 'Laplace transforms' and so on.

Here we proceed as if Heaviside's basic premises are correct as well as leading to results correct from the practical point of view. This assumption leads us to a technique which is in fact more general than rival techniques at present more fashionable. It is also simpler, in that phenomena are considered entirely in the world of time; no transforms are required.

BASIC DEFINITIONS: REVERSIBILITY

In operational calculus, the symbol p is used as an abbreviation for $\dfrac{d}{dt}$; p is thus an 'operator' which operates upon the 'operand', say $V(t)$, which follows. p^n means the operator $\dfrac{d^n}{dt^n}$, and from this there is no difficulty about an expression such as

$$y(t) = (p^n + a_{n-1}p^{n-1} + \ldots + a_1 p + a_0)V(t) \qquad (9.1)$$

if $V(t)$ is given and $y(t)$ is to be found. But for an operational calculus to be useful, we must be also able to find $V(t)$ when $y(t)$ is given in Equation 9.1. In other words, we must be able to solve linear differential equations with constant coefficients. Formally, we might in this case write

$$V(t) = \frac{1}{p^n + a_{n-1}p^{n-1} + \ldots + a_1 p + a_0} \, y(t) \qquad (9.2)$$

but before we can make any use of Equation 9.2, we have to consider what we mean by expressions like $1/p$, $1/(p + a)$, and the reciprocal of a polynomial in p. If we are sufficiently careful about fundamental definitions of this nature, we can use the operational calculus based on them with complete confidence.

Now the most important requirement of a useful operational calculus is that it should be reversible, that is to say, having defined p as $\dfrac{d}{dt}$, we must define p^{-1} or $1/p$ in such a way that, for any relevant operand $h(t)$,

$$pp^{-1}h(t) = p^{-1}ph(t) = h(t) \qquad (9.3)$$

If we can do this, we can make any algebraic transformation we like of an operator such as that in Equation 9.2, and we can have unshakeable confidence that whichever form of the operator we ultimately apply to the operand $y(t)$, we shall obtain the same result. Clearly p^{-1} has something to do with integration, which when we first meet it is usually introduced as the reverse of differentiation; if we can get the precise specification of p^{-1} right, we can perform integrations and/or differentiations involved in an expression such as $1/(p^n + a_{n-1}p^{n-1} + .. + a_1p + a_0)$ in any order we please. The definition of p^{-1} which achieves this objective best is

$$p^{-1}h(t) = \int_{-\infty}^{t} h(\tau)\,d\tau \qquad (9.4)$$

For our present purpose, it is sufficient to assume that Equations 9.3 and 9.4 enable us to make any algebraic transformations we like of an operator; the most general type of operator we shall consider here is a rational function of p, that is, the quotient of two polynomials. This important matter will be discussed in much greater detail elsewhere[7].

It should be noted that the symbol $-\infty$ in the lower limit of Equation 9.4 does not necessarily mean a very large negative number, but only one sufficiently negative for a further negative increase to make no difference. Any operand $h(t)$ must have had some beginning, before which it was negligible, if it is an expression relevant to physics rather than an eternal or metaphysical entity, in the province of an archbishop rather than of a physicist. If $h(t)$ is appropriate to a circuit switched on at zero time, $-\infty$ can be replaced by $-\epsilon$ for that circuit, however small ϵ may be provided that ϵ is positive, but $-\infty$ is the only symbol adequate as a lower limit to ensure that Equation 9.3 is valid for *all* relevant operands as required. For *some* operands, this lower limit can be raised, but we raise it at our peril unless we have made quite sure that raising it will not affect the value of the integral.

At this stage we have an obvious meaning for p and from Equation 9.4 we have obtained a suitable meaning for p^{-1}. Our next task is to consider $1/(p + a)$. Once we can cope with this expression, we can, by means of the partial-fraction technique discussed in Chapter 5, cope with a rational expression in p also. Finally we have to show that rational functions of p are naturally associated with two-terminal networks having lumped elements; this involves a generalisation of Ohm's Law and the 'impedance concept' which is of such fundamental importance for modern electrical technology.

THE OPERATOR $(p+a)^{-1}$

If $h(t)$ is given and

$$\frac{1}{p + a} \quad h(t) = v(t) \qquad (9.5)$$

we are required to find an explicit formula for $v(t)$ in terms of $h(t)$.

We have declared our intention of assuming that any algebraic manipulation of expressions involving p is permissible when p^{-1} is defined by Equation 9.4, so if Equation 9.5 makes any sense at all, we must have

$$h(t) = (p + a) v(t) = \frac{dv(t)}{dt} + a\,v(t) \qquad (9.6)$$

Now there is a useful trick which enables us to progress here; this trick is quite obvious once it has been pointed out. By the ordinary rule (Equation 6.17) for differentiating a product,

$$p\{e^{at}\,v(t)\} = ae^{at}v(t) + e^{at}pv(t) = e^{at}(p + a)v(t) \qquad (9.7)$$

so that Equation 9.6 can be rewritten in the form

$$h(t) = e^{-at}p\{e^{at}v(t)\} \qquad (9.8)$$

or

$$e^{at}h(t) = p\{e^{at}v(t)\} \qquad (9.9)$$

or, transferring the p to the left-hand side of Equation 9.9

$$v(t) = e^{-at} \int_{-\infty}^{t} e^{a\tau}h(\tau)\,d\tau \qquad (9.10)$$

Now Equation 9.10 is really the key to the whole operational calculus as required for two-terminal passive networks consisting of 'lumped' elements. Equation 9.10 makes sense as long as a has a positive real part (or is at worst purely imaginary, since we have already assumed that any relevant $h(t)$ must have a beginning). The vital point is that there must be no contribution from the lower limit in Equation 9.10; in other words, we have to integrate all of the integrand that exists up to time t, without performing any process of selection.

If $h(\tau)$ consists of a number of (decaying) exponential terms each multiplied by a step or impulse factor, as it frequently does in electrical situations, an integral of the form 9.10 can be evaluated explicitly. In other cases, we may not always be able to obtain an explicit answer, but we can see the general nature of the answer, by writing

$$v(t) = \int_{-\infty}^{t} e^{-a(t-\tau)}h(\tau)\,d\tau \qquad (9.11)$$

The right-hand side of Equation 9.11* consists essentially of a weighted sum of the values of $h(\tau)$ beginning with the present time ($\tau = t$) and gradually receding into the past ($\tau < t$), but the weighting factor $e^{-a(t-\tau)}$ decays exponentially (since a has a positive real part) as τ recedes into the past.

Equation 9.10 is essentially what we seek when we are given $h(t)$ and require $v(t)$: it is an explicit series of instructions to perform certain operations upon $h(t)$ which are all explicitly determined. A century or so ago, a mathematician would consider that he had 'solved' a differential equation (which Equation 9.5 essentially is) if he had reduced it to a 'mere integration', however difficult the actual carrying out of the integration might be in a particular case. Under present conditions, with electronic computers available, such a mathematician's attitude is even more correct than he would have realised, since techniques for numerical integration, with or without the use of a computer, are well known.

At this stage we have found that if we accept the symbol p as synonymous with $\dfrac{d}{dt}$, and that p^{-1} is correctly defined by Equation 9.4, we can perform any algebraic manipulations with expressions involving p that we wish, including transfer from one side of an equation to another (provided that, when such a transfer happens, there is no operand preceding an expression involving p on either side, as in Equation 9.8), and we can find an explicit expression (or programme of operations) for $\{1/p\}h(t)$ and for $\{1/(p + a)\}h(t)$ when a has a positive real part. A rational expression in p can be reduced by partial-fraction techniques (Chapter 5) to a number of such expressions. It remains to show that, at any rate for a passive lumped-element two-terminal network, behaviour is naturally expressed in terms of rational expressions in p.

---

*Equation (9.11) can also be written

$$v(t) = \int_{-\infty}^{\infty} e^{-a(t-\tau)} H(t - \tau) \,.\, h(\tau) \, d\tau$$

and this is of the form

$$v(t) = \int_{-\infty}^{\infty} \phi_1(t - \tau)\, \phi_2(\tau) \, d\tau \qquad\qquad (A)$$

where $\phi_1(t) = e^{-at} H(t)$ and $\phi_2(t) = h(t)$. (A) is known as the 'convolution integral' of $\phi_1(t)$ and $\phi_2(t)$; it is really a form of multiplication of these two functions which has a basic importance in physical problems involving any kind of storage.

OHM'S LAW GENERALISATION

If a single ideally pure resistance has a voltage V across it and a current I flowing in it, the relation between V and I is $V = RI$—this is Ohm's Law in its original form, and the constant ratio V/I is known as the resistance and is measured in ohms if V is in volts and I in amperes.

If however the resistance is replaced by an ideally pure inductance of L henrys, the relation between V and I becomes

$$V = L \frac{\mathrm{d}I}{\mathrm{d}t} = (pL)I \qquad (9.12)$$

and likewise if the resistance is replaced by a capacitance of C farads, the relation is

$$V = \frac{1}{C} \int_{-\infty}^{t} I \mathrm{d}\tau = \frac{1}{pC} I \qquad (9.13)$$

for Equation 9.13 simply expresses the fact that a pure capacitance stores indefinitely all the charge that has ever been put into it. Equations 9.12 and 9.13 are of the same form as Ohm's original law, except that we have to suppose that an inductance L henrys possesses an 'impedance' Lp ohms which involves p instead of being constant. Likewise, the 'impedance' associated with a capacitance C farads is $1/Cp$ ohms.

The object of operational calculus is to enable us to work with such impedances just as easily as with pure resistances. Historically,

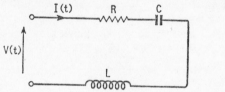

Fig. 9.1. A series LCR circuit

the idea of an impedance pL ohms for an inductance L henrys and $1/pC$ ohms for a capacitance C farads was not reached all at once; the first advance in the right direction was made by the 'steady-state' analysis at the beginning of this century, in which an inductance of L henrys was said to have an impedance of $j\omega L$ ohms if the input was at frequency $\omega/2\pi$ and had been going on for a sufficiently long time, and correspondingly the impedance of a capacitance C farads was $1/j\omega C$. But the operational calculus we have described permits circuit analysis to be carried out whatever the nature of the input. We handle the expressions Lp and $1/Cp$ as if they were ordinary resistances, like R, while we are trying to formulate the relation between the output current and the given input voltage, and then use operational calculus to turn the relation thus implicitly specified into an explicit formula for output in terms of input.

COMBINATION OF IMPEDANCES

There are well-known laws for finding a single impedance Z equivalent to two separate impedances Z_1 and Z_2, namely

$$\left.\begin{array}{l} Z = Z_1 + Z_2 \text{ if } Z_1 \text{ and } Z_2 \text{ are in series} \\ \dfrac{1}{Z} = \dfrac{1}{Z_1} + \dfrac{1}{Z_2} \text{ if } Z_1 \text{ and } Z_2 \text{ are in parallel} \end{array}\right\} \qquad (9.14)$$

(We shall see later (Chapter 10) that both these laws can be combined into the single matrix law that A-matrices of networks in cascade must be multiplied.) The laws 9.14 apply to impedances involving p just as much as resistances which do not, and it is just because complicated impedances for a lumped-element passive two-terminal network arise from repeated application of the combination laws 9.14 that we are apt finally to have to solve a circuit equation of the form

$$I(t) = \frac{1}{Z(p)} \, V(t) \qquad (9.15)$$

where $Z(p)$ is a rational expression in p—the ratio of two polynomials.

ILLUSTRATIVE EXAMPLES

We conclude this chapter with a few illustrative examples. The object of these is to indicate what can be done by means of operational calculus rather than to study it in any detail.

Consider then first the series circuit of Fig. 9.1.

If R is in ohms, C in farads and L in henrys, the total impedance of the three elements in series is $(R + pL + 1/pC)$ ohms, and therefore the generalised form of Ohm's law we have discussed gives

$$I(t) = \frac{1}{R + pL + 1/(pC)} \, V(t) \qquad (9.16)$$

assuming (as is usually the case) that it is the voltage $V(t)$ which we are given.

A change of notation makes Equation 9.16 easier to handle.

We shall mainly consider the case in which the circuit of Fig. 9.1 is oscillatory, so that $R^2 < 4L/C$. Let

$$\alpha = R/2L \qquad \omega = \{1/(LC) - (R^2/4L^2)\}^{1/2} \qquad (9.17)$$

so that Equation 9.16 reduces to

$$I(t) = \frac{1}{L} \frac{p}{(p + \alpha)^2 + \omega^2} V(t) \qquad (9.18)$$

By the partial-fraction technique of Chapter 5, this is readily reduced to

$$I(t) = \frac{1}{2j\omega L} \left[\frac{\alpha + j\omega}{p + \alpha + j\omega} - \frac{\alpha - j\omega}{p + \alpha - j\omega} \right] V(t) \qquad (9.19)$$

and, by applying Equation 9.11 twice, first with $a = \alpha + j\omega$ and then with $a = \alpha - j\omega$, we obtain

$$I(t) = \frac{1}{2j\omega L} \left[(\alpha + j\omega) \int_{-\infty}^{t} e^{-(\alpha+j\omega)(t-\tau)} V(\tau) \, d\tau \right.$$
$$\left. - (\alpha - j\omega) \int_{-\infty}^{t} e^{-(\alpha-j\omega)(t-\tau)} V(\tau) \, d\tau \right] \qquad (9.20)$$

It is no 'vain repetition' to reiterate that Equation 9.20 contains the whole truth of the situation of Fig. 9.1 when the voltage $V(t)$ is given, whatever the nature of $V(t)$ and whether the circuit is in fact oscillatory or not. It is only when we come to carry out the integration in a particular case that we have to worry about such details at all. If for example $V(t)$ is a step-voltage $V_0 H(t)$ (where $H(t)$ is Heaviside's unit-step, zero for negative t and unity for positive t) $I(t)$ becomes $I_1(t)$ where

$$I_1(t) = \frac{V_0}{2j\omega L} \left[(\alpha + j\omega) \int_{0}^{t} e^{-(\alpha+j\omega)(t-\tau)} \, d\tau \right.$$
$$\left. - (\alpha - j\omega) \int_{0}^{t} e^{-(\alpha-j\omega)(t-\tau)} \, d\tau \right] \qquad (9.21)$$

$$= V_0 \frac{e^{-\alpha t} \sin \omega t}{\omega L} H(t) \qquad (9.22)$$

Our first step on obtaining this result should be to verify that it is correct, by evaluating

$$\frac{L\{(p + \alpha)^2 + \omega^2\}}{p} I_1(t) \qquad (9.23)$$

which from Equation (9.18) should be $V_0 H(t)$. This step is necessary in the early stages of using operational calculus, because we have given rules for using this strange, new symbol p in a somewhat arbitrary manner, having confidence that these rules will work. At present operational calculus can be regarded as a means somehow devised for making an enlightened guess as to the required solution. The crucial test is: Does this enlightened guess produce a verifiably correct result? Fortunately, the answer is that it does, and verifying the correctness of a result (however devised) is much easier than finding a result worth verifying.

As our confidence in operational calculus grows with repeated success, we shall learn that the results obtained by it are always in principle correct, and verification becomes necessary merely as a precaution against silly arithmetical and algebraic mistakes in calculation. It is a great advantage that the process of verification is not only simpler than the original calculation, but involves a radically different series of operations. For the expression 9.23 verification is straightforward, except insofar as a term $p\{e^{-at} \sin \omega t\, H(t)\}$ arises. This should be treated as a product in the normal way, so that the ultimate cause of difficulty is a term

$$e^{-at} \sin\, \omega t \,.\, p\, H(t) \qquad (9.24)$$

and for our present purpose it is sufficient to say that a term involving $pH(t)$ can be ignored if it is multiplied by a factor which is zero for $t = 0$ as here; $pH(t)$ is identically zero when t is different from zero.

Now although Equation 9.22 applies primarily to the case when the circuit of Fig. 9.1 is oscillatory, the solution has essentially the same nature, shown most clearly in Equation 9.21, in all cases. Its essential nature is the difference between two exponential multiples of $H(t)$. If ω is real (*see* Equation 9.17) and the circuit is oscillatory, Equation 9.22 is an improvement upon Equation 9.21, and we notice that if ω is small, Equation 9.22 can be simplified by replacing $\sin \omega t / \omega$ by t. This is the only reason why in the 'critical-damping' case ($\omega = 0$) terms of the form $t\, e^{-at}$ occur, and it gives the misleading impression that this case is essentially different. In practice, ω will never be *exactly* zero, though it may be very small, and we would like to suggest that it is important to keep $I_1(t)$ in the general form 9.21 as long as possible, and only to take account of the fact that ω is real, small, or imaginary at the very end of the calculation. Equation 9.21 will have the very similar form 9.20 if the applied voltage is different from a simple step-function, whereas Equation 9.22 may be apparently different.

If the circuit is overdamped, so that $\omega = j\lambda$ where λ is real, Equation 9.21 reduces to

$$I_1(t) = \frac{V_0}{2\lambda L} \left[e^{-(a-\lambda)t} - e^{(a+\lambda)t} \right] H(t) \qquad (9.25)$$

which is the form of solution we would have obtained had we tried to start with this case; this form states explicitly the fact that $I_1(t)$ is the difference between two exponentials.

If the input voltage is some arbitrary expression $V(t)$ but the circuit is still that of Fig. 9.1, we merely have to start from Equation 9.20 instead of Equation 9.21. If the circuit is much more complicated but contains only lumped elements, the equation expressing the output current $I(t)$ in terms of the input voltage $V(t)$ will be of the form 9.15. But $1/Z(p)$ can be expressed in 'partial fractions' as explained in Chapter 5, so that the general case of a two-terminal lumped-element passive network still leaves us ultimately with expressions of the form 9.20 to evaluate, but there may be more terms—in fact, n terms where n is the degree of the numerator of $Z(p)$ in Equation 9.15.

Hence the information given in this chapter is sufficient in principle to enable us to determine the behaviour of an arbitrary two-terminal passive network having lumped elements. It may of course be necessary to factorise $Z(p)$ in order to obtain the required partial fractions to formulate the equation analogous to Equation 9.20 explicitly, but again techniques for doing this have been discussed in Chapters 3, 4, 5 and 7.

Chapter 10

MATRICES

In this chapter our objective is to extend the technique of operational calculus discussed in Chapter 9 so that it can be directly applied to four-terminal lumped networks (having a common between input and output or electrically equivalent thereto) with passive elements. Many networks can be constructed by connecting the fundamental idealised elements of a single pure resistance, inductance or capacitance in various ways, and we therefore first discuss the properties of single-element networks, and then the way in which the properties of more complicated networks are related to those of their constituent parts. Mathematically, the technique required is matrix algebra; for our purposes the matrices will not have more than two rows or columns. This enormously simplifies the algebra, which then can be learnt by an engineer in a few hours. It is noteworthy that matrices of the kind relevant to four-terminal networks such as will be discussed are now being studied for their own sake by schoolboys as young as twelve with great enjoyment (notably under the auspices of Dr. G. Matthews at St. Dunstan's College, Catford) who initially were entirely unaware of their practical electrical applications.

MATRICES FOR SINGLE SERIES OR SHUNT ELEMENTS

Consider then the single series resistance of Fig. 10.1(a). By Ohm's Law in its original form, we have

and by common sense
$$\left. \begin{aligned} V_1 &= V_2 + RI_2 \\ I_1 &= \qquad I_2 \end{aligned} \right\} \tag{10.1}$$

The idea of matrices is to combine Equations 10.1 into the single relation

$$\begin{pmatrix} V_1 \\ I_1 \end{pmatrix} = \begin{pmatrix} 1 & R \\ 0 & 1 \end{pmatrix} \begin{pmatrix} V_2 \\ I_2 \end{pmatrix} \qquad (10.2)$$

expressing as a single entity the relations between input quantities V_1 and I_1 on the one hand and output quantities V_2 and I_2 on the other. The expression

$$\begin{pmatrix} 1 & R \\ 0 & 1 \end{pmatrix} \qquad (10.3)$$

so far is simply an orderly arrangement of the coefficients on the right-hand side of Equations 10.1, and Equation 10.2 is at

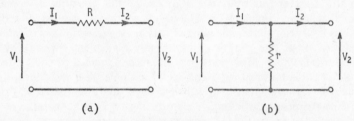

Fig. 10.1.

(a) *A single series resistance*   (b) *A single shunt resistance*

present a mere shorthand for Equation 10.1. An orderly arrangement of quantities like 10.3 is called a matrix, and we shall develop an algebra for handling matrices just as ordinary algebra is an algebra of operations—addition, substraction, multiplication and division—upon single quantities.

If the resistance R ohms in Fig. 10.1 (a) is replaced by an inductance of L henrys, the R in the top right-hand corner of 10.3 must be replaced by pL, where p is the operator $\dfrac{d}{dt}$ to which we have become accustomed in Chapter 9. Likewise, if R in Fig. 10.1(a) is replaced by a capacitance C farads, the top right element in 10.3 becomes $1/pC$.

Before we consider how matrices like 10.3 can usefully be manipulated, we must obtain the corresponding matrix for Fig. 10.1 (b). By Ohm's Law,

$$V_1 = V_2 = r(I_1 - I_2) \qquad (10.4)$$

which, in an orderly arrangement analogous to Equations 10.1 becomes

$$V_1 = V_2 \\ I_1 = \frac{1}{r} V_2 + I_2 \left.\right\}$$
(10.5)

or

$$\begin{pmatrix} V_1 \\ I_1 \end{pmatrix} = \begin{pmatrix} 1 & 0 \\ 1/r & 1 \end{pmatrix} \begin{pmatrix} V_2 \\ I_2 \end{pmatrix}$$
(10.6)

Again, if the resistance r ohms is replaced by an inductance l henrys, r is replaced by pl, so the bottom left element of the matrix 10.6 becomes $1/pl$, and if r is replaced by a capacitance c farads, the bottom left element becomes $1/(1/pc)$ or pc, so that we now have a complete picture of the set of matrices appropriate to single idealised elements in shunt or series, but we have not yet developed a means of handling such matrices.

MATRIX ALGEBRA

If a mathematician wishes to develop a new kind of algebra, he has every right to define the 'addition' and 'multiplication' rules of such an algebra in any way he pleases. But if he exercises that right in an arbitrary manner, he will probably obtain a useless algebra. The rules for adding and multiplying matrices which follow must at this stage be considered as completely arbitrary; we shall later on show how they make sense in the physical world.

The rule for adding matrices is quite simple. First, addition cannot be done at all unless the two matrices have the same number of rows and columns; if they have, the sum is formed by adding corresponding elements. Thus

$$\begin{pmatrix} a_{11} & a_{12} \\ a_{21} & a_{22} \end{pmatrix} + \begin{pmatrix} b_{11} & b_{12} \\ b_{21} & b_{22} \end{pmatrix} = \begin{pmatrix} a_{11} + b_{11} & a_{12} + b_{12} \\ a_{21} + b_{21} & a_{22} + b_{22} \end{pmatrix}$$
(10.7)

The rule for multiplication, however, is much more arbitrary, but we have already a clue to it from the fact that Equation 10.2 was stated to be a shorthand for Equation 10.1. The expressions

$$\begin{pmatrix} V_1 \\ I_1 \end{pmatrix} \text{ and } \begin{pmatrix} V_2 \\ I_2 \end{pmatrix}$$
(10.8)

can be regarded as matrices of a special kind (column matrices, having only one column), whereas in general a matrix can have m rows and n columns. If $m = n$ the matrix is called square. We shall only consider here two-row single-column matrices of the form 10.8 or two-row square matrices like 10.3. For two-row square matrices the law of multiplication is

$$\begin{pmatrix} a_{11} \, a_{12} \\ a_{21} \, a_{22} \end{pmatrix} \times \begin{pmatrix} b_{11} \, b_{12} \\ b_{21} \, b_{22} \end{pmatrix} = \begin{pmatrix} a_{11} \, b_{11} + a_{12} \, b_{21} & a_{11} \, b_{12} + a_{12} \, b_{22} \\ a_{21} \, b_{11} + a_{22} \, b_{21} & a_{21} \, b_{12} + a_{22} \, b_{22} \end{pmatrix}$$

(10.9)

and if the b-matrix has only one column instead of two as in Equation 10.9, the second column on the right-hand side of Equation 10.9 is omitted. We see immediately that the rule 10.9 is consistent with calling Equation 10.2 a shorthand for Equation 10.1, or Equation 10.6 a shorthand for Equation 10.5. Thus we can already see that matrices have some relation to simple electrical networks. This relation is in fact much closer than we as yet realise.

For the benefit of those who may later become interested in matrices in general, it must be stated that a matrix having m rows and n columns can only be multiplied into a matrix having r rows and s columns if $n = r$, and the result will be a matrix having m rows and s columns, each element being the sum of n products of the elements of a row of the first matrix with corresponding elements of a column of the second matrix. It is also urgently necessary to point out that the result of a matrix multiplication usually depends on which matrix comes first, even if multiplication in either order is possible (as in Equation 10.9). As we shall see, however, this

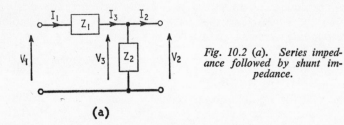

Fig. 10.2 (a). Series impedance followed by shunt impedance.

(a)

corresponds the the fact that the circuit of Fig. 10.2(a) is not the same as that of Fig. 10.2(b) which we now discuss.

In Fig. 10.2, the single impedance Z_1 may be any combination of resistances, inductances and capacitances, and therefore in general a rational function of p or d/dt, and the same applies to Z_2. But as far as matrices are concerned, we do not care in the least what

Z_1 and Z_2 may be.   Our duty is to find relations between V_1 and I_1 on the one hand and V_2 and I_2 on the other, without involving any internal currents and voltages—that is to say, we are concerned with relations between any circuit discussed in this chapter and the outside world.   Once the matrix techniques to be discussed have

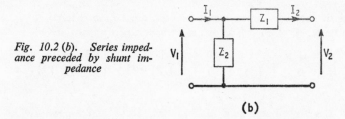

Fig. 10.2 (b).   Series impedance preceded by shunt impedance

(b)

given us relations between V_1, V_2, I_1, and I_2 (which will involve p), we have to go back to Chapter 9 to express those relations explicitly should we need to do so: the relations will be of the same general forms as were discussed in that chapter.

MATRICES FOR NETWORKS IN CASCADE

In Fig. 10.2(a), which is Fig. 10.1(a) (with R replaced by Z_1) followed by Fig. 10.2(b) (with r replaced by Z_2), we have, by analogy with Equations 10.2 and 10.6

$$\begin{pmatrix} V_1 \\ I_1 \end{pmatrix} = \begin{pmatrix} 1 & Z_1 \\ 0 & 1 \end{pmatrix} \begin{pmatrix} V_3 \\ I_3 \end{pmatrix} ; \quad \begin{pmatrix} V_3 \\ I_3 \end{pmatrix} = \begin{pmatrix} 1 & 0 \\ 1/Z_2 & 1 \end{pmatrix} \begin{pmatrix} V_2 \\ I_2 \end{pmatrix} \quad (10.10)$$

This suggests that the correct result for Fig. 10.2(a) may be

$$\begin{pmatrix} V_1 \\ I_1 \end{pmatrix} = \begin{pmatrix} 1 & Z_1 \\ 0 & 1 \end{pmatrix} \begin{pmatrix} 1 & 0 \\ 1/Z_2 & 1 \end{pmatrix} \begin{pmatrix} V_2 \\ I_2 \end{pmatrix} \quad (10.11)$$

which, applying the law of multiplication (10.9), reduces to

$$\begin{pmatrix} V_1 \\ I_1 \end{pmatrix} = \begin{pmatrix} 1 + Z_1/Z_2 & Z_1 \\ 1/Z_2 & 1 \end{pmatrix} \begin{pmatrix} V_2 \\ I_2 \end{pmatrix} \quad (10.12)$$

and this is consistent with the result that would be obtained if we had worked through the process of eliminating V_3 and I_3 from Equations 10.1 (with V_3 for V_2 and I_3 for I_2) and Equations 10.5 (with V_3 for V_1 and I_3 for I_1).   It is this remarkable consistency that makes matrix algebra based upon the law 10.9 for multiplication so useful for network theory.

The corresponding result for Fig. 10.2(b) is

$$\begin{pmatrix} V_1 \\ I_1 \end{pmatrix} = \begin{pmatrix} 1 & 0 \\ 1/Z_2 & 1 \end{pmatrix} \begin{pmatrix} 1 & Z_1 \\ 0 & 1 \end{pmatrix} \begin{pmatrix} V_2 \\ I_2 \end{pmatrix}$$

$$= \begin{pmatrix} 1 & Z_1 \\ 1/Z_2 & 1 + Z_1/Z_2 \end{pmatrix} \begin{pmatrix} V_2 \\ I_2 \end{pmatrix} \tag{10.13}$$

and in fact this process can be continued indefinitely. Thus for the network of Fig. 10.3, we can write down immediately

$$\begin{pmatrix} V_1 \\ I_1 \end{pmatrix} = \begin{pmatrix} 1 & Z_1 \\ 0 & 1 \end{pmatrix} \begin{pmatrix} 1 & 0 \\ 1/Z_2 & 1 \end{pmatrix} \begin{pmatrix} 1 & Z_3 \\ 0 & 1 \end{pmatrix} \begin{pmatrix} 1 & 0 \\ 1/Z_4 & 1 \end{pmatrix} \begin{pmatrix} 1 & Z_5 \\ 0 & 1 \end{pmatrix} \begin{pmatrix} 1 & 0 \\ 1/Z_6 & 1 \end{pmatrix} \begin{pmatrix} V_2 \\ I_2 \end{pmatrix}$$

$$\tag{10.14}$$

and the right-hand side of Equation 10.14 can be reduced to a single matrix by repeated application of Equation 10.9 however complicated the impedances Z_1, Z_2, etc. may be.

Thus we are now able to express V_1 and I_1 in terms of V_2 and I_2 for a ladder network like Fig. 10.3, however many shunt and series

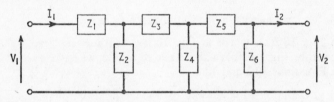

Fig. 10.3. A ladder network

elements the network has, without having to consider any internal currents and voltages. Admittedly the relations obtained involve p, but that is no real limitation since the operational calculus discussed in Chapter 9 is designed for just this situation. As it is always $1/Z_2$, $1/Z_4$, $1/Z_6$ that arise in the matrices associated with shunt elements, it is convenient to work in terms of *admittances* $Y_2 = 1/Z_2$, $Y_4 = 1/Z_4$ and $Y_6 = 1/Z_6$ instead of impedances for such elements.

Y-MATRICES AND Z-MATRICES

Hitherto we have obtained two relations between the four quantities, input voltage, input current, output voltage and output current in the form

$$\begin{pmatrix} V_1 \\ I_1 \end{pmatrix} = \begin{pmatrix} a_{11} & a_{12} \\ a_{21} & a_{22} \end{pmatrix} \begin{pmatrix} V_2 \\ I_2 \end{pmatrix} \tag{10.15}$$

and the matrix in Equation 10.15 is called the A-matrix of the network in question. The useful property of such matrices, as we have seen, is that if two networks are connected in cascade, so that the output of one is the input of the second, then the A-matrix of

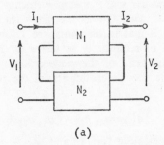

(a)

Fig. 10.4 (a).   Series-series connection

the compound network is the product of the A-matrices of the constituent networks. But we might express any two of the input and output current and voltage in terms of the other two; if we do so, we obtain various other network matrices. The most important of these are listed in Table 10.1, which also gives the rules for converting from one type of matrix to another when necessary. These additional matrices enable us to extend matrix techniques to other types of network connection as well as ladder networks, for if two networks N_1 and N_2 are connected in series-series as in Fig. 10.4(a), the Z- matrix of the combination is the sum of the Z-matrices of the constituent networks, and if the same two networks are connected in parallel-parallel, as in Fig. 10.4(b), the Y-matrix of the combination is the sum of the Y-matrices of the constituent networks.

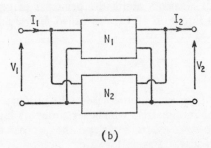

(b)

Fig. 10.4 (b).   Parallel-parallel connection

In Table 10.1, the first row explains which pair of the variables is expressed in terms of the other pair by the matrix named at the top of the same column. In the A-row, the formulae are given for expressing the Y-matrix and the Z-matrix elements in terms of the A-matrix elements, assuming that these are known; similarly, the Y-row gives the A-matrix and Z-matrix elements when the Y-matrix elements are known, and the Z-row gives the A- and Y-matrix elements when the Z-matrix elements are known. The last row gives the condition of reciprocity in terms of the elements of the matrix named at the head of the same column. The expressions $|A|$, $|Y|$ and $|Z|$ are the 'determinants' of the respective matrices, defined as

$$|A| = a_{11}\,a_{22} - a_{12}\,a_{21} \tag{10.16}$$

with two similar expressions for $|Y|$ and $|Z|$.

INVERSE, UNIT AND NULL MATRICES

We notice that if we take the definitions of the Y and Z matrices in Table 10.1, and combine them, we can deduce

$$\begin{pmatrix} I_1 \\ I_2 \end{pmatrix} = \begin{pmatrix} y_{11} & y_{12} \\ y_{21} & y_{22} \end{pmatrix} \begin{pmatrix} z_{11} & z_{12} \\ z_{21} & z_{22} \end{pmatrix} \begin{pmatrix} I_1 \\ I_2 \end{pmatrix} \tag{10.17}$$

whereas obviously

$$\begin{pmatrix} I_1 \\ I_2 \end{pmatrix} = \begin{pmatrix} 1 & 0 \\ 0 & 1 \end{pmatrix} \begin{pmatrix} I_1 \\ I_2 \end{pmatrix} \tag{10.18}$$

Fortunately Equations 10.17 and 10.18 are consistent, as will be seen if we substitute for the y and z elements from the A, Y or Z rows of Table 10.1, and carry out the multiplication according to Equation 10.9. Matrices whose product is the 'unit' matrix (which has unit elements along the principal diagonal and zeros elsewhere, as in Equation 10.18) are called *inverse* and this relation is often expressed in the form

$$\begin{pmatrix} y_{11} & y_{12} \\ y_{21} & y_{22} \end{pmatrix} = \begin{pmatrix} z_{11} & z_{12} \\ z_{21} & z_{22} \end{pmatrix}^{-1} \tag{10.19}$$

This is one of the exceptional cases: the product of two inverse matrices is the unit matrix, whichever order of multiplication is used. For two-row square matrices, the process of finding the inverse is particularly straightforward: looking at the Y-row of Table 10.1, we note that to invert the matrix in the Y-column, we

Table 10.1

Name of Matrix	A	Y	Z
Definition	$\begin{pmatrix}V_1\\I_1\end{pmatrix} = \begin{pmatrix}a_{11} & a_{12}\\a_{21} & a_{22}\end{pmatrix}\begin{pmatrix}V_2\\I_2\end{pmatrix}$	$\begin{pmatrix}I_1\\I_2\end{pmatrix} = \begin{pmatrix}y_{11} & y_{12}\\y_{21} & y_{22}\end{pmatrix}\begin{pmatrix}V_1\\V_2\end{pmatrix}$	$\begin{pmatrix}V_1\\V_2\end{pmatrix} = \begin{pmatrix}z_{11} & z_{12}\\z_{21} & z_{22}\end{pmatrix}\begin{pmatrix}I_1\\I_2\end{pmatrix}$
A	$\begin{pmatrix}a_{11} & a_{12}\\a_{21} & a_{22}\end{pmatrix}$	$\dfrac{1}{a_{12}}\begin{pmatrix}a_{22} & -|A|\\1 & -a_{11}\end{pmatrix}$	$\dfrac{1}{a_{21}}\begin{pmatrix}a_{11} & -|A|\\1 & -a_{22}\end{pmatrix}$
Y	$\dfrac{1}{y_{21}}\begin{pmatrix}-y_{22} & -1\\-|Y| & -y_{11}\end{pmatrix}$	$\begin{pmatrix}y_{11} & y_{12}\\y_{21} & y_{22}\end{pmatrix}$	$\dfrac{1}{|Y|}\begin{pmatrix}y_{22} & -y_{12}\\-y_{21} & y_{11}\end{pmatrix}$
Z	$\dfrac{1}{z_{21}}\begin{pmatrix}z_{11} & -|Z|\\1 & -z_{22}\end{pmatrix}$	$\dfrac{1}{|Z|}\begin{pmatrix}z_{22} & -z_{12}\\-z_{21} & z_{11}\end{pmatrix}$	$\begin{pmatrix}z_{11} & z_{12}\\z_{21} & z_{22}\end{pmatrix}$
Reciprocity Condition	$|A| = 1$	$y_{12} = -y_{21}$	$z_{12} = -z_{21}$

have to divide by the determinant of this matrix (which means that every element of the matrix in the Z-column is divided by $|Y|$); we also have to exchange the principal-diagonal elements and negative the other two. In the case of A-matrices, $|A|$ is usually 1, so that the inversion process is even simpler.

Just as the unit matrix (in Equation 10.18) has a certain similarity to the number unity (in that it leaves unchanged any matrix it multiplies), so the null matrix, all of whose elements are zero, has properties analogous to those of the number zero, in that it reduces to zero all the elements of any matrix it multiplies. But it is possible to obtain the null matrix as the product of two matrices none of whose elements are zero, for example

$$\begin{pmatrix} 1 & -1 \\ 1 & -1 \end{pmatrix} \begin{pmatrix} 1 & 1 \\ 1 & 1 \end{pmatrix} = \begin{pmatrix} 0 & 0 \\ 0 & 0 \end{pmatrix} \tag{10.20}$$

The peculiarity of the matrices on the left-hand side of Equation 10.20 which makes this possible is that they both have zero determinants.

POWERS OF MATRICES

If in Equation 10.14 the various impedances associated with Fig. 10.3 are all different, there is no short-cut to multiplying out the matrices as earlier suggested. It often happens, however, that a ladder network has a number of equal consecutive series elements and a number of equal consecutive shunt elements separating them. For such a network, it would be useful to have a formula, analogous to the Binomial Theorem (Chapter 5), for explicitly evaluating a power of a matrix. Such a formula,[10] exists in a particularly simple form for the 2-row square matrices with determinant unity we have been discussing, as will now be explained. It is also possible to find a power of any square matrix, but the general procedure is inevitably more complicated than that of Wilson[10], which can be expressed by the single formula

$$\begin{pmatrix} \cosh \gamma + k \sinh \gamma & Z_0(1 - k^2)^{1/2} \sinh \gamma \\ (1/Z_0)(1 - k^2)^{1/2} \sinh \gamma & \cosh \gamma - k \sinh \gamma \end{pmatrix}^n$$
$$= \begin{pmatrix} \cosh n\gamma + k \sinh n\gamma & Z_0(1 - k^2)^{1/2} \sinh n\gamma \\ (1/Z_0)(1 - k^2)^{1/2} \sinh n\gamma & \cosh n\gamma - k \sinh n\gamma \end{pmatrix} \tag{10.21}$$

This can be proved by direct multiplication for $n = 2$, by multiplication of the right-hand side of Equation 10.21 when $n = 2$ into the left-hand side for $n = 1$ to obtain the result for $n = 3$, and so on.

The only question is how to get a given matrix into the required form for Equation 10.21 to be applicable.   If

$$\frac{1}{|A|^{\frac{1}{2}}}\begin{pmatrix} a_{11} & a_{12} \\ a_{21} & a_{22} \end{pmatrix} = \begin{pmatrix} \cosh\gamma + k\sinh\gamma & Z_0(1-k^2)^{1/2}\sinh\gamma \\ (1/Z_0)(1-k^2)^{1/2}\sinh\gamma & \cosh\gamma - k\sinh\gamma \end{pmatrix}$$
(10.22)

then it follows that

$$\cosh\gamma = \frac{a_{11}+a_{22}}{2|A|^{\frac{1}{2}}}; \quad Z_0{}^2 = a_{12}/a_{21};$$

$$(1-k^2)\sinh^2\gamma = \frac{a_{12}\,a_{21}}{|A|^{\frac{1}{2}}}$$
(10.23)

The first of Equations 10.23 determines γ—it is simply a quadratic equation for e^γ, since $\cosh\gamma = \frac{1}{2}(e^\gamma + 1/e^\gamma)$—the second determines Z_0 and the third determines k, since γ is already known. Very often $|A| = 1$ (since it is usually for an A-matrix that we are interested in the nth power) but even if this is not so, a power of $|A|$ as a factor correcting the final result presents no difficulty.   No essential difference exists if k or γ happen to be complex.

MATRICES OF STANDARD NETWORKS

Hitherto we have set out a number of general properties of 2×2 matrices, and applied them in a few simple or fundamental cases.

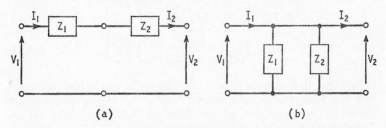

Fig. 10.5.   Illustrating the application of matrices to series and parallel combinations of impedances

If to these we add the case of an ideal transformer of ratio $n : 1$, for which

$$\begin{pmatrix} V_1 \\ I_1 \end{pmatrix} = \begin{pmatrix} n & 0 \\ 0 & 1/n \end{pmatrix} \begin{pmatrix} V_2 \\ I_2 \end{pmatrix}$$
(10.24)

we have all the matrix information necessary for determining the matrices of standard networks. We shall therefore conclude this chapter by giving the A-matrices for a general T-network (Fig. 10.6(a)) and a general Π-network (Fig. 10.6(b)) and discussing

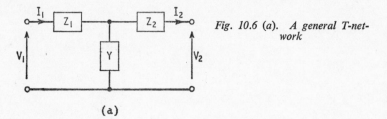

Fig. 10.6 (a). A general T-network

(a)

the application of matrices to circuits involving actual transformers, valves and transistors.

In passing, it is worth noting that the well-known laws for the combination of impedances connected in series and in parallel are both particular cases of the law already given that the A-matrices of networks connected in cascade must be multiplied to give the A-matrix of the combination. For in Fig. 10.5(a)

$$\begin{pmatrix} V_1 \\ I_1 \end{pmatrix} = \begin{pmatrix} 1 & Z_1 \\ 0 & 1 \end{pmatrix} \begin{pmatrix} 1 & Z_2 \\ 0 & 1 \end{pmatrix} \begin{pmatrix} V_2 \\ I_2 \end{pmatrix} = \begin{pmatrix} 1 & Z_1 + Z_2 \\ 0 & 1 \end{pmatrix} \begin{pmatrix} V_2 \\ I_2 \end{pmatrix} \quad (10.25)$$

and in Fig. 10.5(b)

$$\begin{pmatrix} V_1 \\ I_1 \end{pmatrix} = \begin{pmatrix} 1 & 0 \\ 1/Z_1 & 1 \end{pmatrix} \begin{pmatrix} 1 & 0 \\ 1/Z_2 & 1 \end{pmatrix} \begin{pmatrix} V_2 \\ I_2 \end{pmatrix}$$

$$= \begin{pmatrix} 1 & 0 \\ (1/Z_1) + (1/Z_2) & 1 \end{pmatrix} \begin{pmatrix} V_2 \\ I_2 \end{pmatrix} \quad (10.26)$$

In Figs. 10.6(a) and 10.6(b), the networks are ladder networks and the admittances, not impedances, of all shunt elements are shown. The procedure of Equation 10.14 applies, and the A-matrices are therefore respectively

$$\begin{pmatrix} V_1 \\ I_1 \end{pmatrix} = \begin{pmatrix} 1 + YZ_1 & Z_1 + Z_2 + YZ_1Z_2 \\ Y & 1 + YZ_2 \end{pmatrix} \begin{pmatrix} V_2 \\ I_2 \end{pmatrix} \quad (10.27a)$$

for Fig. 10.6(a) and

$$\begin{pmatrix} V_1 \\ I_1 \end{pmatrix} = \begin{pmatrix} 1 + Y_2Z & Z \\ Y_1 + Y_2 + Y_1Y_2Z & 1 + Y_1Z \end{pmatrix} \begin{pmatrix} V_2 \\ I_2 \end{pmatrix} \quad (10.27b)$$

for Fig. 10.6(b).   Any other matrix, such as the *Y*- or *Z*-matrix, can
be obtained if necessary by means of Table 10.1.

At the beginning of this chapter, we remarked that the matrix
techniques to be discussed were strictly applicable only to circuits

Fig. 10.6 (b).   A general Π*-net-work*

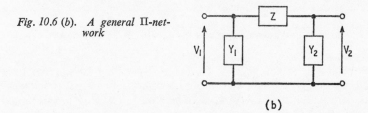

(b)

having a straight-through connection between one input terminal
and one output terminal.   Almost all circuits already discussed had
such a common terminal; one minor exception was the ideal transformer of Equation 10.24.   Certain circuits, however, can be
regarded as electrically equivalent to such three-terminal networks,
so that matrix techniques apply to them also, as will now be
explained.

In communication technique, a single line is commonly protected
from interference by a concentric screen.   This is an unbalanced
system because the outer is earthed.   An alternative way of reducing
interference is by means of a symmetrically-balanced pair.   In this
case it is expected that stray elements occurring on one line will
cancel out equal stray elements occurring on the other.   Currents
going along both lines alike can be called 'push-push'; those which
are equal and opposite along the two lines can be correspondingly
called 'push-pull'.   A balanced structure uses only the 'push-pull'
component, and is usually associated with transformers or other
terminal equipment designed to ignore the unwanted 'push-push'
component and accept the 'push-pull'.   Occasionally such structures
are used in both 'push-pull' and 'push-push' modes, but this is not
in general of great interest and will not be considered further here.
The structures which are of interest are either balanced in the 'push-
pull' mode, or unbalanced, like the concentric cable, with a common
connection or earth.   Either of these has the right number of degrees
of freedom for the application of the 2 × 2-matrix techniques we
have considered.

Balanced circuits need not be considered separately from three-
terminal networks, for (to take a simple example) the three-terminal

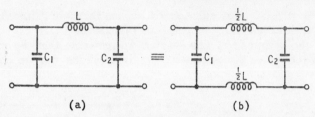

Fig. 10.7. (a) 3-terminal unbalanced circuit; (b) A balanced equivalent

unbalanced circuit of Fig. 10.7(a) is equivalent to the balanced circuit of Fig. 10.7(b), and thus only minor adjustment is sufficient to permit almost all useful work to be done in terms of three-terminal networks.   Certain structures (such as lattices) appear not to be amenable to this treatment, but the use of such elements implies the presence of terminal transformers to look at the push-pull component only.   The corresponding three-terminal network can be

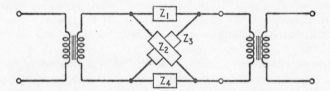

Fig. 10.8.   Lattice network with associated transformers to select push-pull component

obtained in various ways by means of transformers and mutual coupling; for example, as in Fig. 10.8.   For purposes of thought and understanding, it is desirable to replace a lattice by an equivalent unbalanced structure, as, for example, in Fig. 10.9.   The lattice (and

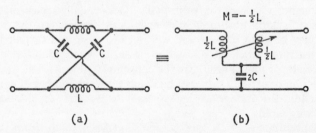

Fig. 10.9. (a) Lattice network: (b) Unbalanced (three-terminal) equivalent

bridged-T) structures come into the category of two-path networks, because they can be realised by connecting two ladder structures in parallel-parallel. The essential quality of a lattice is that it should be equivalent to a straight-through connection at one frequency and a pole change at another frequency.

Thus here we concern ourselves only with the application of matrix techniques to networks which can be regarded as in equivalent three-terminal form.

Matrices Applied to Transformers

In Fig. 10.10, the easiest matrix to obtain direct is the Z-matrix, since

$$\left.\begin{array}{l} V_1 = pL_1I_1 - pMI_2 \\ V_2 = pMI_1 - pL_2I_2 \end{array}\right\} \tag{10.28}$$

or

$$Z = \begin{pmatrix} pL_1 & -pM \\ pM & -pL_2 \end{pmatrix} \tag{10.29}$$

The conversion formulae given in Table 10.1 give us immediately the corresponding A-matrix

$$A = \begin{pmatrix} L_1/M & p(L_1L_2 - M^2)/M \\ 1/pM & L_2/M \end{pmatrix} \tag{10.30}$$

It will save space to write $x = L_1L_2 - M^2$; we should note that if x is zero (so that the coupling in Fig. 10.10 is perfect) then for

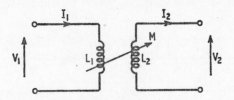

Fig. 10.10. A coupled circuit

sufficiently high frequencies (so that the 'shunt-ness' element $1/pM$ can be neglected) A in Equation 10.30 is the matrix of an ideal transformer of ratio $L_1/M = (L_1/L_2)^{1/2}$ in this case and the elements of the Z-matrix become infinite. In Fig. 10.11 the same basic Equation 10.28 are the easiest to derive directly, and thus the circuits of Figs. 10.10 and 10.11 are equivalent at all frequencies. In the case of Fig. 10.11(b) however, we have

$$A = \begin{pmatrix} 1 & 0 \\ \dfrac{L_2 - M}{px} & 1 \end{pmatrix} \begin{pmatrix} 1 & px/M \\ 0 & 1 \end{pmatrix} \begin{pmatrix} 1 & 0 \\ \dfrac{L_1 - M}{px} & 1 \end{pmatrix} \quad (10.31)$$

and this leads directly to Equation 10.30. Thus, the effect of a coupled circuit can be allowed for by means of the circuits of Figs. 10.11(a) and 10.11(b) which are not effectively different from circuits without coupling. Further, there is no reason why, when a coupled

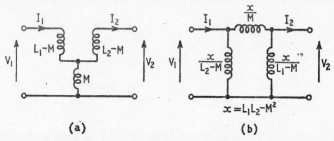

(a)   **(b)**

Fig. 10.11. (a) and (b) Circuits equivalent to the coupled circuit of Fig. 10.10• but without mutual coupling

circuit is required, conceived initially as being of the form of Fig. 10.10, it should not be realised in the form of Fig. 10.11(a) or 10.11(b), and vice versa.

In Fig. 10.12, we have likewise a circuit that can be made equivalent to that of Fig. 10.10 at any one frequency for fixed C_2, and over a whole range of frequencies if C_2 can be varied. For in Fig. 10.12

$$\begin{pmatrix} V_1 \\ I_1 \end{pmatrix} = \begin{pmatrix} 1 & 0 \\ 1/pl_1 & 1 \end{pmatrix} \begin{pmatrix} 1 & 1/pC_2 \\ 0 & 1 \end{pmatrix} \begin{pmatrix} 1 & 0 \\ 1/pl_3 & 1 \end{pmatrix} \begin{pmatrix} V_2 \\ I_2 \end{pmatrix} \quad (10.32)$$

so that

$$A = \begin{bmatrix} 1 + l_1/(l_3 y) & pl_1/y \\ (1/pl_1) + (1/pl_3) + (1/pl_3 y) & 1 + (1/y) \end{bmatrix} \quad (10.33)$$

where

$$y = p^2 l_1 C_2 \quad (10.34)$$

and this is the same as in Equation 10.30 if

$$l_1 = \frac{x}{L_2 - M}; \quad l_3 = \frac{x}{L_1 - M}; \quad y = \frac{M}{L_2 - M} \quad (10.35)$$

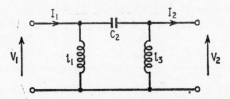

*Fig. 10.12.   A circuit which can be made equivalent to that of Fig. 10.10
(at any one frequency for fixed C_2)*

but of course y varies with frequency, from Equation 10.34, unless
C_2 can be varied appropriately. Thus, if we think of coupled
circuits as having the A-matrix of Equation 10.30 and as realisable
in the form of Figs. 10.11(a), 10.11(b) or 10.12, the sting is taken
out of them; they can be handled just in the same way as circuits
without coupling.

Matrices Applied to Valves and Transistors

Given a triode with anode resistance r_a and mutual conductance
μ, the essential facts of the situation are expressed by means of the
relations

$$- \mu V_1 = V_2 + r_a I_2$$
$$I_1 = 0$$

in the notation of Fig. 10.13. Translated into matrix language,

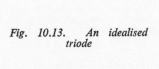

*Fig. 10.13.   An idealised
triode*

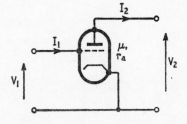

this means that a valve has an A-matrix just like any other network,
active or passive, namely

$$A_v = \begin{bmatrix} -1/\mu & -r_a/\mu \\ 0 & 0 \end{bmatrix} \qquad (10.36)$$

The only peculiarity about A_v in Equation 10.36 is that $|A_v| = 0$,
and there is a very definite physical significance to this in that a

triode arranged as in Fig. 10.13 is a one-way device: I_1 is always zero. But once Equation 10.36 is established, circuits involving triodes can be understood in terms of matrices just like any other circuits; for instance, if the triode is preceded by an admittance Y_1

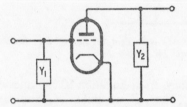

Fig. 10.14. Shunt admittances connected to the idealised triode of Fig. 10.13

in shunt as in Fig. 10.14, and followed by a similar admittance Y_2, we have

$$A = \begin{bmatrix} 1 & 0 \\ Y_1 & 1 \end{bmatrix} \begin{bmatrix} A_v \end{bmatrix} \begin{bmatrix} 1 & 0 \\ Y_2 & 1 \end{bmatrix} \tag{10.37}$$

so that, in Fig. 10.14,

$$\begin{pmatrix} V_1 \\ I_1 \end{pmatrix} = \begin{pmatrix} -(1 + r_a Y_2)/\mu & -r_a/\mu \\ -Y_1(1 + r_a Y_2)/\mu & -Y_1 r_a/\mu \end{pmatrix} \begin{pmatrix} V_2 \\ I_2 \end{pmatrix} \tag{10.38}$$

and it is easily verified that the determinant of the A-matrix on the right-hand side of Equation 10.38 is zero, although all the elements are different from zero. This we should naturally expect, since the one-way character of the idealised triode of Fig. 10.13 is not affected by the surrounding passive elements introduced in Fig. 10.14.

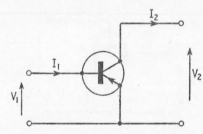

Fig. 10.15. Common-emitter transistor corresponding to the idealised triode of Fig. 10.13

Thus once Equation 10.36 is established, we are at liberty to forget that A_v is associated with a valve and to treat it like any other A-matrix. The only thing we cannot do is to use A_v^{-1}, the inverse of A_v, but this is an eminently sensible prohibition, since using a one-way device the wrong way is even more crazy than driving a car in the wrong direction up a one-way street.

Transistors, like valves, can be associated with A-matrices having determinant zero, and there is a dual relation between these matrices for valves and transistors, as pointed out by Wilson[11]. The common-emitter transistor (idealised as in Fig. 10.15, that is, with emitter and base resistances neglected) has the A-matrix which is dual to that of Equation 10.36, namely

$$A_T = \begin{bmatrix} 0 & 0 \\ -g_c'/\alpha' & -1/\alpha' \end{bmatrix} \qquad (10.39)$$

where

$$\left. \begin{aligned} &g_c \text{ is the collector conductance} \\ &\alpha \text{ is the current gain} \\ &g_c' = g_c/(1-\alpha) \\ &\alpha' = \alpha/(1-\alpha) \end{aligned} \right\} \qquad (10.40)$$

Thus matrices can be used to deal with almost any circuit situation which can be expressed in terms of three-terminal networks. Kirchhoff's laws can be used to obtain correct results if no error is made in the rather heavy algebra usually involved, but it is very difficult to see the significance of results obtained in this way without much hard labour. Matrix technique automatically introduces some order and grouping into the analysis, and greatly reduces the possibility of making silly mistakes because it is difficult in a forest of symbols to find one's way and be sure what one is trying to do. A result which is complicated even when matrices are used is hardly likely to be simple otherwise.

Chapter 11

CONDITIONS FOR MINIMUM VARIATION IN A FUNCTION

There is often a requirement that some quantity associated with a circuit shall be maintained as nearly constant as possible over a given range of frequencies. In filter design, for example, we would like to have the modulus of the transfer function constant at all frequencies within the pass-band, so that the ratio of output voltage to input voltage is constant, and we would also like to have infinite attenuation outside the pass-band. We would also like to have phase varying linearly with frequency within the pass-band. These three requirements are incompatible, and some kind of compromise is in practice usually required. For some applications, constancy of the modulus of the transfer constant is the prime requirement, while for others, it is linearity of phase-change with frequency that matters most.

In many cases, the transfer function will be a polynomial, in the Heaviside operator p, or the reciprocal of such a polynomial. For the purposes of this chapter, we can replace p by $j\omega$, and the square of the modulus of the transfer function will then be a polynomial in ω^2 at frequency $\omega/2\pi$.

If the modulus is to be kept as constant as possible, its square must also be kept as constant as possible, so our problem is essentially: how do we keep a polynomial 'as constant as possible' over a given range and what is the most effective way to formulate specifically the requirement that the polynomial shall be 'as constant as possible'? We shall, therefore, confine our attention to polynomials initially. Later, we shall consider the case where linearity of phase with frequency is the prime requirement. The rate of change of phase with frequency is usually a rational function of ω^2 and not a polynomial, but it is still possible by purely algebraic techniques of a reasonably straightforward nature to choose the parameters available so that this rational function shall have approximately the form required.

MINIMUM VARIATION OF A POLYNOMIAL: MAXIMAL FLATNESS

How then are we to keep the polynomial

$$x^n + a_{n-1}x^{n-1} + a_{n-2}x^{n-2} + \ldots + a_2x^2 + a_1x + a_0 \quad (11.1)$$

as constant as possible in the range $0 < x < 1$, say? There is no loss of generality in taking the coefficient of x^n to be unity or the range of x to be from 0 to 1, since we could if we wished replace x by kx where k is at our disposal, and if 11.1 is multiplied or divided by a constant, any variations in the polynomial 11.1 in the range $0 < x < 1$ would be multiplied or divided by the same constant. For detailed work we shall usually take n to be not greater than 4. A higher value introduces unnecessary complications, while for a lower value of n the inevitable variation of the polynomial 11.1 is considerable.

Now it may happen that for our particular application constancy for low values of x is what matters most, and a variation when x is near 1 is less important. If this is the case, clearly what we must do is to make

$$a_1 = a_2 = a_3 = \ldots = a_{n-1} = 0 \quad (11.2)$$

for then the polynomial 11.1 will only differ from a_0 appreciably when x is very near 1 if n is large. The polynomial will then vary from a_0 to $(a_0 + 1)$ in the range $0 < x < 1$, and almost all the variation will take place when x is near 1.

For many applications it will not be the coefficients a_1, a_2, etc. which are given directly in terms of circuit parameters, but these parameters will be more directly related to the algebraic (linear and quadratic) factors of 11.1. It is therefore worth noting the well-known result that if a_0 is positive and equal to r^n and Equation 11.2 applies, the polynomial 11.1 can always be immediately factorised. These factors are given for $n = 3, 4, 5, 6$, in such a way that they can easily be inferred for higher values of n on the rare occasions when such values occur:

$$n = 3; \quad x^3 + r^3 = (x + r)\left(x^2 - 2rx\cos\frac{\pi}{3} + r^2\right) \quad (11.3)$$

$$n = 4; \quad x^4 + r^4 = \left(x^2 - 2rx \cos \frac{\pi}{4} + r^2\right) \times$$

$$\times \left(x^2 - 2rx \cos \frac{3\pi}{4} + r^2\right) \qquad (11.4)$$

$$n = 5; \quad x^5 + r^5 = (x + r)\left(x^2 - 2rx \cos \frac{\pi}{5} + r^2\right) \times$$

$$\times \left(x^2 - 2rx \cos \frac{3\pi}{5} + r^2\right) \qquad (11.5)$$

$$n = 6; \quad x^6 + r^6 = \left(x^2 - 2rx \cos \frac{\pi}{6} + r^2\right) \times$$

$$\times \left(x^2 - 2rx \cos \frac{3\pi}{6} + r^2\right)\left(x^2 - 2rx \cos \frac{5\pi}{6} + r^2\right) \qquad (11.6)$$

In Equation 11.3 the second factor could be written $(x^2 - rx + r^2)$; in Equation 11.6 the middle factor is $(x^2 + r^2)$, but these factors have been included as written to make the general result more easily seen. There is always a factor $(x + r)$ initially when n is odd, but this factor is absent when n is even.

If we now regard the polynomial (11.1) as the square of the modulus M of a polynomial transfer function, so that x is ω^2, it is interesting to note the well-known result that if M^2 has factors

$$\omega^2 + k^2, \quad \omega^4 - 2a^2\omega^2 \cos \theta + a^4 \qquad (11.7)$$

then the corresponding factors of the transfer function itself are

$$p + k, \quad p^2 + 2ap \sin \tfrac{1}{2}\theta + a^2 \qquad (11.8)$$

so that, from Equations 11.3–11.6 with x replaced by ω^2 we can determine transfer functions associated with 'maximally flat' filters. The proper procedure for realising a network whose transfer function is known is not considered here.

MINIMUM TOTAL VARIATION: THE TCHEBYCHEFF APPROACH

We have now found simple conditions (Equation 11.2) for a polynomial to have 'maximally flat' variation in the range $0 \leqslant x \leqslant 1$, but these conditions will be unsuitable if our requirement is that there shall be as little variation as possible in the polynomial 11.1

over the whole of that range.   Suppose first that the polynomial 11.1 is only a quadratic

$$a_0 + a_1x + x^2 \tag{11.9}$$

Now let X be the variable part of the quadratic 11.9, so that

$$X = a_1x + x^2 \tag{11.10}$$

Then, if $a_1 \geqslant 0$, X increases steadily from zero when $x = 0$ to $(1 + a_1)$ when $x = 1$, and its variation is thus $(1 + a_1)$ in this case. If, however, a_1 is between 0 and -1, X becomes negative as x increases, reaches a minimum value $-\tfrac{1}{4}a_1^2$ when x has the positive value $-\tfrac{1}{2}a_1$, returns to zero when x has the positive value $-a_1$, and finally reaches the positive value $1 + a_1$ when $x = 1$.   The total variation of X in the range 0 to 1 is thus from $-\tfrac{1}{4}a_1^2$ (at $x = -\tfrac{1}{2}a_1$) to $(1 + a_1)$ at $x = 1$, that is

$$(1 + a_1) + \tfrac{1}{4}a_1^2 = (1 + \tfrac{1}{2}a_1)^2 \tag{11.11}$$

Again, if a_1 is between -1 and -2, X will be always negative, and will have a minimum value $-\tfrac{1}{4}a_1^2$ when $x = -\tfrac{1}{2}a_1$, so the variation in X is $\tfrac{1}{4}a_1^2$.

Finally, if $a_1 < -2$, X continually decreases, and its final negative value is $(1 + a_1)$, which gives a range of variation of $-a_1 - 1$ (a positive number greater than 1).   From this it is seen that the least total variation occurs when $a_1 = -1$, and has the value $\tfrac{1}{4}$, whereas in the 'maximally flat' case ($a_1 = 0$) the variation is four times as great.   From Equation 11.10, the condition $a_1 = -1$ implies

$$X = x(x - 1) \tag{11.12}$$

It is convenient to write

$$x = \tfrac{1}{2}(1 - \cos\theta) = \sin^2(\theta/2) \tag{11.13}$$

so that θ is zero when x is zero, and π when x is 1.   Substituting into 11.12 gives that

$$X = -\sin^2\frac{\theta}{2}\cos^2\frac{\theta}{2} = -\tfrac{1}{4}\sin^2\theta = -\tfrac{1}{8}(1 - \cos 2\theta) \tag{11.14}$$

In deriving Equations 11.12 and 11.14 we made no prior assumption about the nature of X; Equation 11.12, however, shows that X is unchanged if x is replaced by $(1 - x)$, or that there is (even) symmetry about $x = \tfrac{1}{2}$.   We shall make the assumption that if the polynomial 11.1 is of higher degree than a quadratic, then it must have symmetry in order to have the least possible variation;

the algebra is thus very greatly simplified. When the polynomial 11.1 is cubic, it is the variation of

$$Y = a_1x + a_2x^2 + x^3 \tag{11.15}$$

which we have to consider, and our assumption means that we must work with Y in the form

$$Y = A(x - \tfrac{1}{2}) + (x - \tfrac{1}{2})^3 + (\tfrac{1}{2}A + \tfrac{1}{8}) \tag{11.16}$$

since this last expression has the required symmetry (odd because Y is of odd degree) about $x = \tfrac{1}{2}$, and has its constant term adjusted so that Y is zero when x is zero as is required in Equation 11.15.

Now if A is positive or zero, Y steadily increases with x, so the range of variation of Y is

$$R_1 = Y(1) - Y(0) = A + \tfrac{1}{4} \tag{11.17}$$

If however A is negative, Y is decreasing when $x = \tfrac{1}{2}$. For small negative values of A, this decrease will continue until Y falls to a minimum $2(-A/3)^{3 \ 2}$ below its value $(\tfrac{1}{2}A + \tfrac{1}{8})$ for $x = \tfrac{1}{2}$; this minimum occurs for $x = 0.5 + (-A/3)^{1/2}$. Y thereafter increases with x. Y also, by symmetry, has a maximum value $2(-A/3)^{3/2}$ above its value $(\tfrac{1}{2}A + \tfrac{1}{8})$ for $x = \tfrac{1}{2}$; this maximum occurs when $x = 0.5 - (-A/3)^{1/2}$. By considering whether the maximum and minimum values occur in the range $0 < x < 1$, and whether they do or do not exceed the values of Y when x is 0 and 1, as in the case of the quadratic already discussed, we find that the least total variation occurs when A is $-3/16$. Substituting from Equation 11.13 into Equation 11.16 for this value of A, we obtain

$$Y \text{ (least variation)} = 1/32 \, [1 - \cos 3\theta] \tag{11.18}$$

so that the least total variation of Y in the range $0 < x < 1$ or $0 < \theta < \pi$ is 0.0625, and the values of a_1, a_2 when this least variation occurs are found, by comparing Equations 11.15 and 11.16, to be 0·5625 and $-1·5$.

Proceeding similarly when the polynomial 11.1 is a quartic, we have to consider the variation of

$$Z = a_1x + a_2x^2 + a_3x^3 + x^4 \tag{11.19}$$

which, by our assumption of (even) symmetry about $x = 0.5$, can also be written, in a manner analogous to Equation 11.16, in the form

$$Z = (x - \tfrac{1}{2})^4 - B(x - \tfrac{1}{2})^2 + (\tfrac{1}{4}B - \tfrac{1}{16}) \tag{11.20}$$

For a small total variation of Z in the range $0 < x < 1$ in Equation 11.20, it is easily found that B must be positive. Z then necessarily has a maximum value $(\frac{1}{4}B - \frac{1}{16})$ at $x = \frac{1}{2}$, but if B is small, Z exceeds this value for values of x near 0 and 1. It turns out that the least total variation of Z occurs when $B = \frac{1}{4}$; substitution into Equation 11.20 for this value of B from Equation 11.13 gives

$$Z = - [1 - \cos 4\theta]/128 \qquad (11.21)$$

and by comparing Equations 11.19 and 11.20, we find

$$a_1 = - 0{\cdot}25, \, a_2 = 1{\cdot}25, \, a_3 = - 2 \qquad (11.22)$$

We are now in a position to infer the general law for the least-varying polynomial of any degree: if Z_n is the varying part of the least varying polynomial 11.1 of degree n, we infer from Equations 11.14, 11.18 and 11.21 that

$$Z_n = \frac{(-1)^{n+1}}{2^{2n-1}} [1 - \cos n\theta] \qquad (11.23)$$

This result 11.23 is equivalent to the results obtained by Tchebycheff, which gave rise to the polynomials that bear his name. The preceding argument has not been intended to prove Tchebycheff's results afresh, but merely to bring out their meaning and significance. For Equation 11.23 is readily understandable; it implies that if we require a polynomial of degree n to vary as little as possible in the range $0 < x < 1$, the least variation obtainable is $1/2^{2n-2}$, and the polynomial in question will have the maximum possible number $(n - 1)$ of turning-values in the range $0 < x < 1$. All the maxima will be equal, and all the minima will be equal, and the extreme values for $x = 0$ ($\theta = 0$) and $x = 1$ ($\theta = \pi$) will be equal to the maximum or minimum values. Maxima or minima occur when $\theta = k\pi/n$ (k integer) or $x = \frac{1}{2} [1 - \cos (k\pi/n)]$.

Equation 11.23 is thus the most convenient form for expressing the result; we must remember that $\cos n\theta$ is a polynomial of degree n in $\cos \theta$, which from Equation 11.13 is $(1 - 2x)$. The Tchebycheff polynomial of degree n is obtained from Equation 11.23 by substituting y for $\cos \theta$ in the polynomial for $\cos n\theta$, and therefore has symmetry. Substituting $(1 - 2x)$ for $\cos \theta$ would enable us to determine the coefficients a_1, a_2, etc., of the polynomial 11.1 so that it should have the least possible variation, but the values of the coefficients by themselves would not make that symmetry obvious.

MAXIMALLY FLAT AND TCHEBYCHEFF
VARIATIONS COMPARED

If we now compare the variation obtained by the 'maximally-flat' approach (Equation 11.2) and the minimum total variation or Tchebycheff approach (Equation 11.23) we see that the total variation is far greater under the maximally-flat approach, especially when n is large. In the general case it may be worth considering replacing x by $y + \frac{1}{2}$ in the polynomial 11.1 and making as many coefficients of powers of y zero as possible. The polynomial 11.1 would thus become

$$b_0 + y^n \tag{11.24}$$

b_0 being the value of the polynomial 11.1 when $x = \frac{1}{2}$. The variation of y is from $-\frac{1}{2}$ to $+\frac{1}{2}$, so the variation of the expression 11.24 is $1/2^n$ when n is even and $1/2^{n-1}$ when n is odd. But if x is ω^2 in the polynomial 11.1, we shall have to replace ω by $z + 1/\sqrt{2}$ in the polynomial 11.1, and this will give us a polynomial of degree $2n$ in z instead of n, in which both even and odd powers of z will appear. This polynomial in z will therefore only be free from powers of z below z^n when we impose the maximally-flat conditions, and the reduction in variation achieved by changing the origin will be correspondingly less than in the case 11.24. No corresponding difficulty occurs in connection with the Tchebycheff approach.

We have thus obtained two approaches to the problem of obtaining a polynomial which shall vary as little as possible in a given range. The maximally-flat approach is advantageous when variations at one end of the range are important, but the variation over the whole range is much less under the Tchebycheff system.

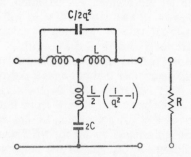

Fig. 11.1. Bridged-T all-pass filter with transfer function of Equations 11.25 and 11.26

EXTENSION TO A RATIONAL FUNCTION

We now have to consider whether some of the ideas underlying the above discussion can be extended to cases where the function whose variation is controlled is not a polynomial, and we shall take as a particular example the case of group-delay correction of one bridged-T all-pass filter as in Fig. 11.1 or of two such filters in cascade. The methods used do not depend upon the properties of the particular functions chosen, which here are rational in the frequency $\omega/2\pi$, so the methods could be applied widely.

Gouriet[9] has shown that the transfer function associated with the bridged-T network of Fig. 11.1, for a steady input frequency $\omega/2\pi$, is

$$\frac{\phi_2(-p)}{\phi_2(p)} = \frac{1 - ap + bp^2}{1 + ap + bp^2} = \frac{(1 - b\omega^2) - \mathrm{j}a\omega}{(1 - b\omega^2) + \mathrm{j}a\omega} = G_2(\omega) \qquad (11.25)$$

where

$$L = aR, \quad C = a/R, \quad q = a/\sqrt{b} \qquad (11.26)$$

and R is the termination resistance. If $q > 1$, so that the shunt inductance in Fig. 11.1 is negative, Gouriet also points out that an effectively equivalent circuit is obtained by having coupling between the two series inductances with coupling factor $(q^2 - 1)/(q^2 + 1)$. The third member of Equation 11.25 shows that the gain is unity at all frequencies, since the numerator and denominator differ only in the sign of their imaginary parts, and they therefore have the same modulus

$$D_2 = \{(1 - b\omega^2)^2 + a^2\omega^2\}^{1/2} \qquad (11.27)$$

We are concerned with the way in which the phase θ_2 of $G_2(\omega)$ in Equation 11.25 varies with frequency. Our aim is to make θ_2 vary with ω (over a given range) as linearly as possible (or rather, ultimately, to make the corresponding phase-angle θ_4 obtained when two of the bridged-T networks of Fig. 11.1 are connected in cascade vary as linearly as possible with ω, as explained below). If θ_2 is to vary as linearly as possible with ω, then $\dfrac{\mathrm{d}\theta_2}{\mathrm{d}\omega}$ must be kept as constant as possible, so that we have to deal with the same type of problem as before, but $\dfrac{\mathrm{d}\theta_2}{\mathrm{d}\omega}$ is a rational function of ω^2 instead of a polynomial in ω or the reciprocal of a polynomial in ω.

In order to evaluate the phase θ_2 of $G_2(\omega)$, it is convenient to define ψ_2 by the equation

$$\tan \psi_2 = \frac{a\omega}{1 - b\omega^2} \quad (0 \leqslant \psi_2 < \pi) \tag{11.28}$$

in which case, from Equation 11.27,

$$\sin \psi_2 = a\omega/D_2 \; ; \; \cos \psi_2 = (1 - b\omega^2)/D_2 \tag{11.29}$$

From Equation 11.28 or Equation 11.29 combined with Equation 11.25,

$$\begin{aligned}
G_2(\omega) &= \frac{1 - \mathrm{j} \tan \psi_2}{1 + \mathrm{j} \tan \psi_2} \\
&= \frac{\cos \psi_2 - \mathrm{j} \sin \psi_2}{\cos \psi_2 + \mathrm{j} \sin \psi_2} \\
&= \frac{\mathrm{e}^{-\mathrm{j}\psi_2}}{\mathrm{e}^{\mathrm{j}\psi_2}} = \mathrm{e}^{-2\mathrm{j}\psi_2}
\end{aligned} \tag{11.30}$$

so that the phase θ_2 of $G_2(\omega)$ is given by

$$\theta_2 = -2\psi_2 \tag{11.31}$$

The group delay is defined as $-\dfrac{\mathrm{d}\theta_2}{\mathrm{d}\omega}$ or $\dfrac{2\mathrm{d}\psi_2}{\mathrm{d}\omega}$, so we require $\dfrac{\mathrm{d}\psi_2}{\mathrm{d}\omega}$.

This is most easily obtained by differentiating both sides of Equation 11.28 with respect to ω as they stand, thus from the right-hand side

$$\begin{aligned}
\frac{\mathrm{d}}{\mathrm{d}\omega}\left[\frac{a\omega}{1 - b\omega^2}\right] &= \frac{(1 - b\omega^2)a - (-2b\omega)a\omega}{(1 - b\omega^2)^2} \\
&= \frac{a(1 + b\omega^2)}{(1 - b\omega^2)^2}
\end{aligned} \tag{11.32a}$$

and from the left-hand side

$$\begin{aligned}
\frac{\mathrm{d}}{\mathrm{d}\omega}\left[\tan \psi_2\right] &= \frac{\mathrm{d}}{\mathrm{d}\psi_2}\left[\tan \psi_2\right] \cdot \frac{\mathrm{d}\psi_2}{\mathrm{d}\omega} \\
&= \sec^2\psi_2 \frac{\mathrm{d}\psi_2}{\mathrm{d}\omega} \\
&= \frac{D_2{}^2}{(1 - b\omega^2)^2} \frac{\mathrm{d}\psi_2}{\mathrm{d}\omega}
\end{aligned} \tag{11.32b}$$

Equating the last member of Equation 11.32a with the last member of Equation 11.32b, we have

$$\text{Group delay} = -\frac{d\theta_2}{d\omega}$$

$$= 2\frac{d\psi_2}{d\omega}$$

$$= \frac{2a(1 + b\omega^2)}{D_2{}^2} \tag{11.33}$$

First, we have to consider how to keep this as constant as possible at low frequencies. When the expression whose variations were to be minimised was a polynomial, we achieved this by equating to zero the coefficients of as many powers of the independent variable as we could, in ascending order. In the case of the group delay in Equation 11.33, however, we cannot just put b equal to zero, because that leaves out of account the variations of the denominator $D_2{}^2$. We need to express the group delay as a series (finite or infinite) of ascending powers of ω^2, and then equate to zero as many of the coefficients of powers of ω^2 as we can, in ascending order. It is possible to write down such a series if we know a sufficient number of the successive derivatives of the group delay when $\omega = 0$, but the evaluation of these derivatives is awkward because of the denominator $D_2{}^2$ in Equation 11.33. Instead, we shall obtain our series by dividing the denominator $D_2{}^2$ into the numerator, cancelling the lowest power of ω^2 remaining at each stage. If $D_2{}^2$ is divided into $(1 + b\omega^2)$ in this way, the first three terms of the quotient are

$$1 + (3b - a^2)\omega^2 + (5b^2 - 5a^2b + a^4)\omega^4 \tag{11.34}$$

and this process of division is simply a way of finding out that

$$D_2{}^2\{1 + (3b - a^2)\omega^2 + (5b^2 - 5a^2b + a^4)\omega^4\}$$
$$= 1 + b\omega^2 + (\text{terms in } \omega^6 \text{ and higher powers})$$

For sufficiently small ω, so that ω^6 is negligible, the expression 11.34 is an adequate representation of $(1 + b\omega^2)/D_2{}^2$. If we want the expression 11.34 to be as constant as possible at low frequencies, we clearly require

$$a^2 = 3b \tag{11.35}$$

and in this case the coefficient of ω^4 in the expression 11.34 reduces to $-a^4/9$. Thus to keep the group delay (Equation 11.33) as constant as possible at low frequencies, a, b must satisfy Equation 11.35 and must be as small as possible, and the group delay will fall from its zero-frequency value.

If we now consider the alternative requirement that there shall be as little variation of the group delay as possible for $0 \leqslant \omega \leqslant 1$, we first want to consider the difference between the group delay (Equation 11.33) and its value $2a$ when $\omega = 0$. This is

$$2a\left[\frac{1 + b\omega^2}{D_2{}^2} - 1\right] = \frac{2a}{D_2{}^2}\ \omega^2\{(3b - a^2) - b^2\omega^2\} \qquad (11.36)$$

In the absence of the denominator $D_2{}^2$, we should expect that the correct procedure was to make

$$a^2 = b(3 - b) \qquad (11.37)$$

so that the group delay would return to its initial value when $\omega = 1$. Substituting from Equation 11.37 into Equation 11.33, the group delay reduces to

$$\frac{2\{b(3 - b)\}^{1/2}(1 + b\omega^2)}{1 + (b - b^2)\omega^2 + b^2\omega^4} \qquad (11.38)$$

This is found by straightforward differentiation to have a maximum when

$$b\omega^4 + 2\omega^2 - 1 = 0 \text{ or } b\omega^2 = (1 + b)^{1/2} - 1 \qquad (11.39)$$

and the maximum value is

$$\frac{2\{b(3 - b)\}^{1/2}}{2(1 + b)^{1/2} - 1 - b} \qquad (11.40)$$

For small b, the expression 11.40 differs little from the value $2a$ or $2\{b(3 - b)\}^{1/2}$ of the group delay for $\omega = 0$ and for $\omega = 1$, but for values of b near 3, the expression 11.40 is large. For $b = 1{\cdot}5$ its value is $3/(\sqrt{(10)} - 2{\cdot}5)$ which is about $4{\cdot}53$, and thus the group-delay varies between 3 and $4{\cdot}53$ for $0 < \omega < 1$; for $b = 1$ the corresponding variation is between $2\sqrt{2}$ when $\omega = 0$ or $\omega = 1$ and $2 + \sqrt{2}$ when $\omega = \sqrt{2} - 1$, a range of $2 - \sqrt{2} = 0{\cdot}586$. Thus for small and moderate values of b, we have obtained a reasonably satisfactory 'maximally-flat' curve and another curve with satisfactory overall variation in the range $0 < \omega < 1$, by techniques analogous to those used for minimising variations of a polynomial. For sufficiently large values of b, these curves cease to be satisfactory.

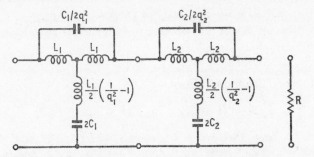

Fig. 11.2.   Two bridged-T all-pass filters in cascade

Unfortunately, these are only two variable parameters a and b in Equation 11.25, and this does not give us very much room for manoeuvre, so we now pass on the the case of two of the bridged-T networks of Fig. 11.1 in cascade.   We shall adopt the same general procedure, but the equations are more complicated.

The transfer function for the two bridged-T networks for Fig. 11.1, arranged as in Fig. 11.2, is

$$\frac{\phi_4(-p)}{\phi_4(p)} = \frac{1 - a_1p + b_1p^2}{1 + a_1p + b_1p^2} \cdot \frac{1 - a_2p + b_2p^2}{1 + a_2p + b_2p^2}$$

$$= \frac{(1 - c_2\omega^2 + c_4\omega^4) - j\omega(c_1 - c_3\omega^2)}{(1 - c_2\omega^2 + c_4\omega^4) + j\omega(c_1 - c_3\omega^2)} = G_4(\omega)$$

(11.41)

where

$$L_1 = a_1R; \quad C_1 = a_1/R; \quad q_1 = a_1/\sqrt{b_1}; \quad L_2 = a_2R;$$
$$C_2 = a_2/R; \quad q_2 = a_2/\sqrt{b_2}$$
(11.42)

and

$$c_1 = a_1 + a_2; \quad c_2 = b_1 + b_2 + a_1a_2; \quad c_3 = a_1b_2 + a_2b_1; \quad c_4 = b_1b_2$$
(11.43)

Normally we should expect L_1, C_1, L_2, C_2, R, q_1 and q_2 to be given, and we should then deduce a_1, b_1, a_2, and b_2 from Equation 11.42 and c_1, c_2, c_3 and c_4 from Equation 11.43.   Here, however, we once again 'work backwards'.   We shall endeavour to find algebraically the most appropriate values for c_1, c_2, c_3 and c_4 so that the group delay $G_4(\omega)$ in Equation 11.41 shall be maximally flat or shall have as little total variation as possible for $0 < \omega < 1$.   Then we shall deduce from Equation 11.43 the values of a_1, a_2, b_1, and b_2; this simply means that we have to factorise the expression

$$\phi_4(p) = 1 + c_1 p + c_2 p^2 + c_3 p^3 + c_4 p^4 \qquad (11.44)$$

into two real quadratic factors

$$\phi_4(p) = (1 + a_1 p + b_1 p^2)(1 + a_2 p + b_2 p^2) \qquad (11.45)$$

This has been discussed in Chapters 3, 4 and 7, and need not be considered further here. Knowing R, and a_1, a_2, b_1 and b_2 from Equation 11.45, the values of L_1, C_1, L_2, C_2, q_1, q_2 are obtainable from Equation 11.42 and therefore the circuit of Fig. 11.2 is determined. For applying algebraic techniques, Equation 11.44 is a more convenient form for $\phi_4(p)$ than Equation 11.45, and we therefore shall work entirely with Equation 11.44 and the corresponding expression in terms of ω given in Equation 11.41.

In order to evaluate the phase θ_4 of $G_4(\omega)$ in Equation 11.41, we define an angle ψ_4 (analogous to ψ_2 in Equation 11.28) by

$$\tan \psi_4 = \frac{\omega(c_1 - c_3 \omega^2)}{1 - c_2 \omega^2 + c_4 \omega^4} \qquad (11.46)$$

so that

$$\sin \psi_4 = \omega(c_1 - c_3 \omega^2)/D_4;$$
$$\cos \psi_4 = (1 - c_2 \omega^2 + c_4 \omega^4)/D_4 \qquad (11.47)$$

where

$$D_4{}^2 = (1 - c_2 \omega^2 + c_4 \omega^4)^2 + \omega^2(c_1 - c_3 \omega^2)^2 \qquad (11.48)$$

Thus D_4 is the modulus of the numerator and denominator of $G_4(\omega)$ in Equation 11.41, and $G_4(\omega)$, like $G_2(\omega)$ in Equation 11.25, always has unit modulus. ψ_4 increases steadily from 0 to 2π as ω increases from 0 to ∞. The equation analogous to Equation 11.30 is

$$G_4(\omega) = \frac{1 - j \tan \psi_4}{1 + j \tan \psi_4}$$

$$= \frac{\cos \psi_4 - j \sin \psi_4}{\cos \psi_4 + j \sin \psi_4}$$

$$= e^{-2j\psi_4} \qquad (11.49)$$

and therefore the phase θ_4 of $G_4(\omega)$ is given by

$$\theta_4 = -2\psi_4 \tag{11.50}$$

Now Equation 11.46, like Equation 11.28, can be differentiated with respect to ω on both sides to give

$$\frac{d}{d\omega}\left[\frac{\omega(c_1 - c_3\omega^2)}{1 - c_2\omega^2 + c_4\omega^4}\right]$$

$$= \frac{(1 - c_2\omega^2 + c_4\omega^4)(c_1 - 3c_3\omega^2) + \omega^2(c_1 - c_3\omega^2)(2c_2 - 4c_4\omega^2)}{(1 - c_2\omega^2 + c_4\omega^4)^2} \tag{11.51}$$

and

$$\frac{d}{d\omega}[\tan\psi_4] = \frac{d}{d\psi_4}[\tan\psi_4]\frac{d\psi_4}{d\omega}$$

$$= \sec^2\psi_4\frac{d\psi_4}{d\omega}$$

$$= \frac{D_4^2}{(1 - c_2\omega^2 + c_4\omega^4)^2}\frac{d\psi_4}{d\omega} \tag{11.52}$$

Equating the last members of Equations 11.51 and 11.52 we have

$$\text{Group delay} = -\frac{d\theta_4}{d\omega}$$

$$= 2\frac{d\psi_4}{d\omega}$$

$$= \frac{2}{D_4^2}\left[\begin{array}{l}(1 - c_2\omega^2 + c_4\omega^4)(c_1 - 3c_3\omega^2) \\ + \omega^2(c_1 - c_3\omega^2)(2c_2 - 4c_4\omega^2)\end{array}\right] \tag{11.53}$$

This is the expression whose variations we wish to minimise, but first it is convenient to change our notation and write

$$c_1 = x_0/\omega_0; \quad c_2 = Kx_0^2/\omega_0^2; \quad c_3 = Lx_0^3/\omega_0^3;$$

$$c_4 = Mx_0^4/\omega_0^4; \quad X = \omega/\omega_0 \tag{11.54}$$

since x_0 then becomes virtually a scale factor; X varies from 0 to 1 over the range of interest, and K, L and M are the significant parameters controlling the way in which the group delay varies for

$0 \leqslant X \leqslant 1$. The group delay τ_4 given by Equation 11.53 now reduces to

$$\tau_4 = \frac{2x_0}{\omega_0} \left[\frac{(1 - Kx_0{}^2X^2 + Mx_0{}^4X^4)(1 - 3Lx_0{}^2X^2)}{(1 - Kx_0{}^2X^2 + Mx_0{}^4X^4)^2 + x_0{}^2X^2(1 - Lx_0{}^2X^2)^2} \right.$$

$$\left. + \frac{x_0{}^2X^2(1 - Lx_0{}^2X^2)(2K - 4Mx_0{}^2X^2)}{(1 - Kx_0{}^2X^2 + Mx_0{}^4X^4)^2 + x_0{}^2X^2(1 - Lx_0{}^2X^2)^2} \right] \quad (11.55)$$

If we wish the group delay τ_4 in Equation 11.55 to be maximally flat, that is, to have no term in X^2, X^4 or X^6 if expressed as a series of ascending powers of X^2, the simplest procedure is to make the coefficients of X^2, X^4 and X^6 equal in the numerator and denominator of Equation 11.55, since the number-terms are unity for both. The conditions for this are

$$K - 3L = 1 - 2K \quad (11.56)$$

$$KL - 3M = 2M - 2L + K^2 \quad (11.57)$$

$$LM = L^2 - 2KM \quad (11.58)$$

Equation 11.56 simplifies to

$$L = K - \frac{1}{3} \quad (11.59)$$

Substituting for L from Equation 11.59 into Equation 11.57, we have

$$M = \frac{1}{3}(K - 0\cdot4) \quad (11.60)$$

and substituting from Equations 11.59 and 11.60 into Equation 11.58 to eliminate L, M we obtain

$$K = \frac{3}{7}, \text{ whence } L = \frac{2}{21}, M = \frac{1}{105} \quad (11.61)$$

Thus Equation 11.61 gives the conditions for maximal flatness, but if K is arbitrary and L and M are given by Equations 11.59 and 11.60, the group delay will be 'quartically flat' and, if expanded in ascending powers of X^2, will have no term in X^2 or X^4; this last result was found by Gouriet[9] who has studied the general behaviour of τ_4 for varying K when Equations 11.59 and 11.60 apply. If we substitute from Equations 11.61 and 11.55, the result can be written

$$2x_0 - \omega_0\tau_4$$

$$= \frac{2x_0^9 X^8}{11025 + 1575x_0^2X^2 + 135x_0^4X^4 + 10x_0^6X^6 + x_0^8X^8} \tag{11.62}$$

and the expression on the right-hand side of Equation 11.62 continually increases with X whatever the value of x_0 may be; for sufficiently large values of x_0X it differs from $2x_0$ by a small quantity.

As above in Equation 11.36, it is the difference between τ_4 and its zero-frequency value that we should examine carefully. This difference is given, in the general case of Equation 11.55, by

$$2x_0 - \omega_0\tau_4$$

$$= \frac{2x_0}{D_4^2}\left[\begin{matrix}(3L - 3K + 1)\,x_0^2X^2 + (5M - 2L - KL + K^2)\,x_0^4X^4 + \\ + (L^2 - ML - 2MK)\,x_0^6X^6 + M^2x_0^8X^8\end{matrix}\right] \tag{11.63}$$

In the absence of the denominator D_4^2, we should seek to adjust the coefficients of the numerator so that it became a multiple of $(1 - \cos 8\theta)$ where $\cos \theta = X$, for although we are only concerned with variations of τ_4 for $0 < X < 1$, the numerator of Equations 11.63 is even in X, and so we are effectively studying variations of X in the range $-1 < X < 1$. In terms of X we have

$$\begin{aligned}1 - \cos 8\theta &= 2\sin^2 4\theta \\ &= 8\sin^2 2\theta \cos^2 2\theta \\ &= 32\sin^2 \theta \cos^2 \theta \cos^2 2\theta \\ &= 32(1 - X^2)X^2(2X^2 - 1)^2 \\ &= 128X^2(X^2 - \tfrac{1}{2})^2(1 - X^2) \end{aligned} \tag{11.64}$$

and if the numerator of Equation 11.63 becomes a multiple of $(1 - \cos 8\theta)$, it is not only zero when $X = 0$ and $X = 1/\sqrt{2}$ and $X = 1$, but has two equal maxima in the range $0 < X < 1/\sqrt{2}$ and $1/\sqrt{2} < X < 1$. To allow for the presence of the denominator D_4^2, however, we shall instead seek to adjust the coefficients of the numerator of Equation 11.63 so that it becomes a multiple of

$$V = X^2(X^2 - \alpha^2)^2(1 - X^2) \tag{11.65}$$

and substitution back into Equation 11.63 will then give

$$\omega_0 \tau_4 = 2x_0 \left[1 - \frac{M^2 x_0^8 V}{D_4^2} \right] \qquad (11.66)$$

If $\alpha = 1/\sqrt{2}$, the right-hand side of Equation 11.64 is $128V$. If α is sufficiently near zero, the maximum value of $\omega_0 \tau_4$ in the range $0 < X < \alpha$ will be lower than the corresponding maximum in the range $\alpha < X < 1$, but if α is sufficiently near 1, the reverse is true. Further, D_4^2 is the sum of two squares (Equation 11.48) and is therefore always positive. Hence a value of α exists such that the two maxima are equal; we shall follow Tchebycheff and assume that this value of α is the best available, should the variation of $\omega_0 \tau_4$ be in danger of becoming undesirably large.

In order that Equation 11.66 may be the same as Equation 11.63 for all values of X^2, we must have

$$M^2 x_0^8 V = (3L - 3K + 1)x_0^2 X^2 + (5M - 2L - KL + K^2)x_0^4 X^4$$
$$+ (L^2 - ML - 2MK)x_0^6 X^6 + M^2 x_0^8 X^8$$
$$(11.67)$$

and the coefficients of X^2, X^4 and X^6 on both sides of Equation 11.67 must be the same. This gives

$$3L - 3K + 1 = - x_0^6 M^2 \alpha^4 \qquad (11.68)$$

$$5M - 2L - KL + K^2 = x_0^4 M^2 (2\alpha^2 + \alpha^4) \qquad (11.69)$$

$$M(L + 2K) - L^2 = x_0^2 M^2 (2\alpha^2 + 1) \qquad (11.70)$$

Equations 11.68–11.70 are much easier to handle than at first appears. Multiply Equation 11.68 by $K/3$ and add to Equation 11.69, and only terms linear in K and L remain. The resulting equation, together with Equation 11.68, forms a pair of linear simultaneous equations for K and L in terms of M, x_0 and α; the value of K is

$$K = \frac{(2 + 15M) - 6\alpha^2 x_0^4 M^2 + \alpha^4 x_0^4 M^2 (2x_0^2 - 3)}{5 - \alpha^4 x_0^6 M^2} \qquad (11.71)$$

and L is then deduced from Equation 11.68.

If x_0 is so small that powers above the second can be neglected, Equations 11.68 and 11.69 have zero right-hand sides, and are equivalent to Equations 11.56 and 11.57, so that L and M are given in terms of K by Equations 11.59 and 11.60, and the variation of group-delay with frequency is 'quartically flat'. Substituting into Equation 11.70, we have

$$7K - 3 = 45x_0^2 M^2 (2\alpha^2 + 1) \tag{11.72}$$

so that, for a group-delay characteristic of the form 11.66 to be obtainable at all, K must exceed the value $\frac{3}{7}$ appropriate to the 'maximally flat' case, and likewise M must exceed the corresponding value $1/105$.

More generally, if we wish to obtain sets of values of K, L, M, x_0 and α satisfying Equations 11.68–11.70, we can adopt the following iterative procedure. First, choose values of M and α, and an arbitrary starting-value ξ_1 of x_0^2 (it is more convenient to have x_0^2 a round number than x_0, since only even powers of x_0 are involved). We obtain the starting approximation to K from Equation 11.71 and that to L from Equation 11.68. It is advisable to check that Equation 11.69 is now satisfied, before evaluating the two sides of Equation 11.70; if these are unequal, a new value of x_0^2 is required, say ξ_2. As both sides of Equation 11.70 vary nearly linearly with x_0^2, we have a useful clue to the right value of ξ_2, and two more applications of this process appear to be sufficient to determine x_0 satisfactorily. In Fig. 11.3 a rough graphical indication of values of M, x_0 and α satisfying all of Equations 11.68–11.70 is given; the corresponding values of K are obtainable from Equation 11.71 and of L from Equation 11.68. The point A, where $M = 1/105$ and $x_0 = 0$, lies on all the curves, and the maximally-flat case is represented for comparison by the dotted straight line $M = 1/105$ on Fig. 11.3.

We have assumed that a variation of order 1 in $\omega_0 \tau_4$ in the range $0 < X < 1$ is tolerable. If M only just exceeds the minimum value $1/105$, the variation in τ_4 is small and the value of α is not important. If M increases over $0{\cdot}02$, the variation in τ_4, even when Equations 11.68–11.70 are satisfied, increases rapidly. We have therefore given special attention to the case

$$M = 0{\cdot}02 \quad \alpha = 0{\cdot}6 \quad x_0 = \sqrt{14{\cdot}20} = 3{\cdot}7683 \tag{11.73}$$

for which the values of K and L satisfying Equations 11.68–11.70 are approximately $0{\cdot}493$ and $0{\cdot}110$ respectively. A maximum value of about $0{\cdot}7$ for $(2x_0 - \omega_0 \tau_4)$ occurs when $X \approx 0{\cdot}3$, and a second maximum of about $0{\cdot}8$ when $X \approx 0{\cdot}9$. This case seems to represent a reasonable compromise.

If x_0 is small, all the quantities c_1, c_2, c_3 and c_4 are small in Equations 11.43 and 11.54, and therefore the two bridged-T networks make very little contribution to group delay. If on the other hand x_0 and the c-terms are large, the variation of group-delay with frequency cannot be kept within bounds.

Having obtained a set of values, such as that of Equations 11.73, which satisfy Equations 11.68–11.70, we can if necessary improve the accuracy by the iterative procedure described. The network

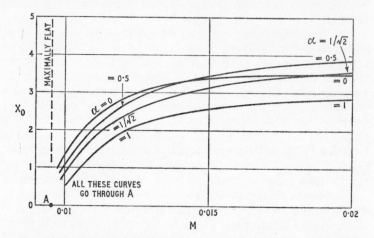

Fig. 11.3. (M, x_0) curves for constant α (see Equations 11.68–11.70)

elements required are found by first evaluating c_1, c_2, c_3 and c_4 from Equations 11.54. For the case of Equations 11.73

$$\omega_0 c_1 = 3{\cdot}7683; \quad \omega_0^2 c_2 = 6{\cdot}9992; \quad \omega_0^3 c_3 = 5{\cdot}8914; \quad \omega_0^4 c_4 = 4{\cdot}0328$$

$$(11.74)$$

We then have to factorise $\phi_4(p)$ given by Equation 11.44 into the quadratic factors 11.45, for which we can use the procedures of Chapters 3, 4 or 7. For the special case

$$\phi_4(p) = (1 + 0{\cdot}6917\, p/\omega_0 + 1{\cdot}0575\, p^2/\omega_0^2) \times$$
$$\times (1 + 3{\cdot}0766\, p/\omega_0 + 3{\cdot}8136\, p^2/\omega_0^2) \quad (11.75)$$

whence it follows from Equations 11.42 that

$$\omega_0 L_1 = 0{\cdot}6917R; \quad \omega_0 C_1 = 0{\cdot}6917/R; \quad q_1 = 0{\cdot}6726 \left.\right\}$$
$$\omega_0 L_2 = 3{\cdot}0766R; \quad \omega_0 C_2 = 3{\cdot}0766/R; \quad q_2 = 1{\cdot}5755 \left.\right\} \quad (11.76)$$

For comparison, the corresponding results for the maximally flat case where x_0 is arbitrary and K, L, M satisfy Equations 11.61 are included, namely

$$\omega_0 c_1 = x_0; \quad \omega_0^2 c_2 = 3x_0^2/7; \quad \omega_0^3 c_3 = 2x_0^3/21; \quad \omega_0^4 c_4 = x_0^4/105$$
$$(11.77)$$

$$\phi_2(p) = 1 + \frac{px_0}{\omega_0} + \frac{3p^2x_0^2}{7\omega_0^2} + \frac{2p^3x_0^3}{21\omega_0^3} + \frac{p^4x_0^4}{105\omega_0^4}$$

$$= \left(1 + 0.6337\frac{px_0}{\omega_0} + 0.1094\frac{p^2x_0^2}{\omega_0^2}\right) \times$$

$$\times \left(1 + 0.3663\frac{px_0}{\omega_0} + 0.08705\frac{p^2x_0^2}{\omega_0^2}\right) \qquad (11.78)$$

$$\left.\begin{array}{lll} \omega_0 L_1 = 0.6337 x_0 R & \omega_0 C_1 = 0.6337/x_0 R & q_1 = 1.916 \\ \omega_0 L_2 = 0.3663 x_0 R & \omega_0 C_2 = 0.3663/x_0 R & q_2 = 1.241 \end{array}\right\} \qquad (11.79)$$

Thus we see that although τ_4 is not a polynomial, we can choose the circuit parameters so as to control its variations satisfactorily by very much the same ideas as Tchebycheff used to control the variations of a polynomial, namely that the varying expression should be made to have as many maxima and minima as possible within the range for which the variation is to be controlled, and that as far as possible all maxima should be equal and all minima equal also; values at the ends of the range should also be equal to maximum or minimum values.

Chapter 12

ANALYTICAL GEOMETRY AND IMPEDANCE CALCULATIONS

When we require to calculate the impedance of a complicated network, we have to apply repeatedly the principle that two impedances Z_1 and Z_2 in series can be replaced by a single impedance $Z_1 + Z_2$, and two admittances Y_1 and Y_2 in parallel can be replaced by a single admittance $Y_1 + Y_2$. The difficulty is that it is frequently necessary for us to change from admittance to impedance and vice versa.

Here we shall obtain by analytical geometry an impedance $R_0{}^2/Z_1$ from a given impedance Z_1. In certain simple cases, this geometrical approach is sufficient to tell us exactly how the expression $R_0{}^2/Z_1$ behaves as a function of frequency and, in more complicated cases, the geometrical approach can throw light on the behaviour of a network without the necessity for us to perform laborious calculation.

In Fig. 12.1, therefore, let the point P represent an arbitrary impedance Z_1 at a particular frequency $\omega/2\pi$, so that OA represents the resistive part and AP the reactive part. Let OA_0 represent an arbitrary resistance R_0 which we shall regard as the unit of resistance for our present purpose; we shall discuss later the question of choosing R_0 conveniently. Let OA' represent the resistance $R_0{}^2/OA$, and draw in the circle on OA' as diameter, meeting OP in Q. Draw OQ' in such a way that OQ' and OQP are equally inclined to the real axis Ox, and let OQ' meet the circle on OA' as diameter in Q'. Then the point Q' represents the impedance $R_0{}^2/Z_1$. It is clear that Q' has the correct argument; that $Q'O$ is the correct magnitude is seen from the fact that $\angle\ OQA'$ is a right angle, since OQA' is a semicircle. The triangles OQA' and OAP

are therefore equiangular and their corresponding sides are proportional, and from this it follows that

$$OQ' \cdot OP = OQ \cdot OP$$

$$= OA' \cdot OA$$

$$= R_0{}^2 \qquad (12.1)$$

Thus to obtain Q' we have only to determine A' by calculating $R_0{}^2/OA$. The direction of OQ' is known immediately from the

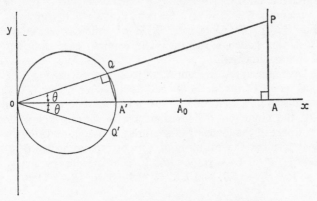

Fig. 12.1.   Geometrical construction of $R_0{}^2/Z_1$

position of P, and we can either drop a perpendicular from A' or draw an arc with centre the mid-point of OA' and radius $\frac{1}{2}OA'$ to meet the known line OQ'. If therefore we know the locus of P for varying frequency, it is not unduly difficult to plot the locus of Q'.

In certain simple cases, such as that of the network in Fig. 12.2, we can do more than this, and determine accurately the nature of the locus of the point representing the impedance in which we are interested. For the impedance Z of this network at frequency $\omega/2\pi$ is given by

$$\frac{1}{Z} = \frac{1}{Z_1} + \frac{1}{R_2} \quad \text{where } Z_1 = R_1 + j\omega L \qquad (12.2)$$

so that if the Z_1 of Fig. 12.1 and that of Equation 12.2 are the same, we have

$$AP = \omega L; \quad OA = R_1; \quad \tan\theta = \omega L/R_1 \qquad (12.2a)$$

In this case, therefore, the point Q' representing the impedance $R_0{}^2/Z_1$ decribes the semicircle on OA' as diameter and below the axis Ox as ω varies from 0 to ∞, for the point A (and therefore A') remains fixed as ω varies and P moves vertically upwards.

We now know, by multiplying through Equation 12.2 by $R_0{}^2$, that

$$\frac{R_0{}^2}{Z} = \frac{R_0{}^2}{Z_1} + \frac{R_0{}^2}{R_2} \qquad (12.3)$$

so that $R_0{}^2/Z$ is represented by the lower semicircle of Fig. 12.1 shifted a distance $R_0{}^2/R_2$ to the right as indicated in Fig. 12.3 by the semicircle on BB' as diameter; B' corresponds to A' (in Fig. 12.1) and represents $R_0{}^2/Z$ at zero frequency while B corresponds to O (in Fig. 12.1) and represents $R_0{}^2/Z$ at infinite frequency, when $R_0{}^2/Z$ is the same as $R_0{}^2/R_2$. The semicircle is thus described clockwise as indicated.

We have now to return from $R_0{}^2/Z$ to Z by applying Fig. 12.1 when P is any point of the circle on BB' as diameter below Ox, since Z is the same as $R_0{}^2 \div (R_0{}^2/Z)$. Now it is clear that, since the relevant part of the circle on BB' as diameter is entirely below Ox, the relevant part of the locus of Z is entirely above it. Further, we can easily determine the position of C' corresponding to B' at zero frequency and of C corresponding to B at infinite frequency. For $OB' = R_0{}^2/R_2 + BB'$ and $BB' = OA' = R_0{}^2/R_1$. Thus

$$\left.\begin{array}{l} OB' = \dfrac{R_0{}^2}{R_2} + \dfrac{R_0{}^2}{R_1} = \dfrac{R_0{}^2(R_1 + R_2)}{R_1 R_2} \, ; \\[2mm] OC' = \dfrac{R_0{}^2}{OB'} = \dfrac{R_1 R_2}{R_1 + R_2} \\[2mm] OB = R_0{}^2/R_2; \quad OC = R_0{}^2/(R_0{}^2/R_2) = R_2 \end{array}\right\} \qquad (12.4)$$

Now it can be proved that the locus of Z for any frequency is the upper semicircle on $C'C$ as diameter, described clockwise. More generally, if the impedance Z_1 discussed in Fig. 12.1 describes a circle (as frequency varies) anywhere in the complex plane, then the impedance $R_0{}^2/Z_1$ also describes a circle. Thus is the case of the network of Fig. 12.2, we have only to determine the positions of C and C', and we have determined the locus of Z completely because we know it is circular. In more complicated cases, we might need to determine three points before a locus known to be circular was adequately specified.

The process of finding $R_0{}^2/Z_1$ from Z_1 is often called 'inversion', and it is worth noting the mathematically well-known result that if two curves intersect, they intersect at the same angle as their inverses. Now in Fig. 12.3, the inverse of the real axis Ox is the real axis itself, because if R is real, $R_0{}^2/R$ is also real. The real axis cuts the circle on BB' as diameter at right angles at both B and B', and therefore it also cuts the inverse circle at right angles at C and C'; this confirms that the Z-locus must be in this case the circle on CC' as diameter, and not just any circle through C and C'.

At this point we should consider the proper choice of the 'unit' R_0 of resistance. The radius of the circle in Fig. 12.1 is $R_0{}^2/2OA$, and we clearly do not want this quantity to be very large or very small. Probably the most convenient value of R_0 is OA if we have only one impedance to invert, and approximately the mean value of OA if we have a whole curve (described by P in Fig. 12.1) to invert.

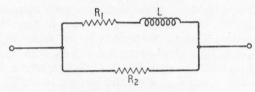

Fig. 12.2. A simple network

If R_0 is equal to OA, A, A_0 and A' all coincide and the circle touches AP at A, so that there is very little wasted space in the figure.

GEOMETRICAL SPECIFICATION OF IMPEDANCE OF THE NETWORK OF FIG. 12.2

Fig. 12.3 shows us at a glance the whole behaviour of the magnitude and phase angle of the impedance of the network of Fig. 12.2 as the frequency varies. For at frequency $\omega/2\pi$, θ is given in Fig. 12.1 by Equation 12.2a, and Q' is the corresponding point representing $R_0{}^2/Z_1$. In Fig. 12.3, Q'' is the corresponding point representing $R_0{}^2/Z$, and the corresponding point T'' representing Z is found by making OT'' equally inclined with OQ'' to Ox. If OQ'' meets the circle on BB' as diameter in q and OT'' meets the circle on CC' as diameter in t, then t represents Z at the frequency for which q represents $R_0{}^2/Z$, and a little care is necessary to choose T'' and not t as the point 'corresponding' to Q''.

At low frequencies, the point T'' representing the impedance of the network of Fig. 12.2 is moving nearly parallel to the imaginary axis Oy with increasing frequency, so the magnitude of this impedance is changing little. The phase angle is that between OT'' and Ox, and this increases to a maximum θ_{max} where the tangent from O to the upper semicircle on CC' as diameter touches the semi-circle. If D is the mid-point of CC' and therefore the centre of the semi-circle, the radius DV is at right angles to the tangent OV, and therefore

$$\sin \theta_{max} = \frac{DV}{OD} = \frac{OC - OC'}{OC + OC'} = \frac{R_2}{2R_1 + R_2} \qquad (12.5)$$

and from Equation 12.2a, the frequency $\Omega/2\pi$ at which the phase angle θ_{max} occurs is given by

$$\Omega = (R_1/L) \tan \theta_{max} = \frac{R_2}{2L}\left(\frac{R_1}{R_1 + R_2}\right)^{1/2} \qquad (12.6)$$

At higher frequencies, the phase angle gradually decreases to zero and the magnitude of the impedance gradually increases to R_2.

From Equation 12.5 we see that it is the ratio R_2/R_1 which controls θ_{max}; if R_2 is small compared with R_1, then θ_{max} is small, whereas if R_1 is small compared with R_2, θ_{max} is near $\pi/2$. If R_2 is $2R_1$, θ_{max} is $\pi/6$. Once θ_{max} is decided by the ratio R_2/R_1, L controls the way in which the semicircle is described as the frequency increases. Thus if L is small, the maximum phase θ_{max} occurs at a relatively high frequency, so that the point T'' reaches V relatively slowly as frequency increases; in the contrary case, when L is large, Ω in Equation 12.6 is relatively small, so the point T'' reaches V quickly and thereafter the phase decreases.

We have thus seen that, in the case of a network like that of Fig. 12.2 where we know that the locus of a point representing the impedance as a function of frequency is a circle or part thereof, we can tell at a glance the behaviour of magnitude and phase. In more complicated cases, we may have to determine more points to understand satisfactorily the impedance locus but, for any particular frequency, the point representing the impedance can always be determined by a series of inversions (as when Q' is derived from P in Fig. 12.1) and shifts (as when the semicircle on BB' as diameter in Fig. 12.3 is derived from that on OA' as diameter in Fig. 12.1 and Q'' from Q') as indicated above. (The shifts, however, need not necessarily be horizontal as in Fig. 12.3.) The general behaviour of impedance magnitude and phase can then be studied, at least qualitatively, by purely geometrical consideration of the impedance locus—when is it nearest to, or furthest from, O, and where are the points of contact of tangents from O to the locus which are associated with phase maxima or minima?

IMPEDANCE OF TRANSMISSION LINE
CIRCLE DIAGRAMS

Another case in which geometrical considerations can greatly simplify impedance calculations is that of a uniform length of transmission line.

'Circle diagrams' have been discussed by Jackson and Huxley[12]; we shall here take a somewhat more geometrical viewpoint than they did. Their electrical results will be taken for granted, but the

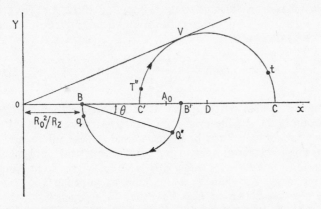

Fig. 12.3. Representation of R_0^2/Z for the network of Fig. 12.2

derivation of their geometrical and mathematical results will be considered in some detail.

Our starting-point is thus that the input impedance Z_s of a length l of uniform transmission line, of characteristic impedance Z_0 and propagation constant P terminated in an impedance Z_t, is given by

$$Z_s = Z_0 \frac{Z_T + Z_0 \tanh Pl}{Z_0 + Z_T \tanh Pl} \qquad (12.7)$$

Jackson and Huxley find it convenient to 'normalise' and write

$$z_s = Z_s/Z_0, \quad z_t = Z_t/Z_0 \qquad (12.8)$$

They also define

$$Pl = u_0 + jv_0 = \alpha l + jl(2\pi/\lambda) \qquad (12.9)$$

where α is the attenuation coefficient and $2\pi/\lambda$ the phase constant of the line. Equation 12.7 then becomes

$$z_s = \frac{z_t + \tanh(u_0 + jv_0)}{1 + z_t \tanh(u_0 + jv_0)} \qquad (12.10)$$

If we now define $u_1 + jv_1$ by the equation

$$z_t = \tanh (u_1 + jv_1) \tag{12.11}$$

Equation (12.10) can be reduced to

$$z_s = \tanh [(u_0 + u_1) + j(v_0 + v_1)] \tag{12.12}$$

so that it is clearly important to be able to find z_s given $(u_0 + u_1)$ and $(v_0 + v_1)$ in Equation 12.12 and vice versa. This is what the 'circle diagram' enables us to do. Equation 12.12 is easily derived from Equation 12.10 after substitution from Equation 12.11 for z_t since by definition

$$\tanh \psi = \frac{e^{\psi} - e^{-\psi}}{e^{\psi} + e^{-\psi}} \tag{12.13}$$

whether ψ is real or complex. It is further to be noted that in Equation 12.13, if ψ has even a moderately large real part, say 3 or 4, then the terms $e^{-\psi}$ can be neglected and $\tanh \psi$ differs very little from unity. Hence, apart from the geometrical considerations which follow, if Pl has a sufficiently large real part, Z_t in Equation 12.7 reduces to Z_0, whatever the terminating impedance Z_T may be. It is also clear that at any frequency or frequencies for which $Z_T = Z_0, Z_s$ is equal to Z_0 whatever the value of l may be. Although this can be most easily seen by means of Equation 12.7, Equation 12.10 gives us the same information in a more indirect way. For, if $Z_T = Z_0, z_t = 1$. This implies, in Equation 12.11, that u_1 is infinite; the value of v_1 is immaterial. Hence, in Equation 12.12, $u_0 + u_1$ is also infinite, and therefore z_s is also unity.

In the general case, however, we are concerned with using the relation

$$Z = R + jX = \tanh (u + jv) \tag{12.14}$$

to obtain graphically u and v if R and X are known, and vice versa. In Equation 12.14, $R + jX$ must be regarded as a normalised, dimensionless quantity, like z_s and z_t in Equation 12.8.

Now it is shown below that if u is kept constant, the point $R + jX$ describes the circle whose centre is the point $\coth 2u + j0$ and radius $|\operatorname{cosech} 2u|$, while if v is constant, the point $R + jX$ describes part of the circle whose centre is the point $0 - j \cot 2v$ and radius $|\operatorname{cosec} 2v|$. The constant-$u$ circle dwindles to the single point $1 + j0$ as u tends to infinity and to the single point $-1 + j0$

as u tends to minus infinity. For $u = 0$, the circle degenerates into the imaginary axis $R = 0$. For constant v the point $R + jX$ also describes a circle which always goes through the points $\pm 1 + j0$. Its centre is the point $0 - j \cot 2v$ and radius $|\text{cosec } 2v|$. Hence the same circle is used for a particular value v_0 of v and for $v_0 \pm \pi/2$; if v_0 is between 0 and $\pi/2$, the arc above the points $\pm 1 + j0$ is described for $v = v_0$ and the arc below these points for $v = v_0 + \pi/2$. If any constant-u circle meets a constant-v circle, they cut at right angles, so that the tangent to either circle at the point of intersection goes through the centre of the other. We shall take v as lying between 0 (inclusive) and π (exclusive), for adding π or any multiple of π to v does not affect the value of R and X derived from Equation 12.14. All these properties are summed up in Fig. 12.4, and we have to determine a method, as explained immediately

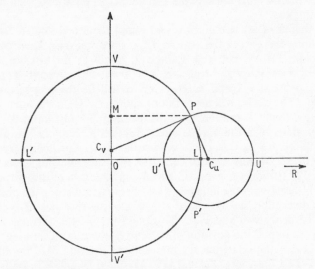

Fig. 12.4. Geometrical determination of u and v when R and X are given, and vice versa

below, of taking advantage of them to find u and v given R and X or R and X given u and v.

In Fig. 12.4 we have shown an arbitrary point P representing $R + jX$, and the circle $U P U'$ which is the locus of points having the same value of u as that at P, together with the circle $V'LPVL'$, part of which is the locus of points having the same value of v as that at P. Since P is above the real axis, this value of v at P is between

0 and $\pi/2$.   At the other intersection, P', of the two circles in Fig. 12.4, u is the same as at P, but v is $v_p + \pi/2$. PM represents R and OM represents X. OL is of unit length and so is OL' since, as already stated, all the v-circles go through $\pm 1 + j0$.   If C_u is the centre of the u-circle through P, then OC_u is coth $2u$, which is always greater than 1 for positive u, so that C_u is always to the right of L. (Similarly, for negative u, C_u would always be to the left of L'.) The radius C_uP is $|$cosech $2u|$.   The circle always encloses the point L (for u positive) or L' (for u negative) and does not meet the imaginary axis $R = 0$.   The centre C_v of the v-circle through P is, as already stated, the point $0 - j$ cot $2v$, so that in Fig. 12.4, the fact that C_v is above O means that OC_v is $-$ cot $2v$ and cot $2v$ is negative: v is therefore between $\pi/4$ and $\pi/2$.   The radius C_vP of the v-circle is $|$cosec $2v|$.   The v-circle radius C_vP touches the u-circle at P and the u-circle radius C_uP touches the v-circle at P;   these two radii are at right angles.

If, therefore, we are given u and v and require R and X, we can determine the two circles in Fig. 12.4, since we know their centres and radii.   If v is between 0 and $\pi/2$, it will be the intersection P of the circles above the real axis $X = 0$ which represents $R + jX$; if v is between $\pi/2$ and π, however, it will be the intersection P' below.   The circles will never fail to intersect.   If on the other hand we know R and X and therefore the position of P (assuming $X > 0$), we can determine the unique circle through P, L and L' to obtain v.   The centre of this circle is necessarily on the imaginary axis ($R = 0$), so we only need to construct the perpendicular bisector of PL or PL' (whichever is easier) and the intersection of this perpendicular bisector with the imaginary axis fixes C_v and v, for the position of C_v determines cot $2v$ and if P is above the real axis ($X = 0$), v must be between 0 and $\pi/2$.   To obtain the u-circle through P (or rather, to obtain the position of its centre, which is all we need) join PL and PL' and construct the internal and external bisectors of the angle $L'PL$;   these meet the real axis ($X = 0$) in U' and U respectively, and C_u is of course the mid-point of UU'.   Knowing C_u, we know coth $2u$ and this determines u uniquely (see below).

Jackson and Huxley[12] have covered the $(R + jX)$ plane with 'circle diagrams' by means of which u and v can be roughly determined given R and X, and vice versa; the circles in their diagrams are simply some of the constant-u and constant-v circles we have already considered.   In the procedure we have discussed, however, it is not actually necessary to draw any circles at all if R and X are given and we require u and v; we only need the perpendicular bisector of PL (or PL') and the internal and external bisectors of angle $L'PL$.

When we know u and v we only require the arcs of the circles in the immediate neighbourhood of their intersection. Thus, for a small number of determinations, or for high accuracy, the method we have here considered has the advantage of requiring no interpolation, and no preliminary drawing or printing of systems of circles. On the other hand, where a large number of determinations of R, X from u, v or vice versa is required, and rough interpolation is sufficient, it may involve less labour to work with 'circle diagrams' especially as these can be prepared in advance.

It should also be noted that what we may really need to do in a problem where this kind of calculation arises is to make Z_T in Equation 12.7 equal to Z_0 at a number of well-chosen frequencies. For we have seen that at sufficiently high frequencies, or when the cable is sufficiently long, the input impedance Z_s will be Z_0 whatever the terminating impedance may be. If Z_s is also forcibly made equal to Z_0 at lower frequencies by making $Z_T = Z_0$ at those frequencies, then we can in effect make the cable behave almost as if its length were considerably increased—there will not be serious variations in Z_s between the frequencies for which Z_T is made equal to Z_0 and above the highest of these frequencies if these frequencies are carefully chosen. This matter has been investigated to some extent in the case of the 'Kelvin Cable' by Mayo and Head.[13]

WHY ARE THE u = CONSTANT AND v = CONSTANT LOCI CIRCLES?

From Equation 12.14

$$\frac{1 + R + jX}{1 - R - jX} = \frac{1 + \tanh(u + jv)}{1 - \tanh(u + jv)}$$

$$= \frac{e^{u+jv}}{e^{-u-jv}} = e^{2u+2jv} \tag{12.15}$$

Now write $1 \pm (R + jX)$ in terms of magnitude and phase, so that

$$1 + R + jX = \rho_1 e^{j\phi_1}$$

where

$$\rho_1 = \{(1 + R)^2 + X^2\}^{1/2},$$

$$\sin\phi_1 = X/\rho_1; \quad \cos\phi_1 = (1 + R)/\rho_1 \tag{12.16}$$

ϕ_1 being between $-\pi$ and $+\pi$, and

$$1 - R - jX = \rho_2 e^{-j\phi_2}$$

where

$$\rho_2 = \{(1 - R)^2 + X^2\}^{1/2}, \; \sin \phi_2 = X/\rho_2, \; \cos \phi_2 = (1 - R)/\rho_2$$

ϕ_2 being between $-\pi$ (exclusive) and $+\pi$ (inclusive)   (12.17)

Then Equation 12.15 reduces to

$$e^{2u+2jv} = e^{2u}(\cos 2v + j \sin 2v)$$

$$= (\rho_1/\rho_2) \, e^{j(\phi_1+\phi_2)} \tag{12.18}$$

so that

$$e^{2u} = \frac{\rho_1}{\rho_2} \; \text{or} \; e^{4u} = \frac{(1 + R)^2 + X^2}{(1 - R)^2 + X^2} \tag{12.19}$$

and

$$2v = \phi_1 + \phi_2 \tag{12.20}$$

Equation 12.19 can be rearranged in the form

$$R^2 + X^2 - 2kR + 1 = 0 \tag{12.21}$$

or

$$(R - k)^2 + X^2 = k^2 - 1 \tag{12.22}$$

where

$$k = \frac{e^{4u} + 1}{e^{4u} - 1} = \coth 2u \tag{12.23}$$

It is the form 12.22 of the relation between R and X which makes clear that the distance of the point $R + jX$ from $k + j0$ has the constant value $(k^2 - 1)^{1/2}$ or $|\text{cosech } 2u|$, so that the locus is a circle centre $k + j0$ or $(\coth 2u + j0)$ and radius $|\text{cosech } 2u|$.

Likewise, Equation 12.20 must be rearranged to explain the nature of the v-locus. We have

$$\tan 2v = \tan (\phi_1 + \phi_2)$$

$$= \frac{\tan \phi_1 + \tan \phi_2}{1 - \tan \phi_1 \tan \phi_2}$$

$$= \frac{\dfrac{X}{1 + R} + \dfrac{X}{1 - R}}{1 - \dfrac{X}{1 + R} \cdot \dfrac{X}{1 - R}} \tag{12.24}$$

and, multiplying top and bottom of the right-hand side of Equation

12.24 by $(1 + R)(1 - R) = 1 - R^2$,

$$\tan 2v = \frac{2X}{1 - R^2 - X^2}$$

or $$X^2 + R^2 + 2X \cot 2v - 1 = 0 \qquad (12.25)$$

which is more conveniently written

$$R^2 + (X + \cot 2v)^2 = 1 + \cot^2 2v = \operatorname{cosec}^2 2v \qquad (12.26)$$

Equation 12.26 expresses that the point $R + jX$ is always a distance $|\operatorname{cosec} 2v|$ from the fixed point $0 - j \cot 2v$, and thus that the locus of $R + jX$ for constant v is a circle.

FINDING u GIVEN COTH $2u$

Tables of coth x are not usually available, but applying Equation 12.13 above with ψ replaced by $2u$, we have that if

$$\coth 2u = k \qquad (12.27)$$

then $$\frac{e^{2u} + e^{-2u}}{e^{2u} - e^{-2u}} = k$$

and therefore $$e^{4u} = \frac{k + 1}{k - 1} \qquad (12.28)$$

so that $$u = \tfrac{1}{4}\{\log_e (k + 1) - \log_e (k - 1)\} \qquad (12.29)$$

and thus u can readily be calculated.

Chapter 13

STABILITY CRITERIA

In Chapter 9 we noted that, in order to determine the current $I(t)$ resulting from the application of a given voltage $V(t)$ to a network whose impedance is $Z(p)$, we had to find some way of solving an equation of the form 9.15. If the network has lumped elements, $Z(p)$ will be rational in p. By using the partial-fraction technique of Chapter 5, the solution of Equation 9.15 can in this case be reduced to a number of terms of the form of Equation 9.11, and all is well as long as the quantity called a in that equation has a positive real part for each of the terms. If however a has a negative real part, Equation 9.10 is no longer a proper representation of the situation, because the factor $e^{a\tau}$ in the integrand tends to infinity instead of zero as assumed in the discussion of that equation. In fact, if Equation 9.15 gives rise to any term of the form 9.11 where a has a negative real part, the system is unstable, and contains a term having exponential growth instead of the more usual exponential decay.

Sufficient information has been given in Chapter 9 to enable the output current $I(t)$ to be calculated given the input voltage $V(t)$ and the network impedance $Z(p)$, but we do not want if we can help it to embark upon such a calculation, only to find that it is entirely useless because the system is unstable. In this chapter various 'stability criteria' are discussed which enable us to determine whether $Z(p)$ is free from zeros with positive real parts and therefore associated with a stable system without our having either to determine the zeros of $Z(p)$ or to determine $I(t)$ for any $V(t)$. The Routh criterion is discussed first, with an illustrative example. This criterion is then compared with that put forward by Jury[14]. In the U.S.S.R., the work of Liapunov on stability is well known, but this is not as well known as it should be in this country, so Parks[15] ought to be thanked for drawing our attention to it. Some straight-

234

forward examples illustrating Liapunov's basic principles have therefore been included.

ROUTH'S CRITERION

Mathematically, we require to know whether the polynomial numerator of the above-mentioned network impedance $Z(p)$ has zeros with negative real parts or not, without having to calculate those zeros if possible. It will therefore be sufficient for our purposes to determine whether a polynomial has such zeros or not. Suppose therefore that the polynomial is of degree 5, namely

$$a_0 + a_1x + a_2x^2 + a_3x^3 + a_4x^4 + a_5x^5 = 0 \qquad (13.1)$$

(For the present investigation the association of p with d/dt is irrelevant: we have thus used a different variable, x, in this chapter.)

Now separate the terms of even degree from those of odd degree, and suppose that

$$a_0 - a_2y + a_4y^2 = 0 \text{ has roots } y = \alpha_1, y = \alpha_2$$

$$a_1 - a_3y + a_5y^2 = 0 \text{ has roots } y = \beta_1, y = \beta_2$$

Then the original equation in x has no roots with positive real parts, and can be the characteristic equation of a stable system if, and only if

(i) All the a-terms in the original equation 13.1 (in x) have the same sign

(ii) α_1, α_2, β_1 and β_2 are all real

(iii) $\alpha_1 < \beta_1 < \alpha_2 < \beta_2$

We shall not attempt to prove this result here; it is a result which, once understood, is easily applied and, in the form given above, can be generalised to equations of any degree. The only difference is that there are then more of the quantities we have called α and β; all of these quantities must be real for stability and, if arranged in ascending order, the α and β terms must occur alternately with the smallest α less than the smallest β. Thus, for example, the equation

$$1 + 4x + 5x^2 + ax^3 + 4x^4 + x^5 = 0 \qquad (13.2)$$

has its α terms given by

$$1 - 5y + 4y^2 = 0 \qquad (13.3)$$

so that $\alpha_1 = 0.25$ and $\alpha_2 = 1$, while β_1 and β_2 are the roots of

$$4 - ay + y^2 = 0 \qquad (13.4)$$

If $a < 4$, this last equation has no real roots and, therefore, the original equation 13.2 cannot possibly be associated with a stable system. When $a = 4$, β_1 and β_2 are both 2 so that the associated system is still unstable. As a increases above 4, β_1 decreases and β_2 increases, until when $a = 5$, β_1 is 1 and β_2 is 4, so that this is the borderline case when $\beta_1 = \alpha_2$. If $a > 5$, β_1 is less then $\alpha_2 = 1$, so the associated system is stable until a increases so much that β_1 falls to $\alpha_1 = 0.25$; this happens when $a = 16.25$. For greater values of a, the associated system is again unstable, since β_1 is now less than α_1.

ROUTH'S CRITERION FOR QUADRATIC, CUBIC AND QUARTIC EQUATIONS

For equations of degree less than 5, the above procedure could still be carried out, but there are now fewer of the quantities we have called α and β. In such cases, however, it is possible to express the 'stability condition' directly in terms of the coefficients of the original equation. Again, we shall confine ourselves to stating the results; namely, that for the equation

$$a_0 + a_1 x + a_2 x^2 + a_3 x^3 + a_4 x^4 = 0$$

(a) If the equation is quadratic ($a_3 = a_4 = 0$) it is sufficient that a_0, a_1 and a_2 all have the same sign.

(b) if the equation is cubic ($a_4 = 0$) a_0, a_1, a_2 and a_3 must all have the same sign and

$$a_1 a_2 > a_0 a_3$$

(c) If the equation is quartic, a_0, a_1, a_2, a_3 and a_4 must all have the same sign and if they are positive

$$a_1 a_2 a_3 > a_4 a_1{}^2 + a_0 a_3{}^2$$

CONDITIONS FOR MINIMUM DAMPING RATE

Finally, we may sometimes be in no doubt that a system is stable, but we may want a more stringent condition than this; namely, that every term in the transient response be damped at least as rapidly as e^{-kt}. This means that our equation must not merely be free from roots with positive real parts, but the real parts of the roots must all be less than $-k$ and, therefore, if we put $x + k = z$, the resulting equation in z must be free from roots with positive real parts. Now, $x = z - k$ so, if we put $(z - k)$ instead of x in the original equation (for example, the fifth-degree equation (13.1) first discussed) we find that

$$a_0 + a_1(z - k) + a_2(z - k)^2 + a_3(z - k)^3 + \\ + a_4(z - k)^4 + a_5(z - k)^5 = 0$$

regarded as an equation in z, must be free from roots with positive real parts. The criteria already obtained must therefore be applied to the equation

$$b_0 + b_1 z + b_2 z^2 + b_3 z^3 + b_4 z^4 + b_5 z^5 = 0$$

where

$$b_5 = a_5; \; b_4 = a_4 - 5ka_5; \; b_3 = a_3 - 4ka_4 + 10k^2 a_5;$$
$$b_2 = a_2 - 3ka_3 + 6k^2 a_4 - 10k^3 a_5;$$
$$b_1 = a_1 - 2ka_2 + 3k^2 a_3 - 4k^3 a_4 + 5k^4 a_5;$$
$$b_0 = a_0 - ka_1 + k^2 a_2 - k^3 a_3 + k^4 a_4 - k^5 a_5$$

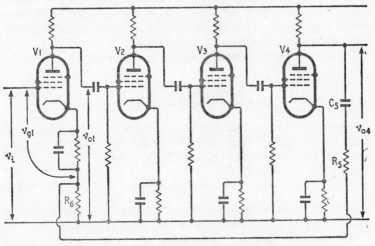

Fig. 13.1. A four-stage feedback amplifier

We have thus found a criterion for stability (essentially that of Routh) which does not require the drawing of Nyquist diagrams if the characteristic equation is known and, if the characteristic equation has degree not exceeding 5, no mathematical process more complicated than solving a quadratic equation with real roots is involved. The criterion can readily be adapted to securing a minimum damping rate.

APPLICATION TO FOUR-STAGE FEEDBACK AMPLIFIER

We now apply the criteria just obtained to the four-stage feedback amplifier of Fig. 13.1.

We shall consider only performance at frequencies so high that interstage coupling capacitances, screenfeed components and bias circuits can all be ignored. Performance is then governed mainly by the values of the shunt valve and wiring capacitances in relation to the coupling resistances.

The effective circuit of an individual stage at such frequencies can be reduced to the well-known form shown in Fig. 13.2. Here the input grid-cathode voltage of the valve is v_g and g_m is the mutual conductance, giving the input current $g_m v_g$ shown in Fig. 13.2. R is the value of the anode a.c. resistance and coupling resistance of the valve, combined in parallel with each other and with the following grid leak. C represents the total shunt capacitance of the stage and comprises the output capacitance of one valve plus the input capacitance of one valve plus the input capacitance of the next plus stray wiring capacitance. The output voltage v_0 of one stage forms the input grid–cathode voltage for the next stage.

The gain of the stage equivalent to the circuit of Fig. 13.2 is

$$A = \frac{v_0}{v_g} = \frac{-g_m R}{1 + pCR} \tag{13.5}$$

the minus sign being included to take account of the reversal of phase in the stage. Ignoring feedback for the moment, the gain from the grid of V_1 to the anode of V_4 is therefore

$$A_{14} = A_1 A_2 A_3 A_4 \tag{13.6}$$

where each of the A-terms is of the form given for Fig. 13.2 with the values of g_m, R and C appropriate to the stage in question.

We now have feedback to consider. C_5 (in Fig. 13.1) can normally be neglected at high frequencies; we shall also assume

$R_6 \ll R_5$. The presence of R_5 will slightly modify the gain of the V_4 stage by shunting its coupling resistance; this can be allowed for by altering the effective value of R (in Fig. 13.2) for this stage.

The determination of the feedback factor is complicated by current feedback in V_1 because of the presence of R_6 in its cathode circuit. In effect, therefore, there are two kinds of feedback to take into account. The equivalent circuit of the first stage is shown in Fig. 13.3. If we note that

$$v_i = v_{g1} + (i_a + i_1) R_6 \tag{13.7}$$

and write the other equations in accordance with Kirchhoff's Laws, it is a matter of simple algebraic manipulation to find that the overall gain A_0 is given by

$$A_0 = \frac{v_{01}}{v_i}$$

$$= \frac{-\mu A_2 A_3 A_4 z}{r_a + z + (1 + \mu)\dfrac{R_5 R_6}{R_5 + R_6} + A_2 A_3 A_4 (1 + \mu)\dfrac{z R_6}{R_5 + R_6}} \tag{13.8}$$

where $z = R'/(1 + pCR')$
Now if

$$A_1 = \frac{-\mu z}{r_a + z + \dfrac{R_5 R_6}{R_5 + R_6}(1 + \mu)} \tag{13.9}$$

A_1 is the gain of the first stage with its own internal current feedback through $R_5 R_6/(R_5 + R_6)$ acting as an unbypassed cathode resistor. This expression is conveniently expanded to

$$A_1 = \frac{-g_m r_a R'}{r_a + R' + (1 + \mu)\dfrac{R_5 R_6}{R_5 + R_6}} \cdot K$$

where

$$\frac{1}{K} = 1 + pC \frac{R'\left[r_a + \dfrac{R_5 R_6}{R_5 + R_6}(1 + \mu)\right]}{r_a + R' + \dfrac{R_5 R_6}{R_5 + R_6}(1 + \mu)} \tag{13.10}$$

This apparently cumbersome expression actually shows clearly that the effect of this local feedback on the transient response is merely to change the effective a.c. resistance of the valve from

$$r_a \text{ to } r_a + (1 + \mu)\, R_5 R_6/(R_5 + R_6)$$

The value of R for this stage is thus R' in parallel with this effective resistance instead of in parallel with r_a.

If we substitute in the expression 13.8 for A_0 in terms of A_1 we get

$$A_0 = \frac{A_1 A_2 A_3 A_4}{1 + A_1 A_2 A_3 A_4 \beta} \qquad (13.11)$$

where $\beta = R_6/(R_5 + R_6)$.

In doing this, we have introduced one approximation, which is that in the denominator $1 \ll \mu$. Because the feedback is applied

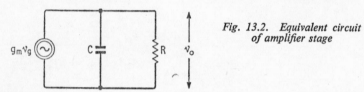

$g_m v_g$ C R v_0

Fig. 13.2. Equivalent circuit of amplifier stage

to the cathode of V_1, the loop gain is dependent on $1 + \mu$ in the first stage instead of on μ. For a first-stage valve, μ will rarely be less than 40 and will be much higher if a pentode is used. The error is negligible, therefore, and considerably simplifies the equations.

Now each of the A terms is of the form

$$- g_m R/(1 + pCR)$$

so if $A_L = g_{m_1} R_1 g_{m_2} R_2 g_{m_3} R_3 g_{m_4} R_4$ we have

$$A_0 = \frac{A_L}{(1 + pC_1 R_1)(1 + pC_2 R_2)(1 + pC_3 R_3)(1 + pC_4 R_4) + A_L \beta} \qquad (13.12)$$

$$= \frac{A_L}{(1 + A_L \beta) + b_1 p + b_2 p^2 + b_3 p^3 + b_4 p^4} \qquad (13.13)$$

where the b terms are all combinations of the CR terms, and can readily be evaluated by expanding the denominator of 13.12 and equating the coefficients of corresponding powers of p in 13.12 and 13.13.

If β is zero, the equation has all its roots real and negative but, if β is gradually increased, the equation

$$(1 + A_L\beta) - b_2y + b_4y^2 = 0$$

whose roots correspond to those we called α_1 and α_2 when discussing Equation 13.1 above, is such that α_1 and α_2 move closer together but $(\alpha_1 + \alpha_2)$ remains constant and equal to b_2/b_4. The equation

$$b_1 - b_3y = 0$$

has a fixed root which we called β_1 with reference to Equation 13.1. Hence, as β is gradually increased, a value must eventually be reached when the condition for stability, which is

$$\alpha_1 < \beta_1 < \alpha_2,$$

is no longer met. It is clear that

$$A_L\beta < b_2{}^2/(4b_4) - 1 \qquad (13.14)$$

otherwise α_1 and α_2 will not be real and there cannot be stability. As the original equation is quartic, the condition for stability can be written down explicitly; it is

$$(1 + A_L\beta)b_3{}^2 < b_1b_2b_3 - b_1{}^2b_4 \qquad (13.15)$$

but, in many cases, the simpler condition 13.14 is sufficient to

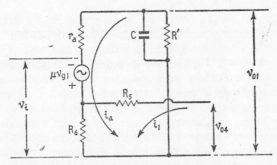

Fig. 13.3. Equivalent circuit for first stage and feedback network of the amplifier of Fig. 13.1

give us the information required. For a quintic equation, we could still obtain a rough criterion of the form 13.14, but there would no longer be a simple exact one of the form 13.15 and, for exact information, we should be compelled to determine the quantities α_1, α_2, β_1 and β_2, as suggested with reference to Equation 13.1.

Hitherto, we have assumed that the mathematical requirement for stability was that a certain algebraic equation associated with the system should be free from roots with positive real parts, and the reasons for this in the case of the kind of problem discussed in Chapter 9 have been outlined.

PROFESSOR JURY'S CRITERION: NUMERICAL PRODECURE

Recently, however, Professor Jury[14] has investigated a rather different, but closely related, stability requirement which arises in particular in connection with sampled-data control systems. Mathematically, Professor Jury requires all the roots of an algebraic equation to lie within the unit circle, that is to say, to have modulus less than unity. This requirement also arises in connection with linear difference equations.

We shall describe Professor Jury's procedure and compare it carefully with that just discussed. Such a comparison is a great help towards understanding of all the entities compared. It is also advantageous to have more than one method available for doing numerical calculations, because of the enormous number of possibilities of making silly mistakes. When two procedures give different answers for the same calculation, one is at least warned that there is a mistake, and it can then be found; when there is only one way of doing the calculation, one often does not know whether the result is right or not.

First, let us consider Professor Jury's procedure for determining whether a given algebraic equation has all its roots within the unit circle (that is, between -1 and $+1$ if they are real, and of the form $re^{j\theta}$ where $0 < r < 1$ if they are complex). We shall consistently use the variable z when we are dealing with equations subject to Professor Jury's requirement; when we consider, for purposes of comparison, an equation whose roots are required to be negative if real or to have negative real parts if complex we shall use the variable w. For equations of degrees up to 4, the conditions under discussion are specially simple, so all illustrative numerical work will be done with two equations of degree 6, to which the general procedure applies. The minor modifications required when the equation is of degree n, where n exceeds 4 and is not equal to 6, will be indicated as they occur.

Professor Jury's procedure is set out in Table 13.1 for the general sextic equation

$$F_G(z) = a_6z^6 + a_5z^5 + a_4z^4 + a_3z^3 + a_2z^2 +$$
$$+ a_1z + a_0 = 0 \quad (a_6 > 0) \qquad (13.16)$$

Row 1 is simply the coefficients of Equation 13.16 in ascending order, while Row 2 is the same coefficients in descending order. The general formula for obtaining Row 3 is

$$b_k = a_0a_k - a_6a_{6-k} \quad (k = 0, \ 1 \ldots .5) \qquad (13.17)$$

which means, in words, that to obtain b_k in Row 3, Column k, we multiply the element a_k in Row 1, and the same Column k by a_0, and we multiply the element a_{6-k} in Row 2, and the same Column k by a_6 and subtract.   Thus

$$b_0 = a_0{}^2 - a_6{}^2; \ b_1 = a_0a_1 - a_6a_5, \text{ etc.} \qquad (13.18)$$

Table 13.1.   TESTING WHETHER ROOTS OF EQUATION 13.1 LIE WITHIN THE UNIT CIRCLE

Column No.	0	1	2	3	4	5	6
Row No.							
1	a_0	a_1	a_2	a_3	a_4	a_5	a_6
2	a_6	a_5	a_4	a_3	a_2	a_1	a_0
3	b_0	b_1	b_2	b_3	b_4	b_5	
4	b_5	b_4	b_3	b_2	b_1	b_0	
5	c_0	c_1	c_2	c_3	c_4		
6	c_4	c_3	c_2	c_1	c_0		
7	d_0	d_1	d_2	d_3			
8	d_3	d_2	d_1	d_0			
9	e_0	e_1	e_2				
10	e_2	e_1	e_0				

If the Equation 13.16 had been of degree n instead of degree 6, Equation 13.17 would be replaced by

$$b_k = a_0a_k - a_na_{n-k} \qquad (13.19)$$

but the verbal description would be as above except that the element a_{n-k} in Row 2, Column k is now multiplied by a_n instead of a_6 so that

$$b_0 = a_0{}^2 - a_n{}^2; \ b_1 = a_0a_1 - a_na_{n-1}, \text{ etc.} \qquad (13.20)$$

and Row 3 has $(n - 1)$ elements instead of 5. Row 4 is simply Row 3 written down in the reverse order. Row 5 is now formed from Rows 3 and 4 in the same way as Row 3 was formed from Rows 1 and 2. The general formula is

$$c_k = b_0 b_k - b_5 b_{5-k} \qquad (13.21)$$

and this means that to obtain c_k in Row 5, Column k, we multiply the element b_k two rows higher in the same column by b_0, multiply the element b_{5-k} one row higher in the same column by b_5, and subtract, so that

$$c_0 = b_0{}^2 - b_5{}^2; \quad c_1 = b_0 b_1 - b_5 b_4, \text{ etc.} \qquad (13.22)$$

Again, if the equation is of degree n instead of degree 6, Equation 13.21 becomes

$$c_k = b_0 b_k - b_{n-1} b_{n-1-k} \qquad (13.23)$$

and the fixed multiplying element for b_{n-1-k} (which appears in Row 4, Column k) is b_{n-1} instead of b_5, so that

$$c_0 = b_0{}^2 - b{}^2_{n-1}; \quad c_1 = b_0 b_1 - b_{n-1} b_{n-2}, \text{ etc.} \qquad (13.24)$$

and there are $(n - 2)$ elements in Row 5 instead of 4. Row 6 is Row 5 reversed. The remaining rows are formed similarly. All rows with even numbers are formed by reversing the previous row with an odd number. The formulae for the rows with odd numbers are, for Equation 13.16,

$$d_k = c_0 c_k - c_4 c_{4-k} \text{ and } e_k = d_0 d_k - d_3 d_{3-k} \qquad (13.25)$$

Table 13.2. TESTING WHETHER ROOTS OF EQUATION 13.29 LIE WITHIN THE UNIT CIRCLE

Column No.	0	1	2	3	4	5	6	Remarks
Row No.								
1	1	3	9	14	20	16	12	
2	12	16	20	14	9	3	1	
3	−143	−189	−231	−154	−88	−20		
4	−20	−88	−154	−231	−189	−143		
5	20049	25267	29953	17402	8804			
6	8804	17402	29953	25267	20049			
7	3·2445	3·5337	3·3682	1·2644				} All × 10⁸
8	1·2644	3·3682	3·5337	3·2445				
9	8·928	7·206	6·460					} All × 10¹⁶
10	6·460	7·206	8·928					

and the process stops at Row 10 (or even Row 9 since Row 10 is only Row 9 reversed) because this row has only three elements. For an equation of degree n, Equation 13.25 must be replaced by

$$d_k = c_0 c_k - c_{n-2} c_{n-2-k}; \quad e_k = d_0 d_k - d_{n-3} d_{n-3-k}, \text{ etc.} \quad (13.26)$$

and the process continues until the row numbered $2n - 3$ which again has only three elements. The necessary and sufficient conditions for the roots of Equation 13.16 all to have modulus less than unity are

$$|a_0| < a_6; \quad |b_0| > |b_5|; \quad |c_0| > |c_4|;$$
$$|d_0| > |d_3| \text{ and } |e_0| > |e_2|$$
$$F_G(z) > 0 \text{ for } z = 1 \text{ and } z = -1 \quad (13.27)$$

and the corresponding conditions for an equation of degree n (with the coefficient a_n of z^n positive) are

$$|a_0| < a_n; \quad |b_0| > |b_{n-1}|; \quad |c_0| > |c_{n-2}|, \text{ etc.}$$
$$f(z) > 0 \text{ when } z = 1;$$

when $z = -1, f(z) > 0$ (n even); $f(z) < 0$ (n odd). $\quad (13.28)$

so that there are $(n - 1)$ of these inequalities altogether instead of 5.

This process is carried out in Table 13.2 and 13.3 for the particular equations

$$F_1(z) = (2z^2 + 2z + 1)(3z^2 + z + 1)(2z^2 + 1)$$
$$= 12z^6 + 16z^5 + 20z^4 + 14z^3 + 9z^2 + 3z + 1$$
$$= 0 \quad (13.29)$$

and

$$F_2(z) = (2z^2 + 2z + 1)(3z^2 + z + 1)(z^2 + 2)$$
$$= 6z^6 + 8z^5 + 19z^4 + 19z^3 + 15z^2 + 6z + 2$$
$$= 0 \quad (13.30)$$

the first of which has all its roots within the unit cirlce while the second has one pair, $z = \pm j\sqrt{2}$, outside. Equations 13.29 and 13.30 have been chosen to have exact factors and integer coefficients, to simplify the numerical work without any essential loss of generality. Applying the inequalities 13.27 to Table 13.2 (for Equation

13.29) we find as we should that they are all satisfied, but in Table 13.3, Row 5 has $c_4 = 944$ and $c_0 = 624$ which violates the third of inequalities 13.27, so that it is not necessary to go any further— we then know that Equation 13.30 must have at least one root with modulus greater than 1, or outside the unit circle.

As a numerical calculation, Table 13.2 is perfectly straightforward except insofar as the numbers involved in the later rows tend to become large. Professor Jury[14] gives a division process which does the same work as Table 13.1 or 13.2 but only involves the ratios of the numbers in those Tables. This division process is applied to Equation 13.29 in Table 13.4, which is explained immediately below.

A condensed notation is used in Table 13.4 to save space. The number tabulated in any particular column of a row is the coefficient of the power of z which appears at the head of the same column, in the expression represented in condensed form by that row. Thus Row 1 means

$$1 + 3z + 9z^2 + 14z^3 + 20z^4 + 16z^5 + 12z^6 \qquad (13.31)$$

which is simply the left-hand side of Equation 13.29, but written in ascending powers of z instead of descending powers. Next, we note that in expression 13.31, the ratio of the coefficient of the highest power of z to the coefficient of the lowest power of z is $12 \div 1 = 12$. This is recorded in the column labelled *Divisor* on the left of Table 13.4. Row 2 of Table 13.4 is then obtained by writing the coefficients of Row 1 down in reverse order, and dividing them all by this divisor. Thus the 1 which appears in the 1-column of Row 2 is the coefficient of z^6 in Row 1 divided by 12, the $1 \cdot 3333$ which appears in the z-column of Row 2 is the coefficient of z^5 in Row 1 divided by 12, and so on. Row 3 is now obtained by subtracting Row 2 from Row 1. Row 4 is obtained from Row 3 as Row 2 was obtained from Row 1. The ratio of the coefficient of z^6 in Row 3 to the coefficient of z (now the lowest power) is this time $11 \cdot 9167 \div 1 \cdot 6667 = 7 \cdot 15$; this is recorded in Row 4, in the *Divisor* column. The order of the coefficients in Row 3 is now reversed, and they are all divided by $7 \cdot 15$ to make the coefficients of Row 4. Thus the z-column in Row 4 is the coefficient of z^6 in Row 3 ($11 \cdot 9167$) divided by $7 \cdot 15$; the z^2 column in Row 4 is the coefficient of z^5 in Row 3 divided by 7.15, and so on. The process is continued until a row is reached having only three elements. It can be verified that the divisor 12 in Row 2 of Table 13.4 is a_6/a_0 in the notation of Table 13.1 (this is obvious by definition), the

Table 13.3. TESTING WHETHER ROOTS OF EQUATION 13.30 LIE WITHIN THE
UNIT CIRCLE

Column No.	0	1	2	3	4	5	6
Row No.							
1	2	6	15	19	19	8	6
2	6	8	19	19	15	6	2
3	−32	−36	−84	−76	−52	−20	
4	−20	−52	−76	−84	−36	−32	
5	624	112	1168	752	944		
6	944	752	1168	112	624		

divisor 7·15 in Row 4 of Table 13.4 is b_0/b_5, the divisor 2·2773 in
Row 6 of Table 13.4 is c_0/c_4, and so on. Hence the inequalities
13.27 will be satified provided that all the divisors which arise are
numerically greater than 1, and provided that the number 5·7873
on the left of Row 9 (which has three elements) is numerically less
than the number on the right (7·9984).

When the same process is carried out in Table 13.5 for Equation
13.30, there is no need to proceed beyond Row 5, for the next
divisor will be 3·25 ÷ 4·9167, which is numerically less than 1, so
that one of inequalities 13.27 is violated.

COMPARISON OF ROUTH AND JURY CRITERIA

Up to this point, we have only been concerned with Professor
Jury's procedure for determining whether an algebraic equation has

Table 13.4. DIVISION TEST FOR EQUATION 13.29

Row No.	Power → of z	1	z	z^2	z^3	z^4	z^5	z^6
1	Divisor ↓	1	3	9	14	20	16	12
2	12	1	1·3333	1·6667	1·1667	0·75	0·25	0·0833
3				1·6667	7·3333	12·8333	19·25	15·75	11·9167
4	7·15			1·6667	2·2028	2·6923	1·7949	1·0256	0·2331
5					5·1305	10·1410	17·4551	14·7244	11·6836
6	2·2773				5·1305	6·4658	7·6650	4·4532	2·2529
7						3·6752	9·7901	10·2712	9·4307
8	2·5660					3·6752	4·0028	3·8153	1·4323
9							5·7873	6·4559	7·9984

all its roots within the unit circle or not, and it is not obvious that the considerations mentioned at the beginning of this chapter, have any relevance whatever. If, however, we let

$$z = \frac{w + 1}{w - 1} \qquad (13.32)$$

then z will satisfy the condition $|z| < 1$ and lie within the unit circle if and only if w has a negative real part. This is most easily seen from Fig. 13.4. Suppose that $w = x + jy$ is represented by the point P whose coordinates are (x, y), where x and y are both positive. Then the modulus of $(w + 1)$, the numerator of z in Equation 13.32, is represented by AP and the modulus of $(w - 1)$, the denominator of z in Equation 13.32, is represented by BP. Hence the modulus of z is AP/PB and it is less than 1 if $AP < PB$. Now by applying Pythagoras's theorem to the triangles APN and BNP in Fig. 13.4 we have

$$AP^2 - BP^2 = AN^2 - BN^2 = (1 + x)^2 - (1 - x)^2 = 4x \qquad (13.33)$$

so that $AP < PB$ and $|z| < 1$ if and only if x is negative.

Equation 13.32 has indicated a connection between Professor Jury's criterion and the Routh criterion discussed earlier; this connection we now proceed to exploit.

Consider first a simple case. Suppose we have a quadratic equation

$$a_0 + a_1 z + a_2 z^2 = 0 \quad (a_2 > 0) \qquad (13.34)$$

and we want to know the conditions that both roots of this quadratic shall be within the unit circle. One way of exploring the

Table 13.5.   DIVISION TEST FOR EQUATION 13.30

Row No.	Power → of z	1	z	z^2	z^3	z^4	z^5	z^6
1	Divisor	2	6	15	19	19	8	6
2	↓ 3	2	2·6667	6·3333	6·3333	5	2	0·6667
3			3·3333	8·6667	12·6667	14	6	5·3333
4	1·6		3·3333	3·75	8·75	7·9167	5·4167	2·0833
5				4·9167	3·9167	6·0833	0·5833	3·25

situation is to use Equation 13.32 to turn Equation 13.34 into a
new equation which, when cleared of fractions, becomes

$$a_0(w - 1)^2 + a_1(w - 1)(w + 1) + a_2(w + 1)^2 = 0 \qquad (13.35)$$

which simplifies to

$$(a_0 + a_1 + a_2)w^2 + 2(a_2 - a_0)w + (a_0 - a_1 + a_2) = 0 \qquad (13.36)$$

Since the relation between z and w is given by Equation 13.32, we
know that requiring z to be within the unit circle is the same thing

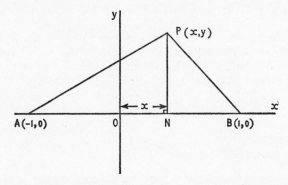

Fig. 13.4.   Graphical demonstration that if x is positive as shown, $|z| = AP/PB$

as requiring w to have a negative real part.   In other words, if we
can be sure that Equation 13.36 is free from roots in w with positive
real parts, then we can be equally sure that Equation 13.34 is free
from roots in z which are outside the unit circle.   But the conditions
for Equation 13.36 to be free from roots in w with positive real
parts are that the coefficients of w^2 and of w and the number term
in Equation 13.36 shall be positive.   These conditions reduce to

$$a_0 + a_2 > |a_1|; \; a_2 > a_0 \qquad (13.37)$$

and it follows that the inequalities 13.37 are the necessary and
sufficient conditions for Equation 13.34 to have both its roots
within the unit circle.

The above discussion has shown that, in the case of Equation
13.34, we can find out something about the position of the roots
in relation to the unit circle by the indirect method of using Equation
13.32 to change Equation 13.34 into Equation 13.36, and applying

to Equation 13.36 the well-known conditions for a quadratic equation to have both its roots with negative real parts. This indirect method of attack seems to be surprisingly effective. It can be extended to equations of any degree. Let us therefore first explore the possibilities of extending it to Equations 13.29 and 13.30.

In Table 13.4 the first row was a shorthand notation for the expression of $F_1(z)$ in Equation 13.29 and the second row was a multiple of the expression $F_1^*(z)$ formed by using the same coefficients as in Equation 13.29 but making the powers of z descend instead of ascend, so that

$$F_1^*(z) = z^6 + 3z^5 + 9z^4 + 14z^3 + 20z^2 + 16z + 12 \qquad (13.38)$$

In fact the second row of Table 13.4 was $F_1^*(z) \div 12$, so that the lowest-power or number term was the same in Row 2 of Table 13.4 as in Row 1. Now if we substitute for z in terms of w from Equation 13.32 and clear of fractions, Equation 13.29 becomes

$$f_1(w) = 75w^6 + 140w^5 + 219w^4 + 176w^3 + 113w^2 + 36w + 9$$

$$(13.39)$$

and Equation 13.38 becomes

$$f_1^*(w) = 75w^6 - 140w^5 + 219w^4 - 176w^3 + 113w^2 - 36w + 9$$

$$(13.40)$$

so that $f_1^*(w)$ is obtained from $f_1(w)$ simply by putting $-w$ for w. This is not an accident—it always happens, for equations of any degree. Thus we arrive at the idea that if we wish to test directly whether $f_1(w)$ given by Equation 13.39 has a zero with a positive real part, we might well carry out some division process involving $f_1(w)$, and $f_1^*(w)$ given by Equation 13.40. In fact it is easier to work with $f_1(w) + f_1^*(w)$ which means the terms of even degree in $f_1(w)$, and $f_1(w) - f_1^*(w)$ which means the terms of odd degree in $f_1(w)$, and it is already known that if $f_1(w)$ is to be free from zeros with positive real parts, then all coefficients which turn up in the division process described below must be positive. This division process is usually known as the 'H.C.F.' (highest common factor) process, and is applied to $f_1(w)$ in Table 13.6; the same shorthand notation is used as in Tables 13.4 and 13.5.

Row 1 of Table 13.6 gives the even-degree terms of $f_1(w)$ in Equation 13.40 on the left, and the odd-degree terms on the right.

Since the odd-degree terms are of lower degree than the even-degree terms, they are divided into the even-degree terms; the quotient is $0 \cdot 5357w$ or $75w/140$ as indicated on the left of Row 2 of Table 13.6. The left-hand part of Row 3 is obtained by subtraction, and the resulting coefficients are all positive, so we can continue. The left-hand half of Row 3 is a quartic expression in w and is thus of lower degree than the quintic odd-degree terms in the right-hand half of Row 1 and is divided into these terms; the quotient is

$$140w/124 \cdot 7143 = 1 \cdot 1225w$$

as indicated on the right of Row 2. The right-hand part of Row 3 is obtained by subtraction, and is divided into the left-hand part, giving the quotient $1 \cdot 7615w$ recorded on the left of Row 4, and so on.

Table 13.6. 'H.C.F.' PROCESS APPLIED TO $f_1(w)$ (EQUATION 13.39)

Row	Quotient	Even-Degree Terms				Odd-Degree Terms			Quotient
No.	w	w^6	w^4	w^2	1	w^5	w^3	w	w
1		75	219	113	9	140	176	36	
2	0·5357	75	94·2857	19·2857		140	105·2004	10·1031	1·1225
3			124·7143	93·7143	9		70·7996	25·8969	
4	1·7615		124·7143	45·6177			70·7996	13·2483	1·4720
5				48·0966	9			12·6486	

The process continues until, in Row 5, the right-hand half reduces to a single term $12 \cdot 6486w$. As all the quotients are positive multiples of w, and all the coefficients remaining in Row 5 are also positive, we conclude that $f_1(w)$ given by Equation 13.39 has no zeros (in w) with positive real parts. This result we expected, since Equation 13.39 was derived by substituting for z from Equation 13.32 into Equation 13.29, and we already knew that Equation 13.29 had all its roots (in z) within the unit circle. Likewise we found that Equation 13.30 had roots (in z) which were outside the unit circle. If Equation 13.32 is applied to Equation 13.30 and the resulting equation (in w) is cleared of fractions, it becomes

$$f_2(w) = 13 + 24w + 73w^2 + 64w^3 + 99w^4 + 40w^5 + 75w^6 = 0$$

$$(13.41)$$

It is therefore no surprise that when the 'H.C.F.' process described above is applied to Equation 13.41, as shown in Table 13.7, a negative coefficient appears in Row 3. This indicates that we need go no further—Equation 13.41 has at least one root (in w) with positive real part.

Thus the 'indirect approach' of turning a given equation (in z), like Equation 13.29, into a 'corresponding' equation in w like Equation 13.39 has led us to a process of testing equations in w for freedom from roots with positive real parts (analogous to Professor Jury's process for testing equations in z for freedom from roots outside the unit circle). Both these processes can be applied to equations of any degree, but they only tell us that a particular equation passes or fails the relevant test; no clue is given from these tests as to what sort of alterations are required to correct the instability just detected.

Table 13.7. 'H.C.F.' PROCESS APPLIED TO $f_2(w)$ (EQUATION 13.41)

Row	Quotient	Even-Degree Terms				Odd-Degree Terms			Quotient
No.	w	w^6	w^4	w^3	1	w^5	w^3	w	w
1		75	99	73	13	40	64	24	
2	1·875	75	120	45					
3			−21	28	13				

If the equation under consideration is a cubic or a quartic, it is possible to obtain explicit inequalities involving the coefficients, analogous to the inequalities 13.37, by means of which stability can be tested directly. We shall not give these explicit inequalities here because they are somewhat complicated and have already been given elsewhere by Professor Jury[14], and they are also special cases of the procedure discussed below, in which the 'indirect approach is developed a stage further in such a way that there is some indication as to how instability can be corrected.

REMEDIAL MEASURES FOR INSTABILITY

At this stage we have insufficient information as to what has gone wrong in cases of failure, and as to whether there is a similar equation, with only a few coefficients significantly altered, which would pass the stability test. Here we shall therefore make further use of the 'indirect' attack upon the two sextic equations we have already studied in a manner which could equally well be applied to equations of any degree, and which gives some indication of the causes of failure and necessary remedial measures.

If we apply the 'indirect attack' of Equation 13.32 to the general sextic equation (in z), namely Equation 13.16, the 'corresponding' equation (in w) is

$$f_G(w) = a_0(w-1)^6 + a_1(w-1)^5(w+1) + a_2(w-1)^4(w+1)^2 +$$
$$+ a_3(w^2-1)^3 + a_4(w-1)^2(w+1)^4 +$$
$$+ a_5(w-1)(w+1)^5 + a_6(w+1)^6$$
$$= 0 \qquad\qquad (13.42)$$

By collecting terms in the various powers of w, we can write this in the form

$$f_G(w) = q_0 + q_1 w + q_2 w^2 + q_3 w^3 + q_4 w^4 + q_5 w^5 + q_6 w^6 = 0$$
$$(13.43)$$

where it is perfectly possible to find formulae giving q_0, q_1, etc., in terms of a_0, a_1, etc., or vice versa, but such formulae are not required for our present purpose.

To apply the tests for Equation 13.43 to have freedom from roots with positive real parts (in w) specified in connection with Equation 13.1, we must separate the even-degree terms of Equation 13.43 from the odd-degree terms, and factorise each set of terms separately, so that

$$q_0 + q_2 w^2 + q_4 w^4 + q_6 w^6 = q_6(w^2 + \alpha_1)(w^2 + \alpha_2)(w^2 + \alpha_3) \quad (13.44)$$

$$q_1 w + q_3 w^3 + q_5 w^5 = q_5 w(w^2 + \beta_1)(w^2 + \beta_2) \qquad (13.45)$$

Then Equation 13.43 is free from roots (in w) with positive real parts if and only if all the quantities α_1, α_2, α_3, β_1, β_2, q_5 and q_6 are real and positive, and

$$0 < \alpha_1 < \beta_1 < \alpha_2 < \beta_2 < \alpha_3 \qquad\qquad (13.46)$$

We shall first apply Equation 13.46 to Equation 13.39 which gives

$$\left. \begin{array}{l} 75w^6 + 219w^4 + 113w^2 + 9 \\ \quad = 75\,(w^2 + 0\cdot09743)(w^2 + 0\cdot5395)(w^2 + 2\cdot2831) \\ 140w^5 + 176w^3 + 36w = 140w(w^2 + 9/35)(w^2 + 1) \end{array} \right\} \ (13.47)$$

Hence in this case $\alpha_1 = 0\cdot09743$, $\alpha_2 = 0\cdot5395$, $\alpha_3 = 2\cdot2831$, $\beta_1 = 9/35$ and $\beta_2 = 1$, and since $9/35 = 0\cdot25714$, inequality 13.46 is satisfied.

From Equation 13.41

$$\left.\begin{aligned}
75w^6 &+ 99w^4 + 73w^2 + 13 \\
&= 75\,(w^2 + 0\cdot2438)(w^4 + 1\cdot0762w^2 + 0\cdot7110) \\
40w^5 &+ 64w^3 + 24w = 8w(5w^2 + 3)(w^2 + 1)
\end{aligned}\right\} \quad (13.48)$$

and since $(w^4 + 1\cdot0762w^2 + 0\cdot7110)$ gives rise to complex quantities corresponding to α_2 and α_3 in the notation of Equation 13.44, we have no hope of satisfying inequality 13.46.

Now it can well be argued that the 'H.C.F.' process discussed above is much simpler than the determination of the quantities α_1, β_1, etc., required for the crucial test of inequality 13.46. If we know or suspect that the equation under discussion, like Equation 13.39, has no roots with positive real parts, this argument has considerable force, but if we have to deal with an equation like Equation 13.41, it may not be enough just to know that there are roots with positive real parts. The real questions may be (a) How ought we to try and alter the coefficients of Equation 13.41 in order to find an equation which is similar but which does satisfy the condition of freedom from roots with positive real parts, and (b) Why has Equation 13.41 failed this test? The 'H.C.F.' process gives us no information here. In the case of Equation 13.41, what has gone wrong is that the quantities α_2 and α_3 (in the notation of Equation 13.37) are complex. To achieve stability, we would need to have a quadratic factor something like

$$w^2 + 1\cdot73w^2 + 0\cdot7 = (w^2 + 0\cdot65)(w^2 + 1\cdot076) \quad (13.49)$$

in place of the offending quadratic factor

$$w^2 + 1.0762w^2 + 0\cdot7110 = (w^2 + 0\cdot5381)^2 + 0\cdot42145 \quad (13.50)$$

In other words, the main requirement is to increase the coefficient of w^2 in Equation 13.41, and we should have to see how the parameters under our control can be altered to achieve this. Returning to Equation 13.30 the main effect of so increasing this coefficient is to increase sharply the w^4 term in the original Equation 13.41; to a less extent, the w^2 term also needs to be increased.

In fact it is not nearly as difficult as it looks to apply inequality 13.46, because the quantities α_1, β_1, etc., arise (as is seen from

Equation 13.45) from equations which have only about half the degree (in w^2) of the equation under consideration, and we are only interested in the real roots of such equations, which can be found roughly by drawing a graph. For a more accurate determination, the procedure suggested in Chapters 3 and 4 can be used.

If an equation with numerical coefficients is being tested by inequality 13.46, failure is much more likely to be due (as in the case of Equation 13.41) to the fact that some of the quantities α_1, β_1, etc., are complex than to the fact that they are real but fail to 'interlace' as required by inequality 13.46. The following example makes this point clear, although in itself it is of little practical interest. Consider the equation

$$(w + a)^6 + \lambda = 0 \tag{13.51}$$

Clearly if λ is sufficiently small, Equation 13.51 has all its roots with negative real parts, since the roots are

$$w = -a + \lambda^{1/6}\{\pm \tfrac{1}{2}\sqrt{3} \pm j\tfrac{1}{2}\}; \quad w = -a \pm j\lambda^{1/6} \tag{13.52}$$

and a root with positive real part will first appear when $\lambda^{1/6}$ exceeds $2a/\sqrt{3}$ or λ exceeds $64\,a^6/27$ or $2{\cdot}3704\,a^6$. When λ has this critical value

$$
\left.
\begin{aligned}
w^6 &+ 15a^2w^4 + 15a^4w^2 + (a^6 + \lambda) \\
&= \left(w^2 + \frac{a^2}{3}\right)\left(w^4 + \frac{44a^2w^2}{3} + \frac{91a^4}{9}\right) \\
6aw^5 &+ 20a^3w^3 + 6a^5w \\
&= 6aw\left(w^2 + \frac{a^2}{3}\right)\left(w^2 + 3a^2\right)
\end{aligned}
\right\} \tag{13.53}
$$

so that, from the point of view of inequality 13.46, breakdown occurs because $\alpha_1 = \beta_1$. It is only necessary to increase λ to $2.8854\,a^6$ before the terms of even degree in w give rise to complex values of α_1 and α_2, so that the range

$$2{\cdot}3704\,a^6 < \lambda < 2{\cdot}8854\,a^6 \tag{13.54}$$

in which the quantities α_1 and α_2 are real but fail to have $\beta_1 = a^2/3$ between them is very restricted. If we only try to test whether the quantities α_1, α_2, α_3 are real, we have to deal with the even-degree terms (of Equation 13.53 in this case) without reference to the odd-degree terms, and thus to work with an equation having about half the degree of the equation (here Equation 13.51) under consideration.

When the equation under consideration is not a sextic, the number of quantities α_1, β_1, etc., will be different; it is still true that all these quantities must be real and positive, and must 'interlace' in the same way as is indicated in inequality 13.46.

We have seen that by applying inequality 13.46 we can not only test whether an equation (in w) is free from roots with positive real parts or not, but also get some idea of how to eradicate such roots by suitable alteration of the coefficients. But these facilities do not appear to be directly available if we are given an equation in z, and find that this equation has roots outside the unit circle. Thus if we want to know what to do about the equation 13.30 so that, by the least possible alteration of the coefficients, it can be turned into a similar equation which does have all its roots (in z) within the unit circle, the only possible procedure appears to be to apply Equation 13.32 and obtain the 'corresponding' w-equation, which is Equation 13.41, and do all real investigation with the w-equation instead of (or on behalf of) the given z-equation.

Thus we have considerable choice of methods available for tackling stability problems. If we are concerned with applications such as feedback amplifiers, where the stability requirement is that a certain equation be free from roots with positive real parts, diagnosis of the cause of instability and assessment of possible remedies can best be done by means of inequality 13.46. If we are concerned with applications such as sampled-data control systems, where stability requires that the roots of an equation shall be within the unit circle, such diagnosis and assessment of remedies can perhaps best be done by substituting from Equation 13.32 to find a 'corresponding' equation which can be tested (instead of the given equation) for freedom from roots with positive real parts. If we are concerned only with the detection of instability and are given an equation with numerical coefficients, there is little to choose between the various methods discussed.

LIAPUNOV'S APPROACH

It remains to consider in outline the Liapunov approach, by means of which results equivalent to those already discussed can be derived. Here we shall only consider the basic ideas and simple examples; these ideas can be extended to nonlinear systems and in various other ways as indicated by Parks[15]. Our objective, however, is merely to have an alternative way of looking at stability

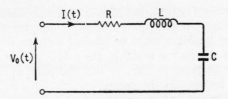

Fig. 13.5.   A simple series circuit

problems, because often there is a kind of marriage between alternative ways of looking at things which results in a great increase in understanding.

Let us therefore consider first the Liapunov approach to the simple series circuit of Fig. 13.5 (which is the same as Fig. 9.1).

We already know that the relation between $V_0(t)$ and $I(t)$ can be expressed in the direct form

$$V_0(t) = [R + pL + (1/pC)]I(t) \qquad (13.55a)$$

or in the operational form

$$I(t) = \frac{p}{L\{(p + \alpha)^2 + \omega^2\}} \, V_0(t) \qquad (13.55b)$$

where

$$p \text{ means } \frac{d}{dt}; \ \alpha = R/2L \text{ and } \omega^2 = 1/(LC) - (R^2/4L^2) \qquad (13.56)$$

and that the operational-calculus solution is given by Equation 9.20, so that α must be positive for stability.   To apply Liapunov's procedure, however, we need to introduce new variables to convert Equation 13.55a into a number (here 2) of first-order differential equations.   Let

$$\frac{1}{p} I(t) = \int_{-\infty}^{t} I(\tau) \, d\tau = q(t) \qquad (13.57)$$

Then Equations 13.55a and 13.57 become

$$\left. \begin{aligned} \frac{dq}{dt} &= I \\[2mm] \frac{dI}{dt} &= \frac{1}{L}\left(V_0 - RI - \frac{1}{C}q\right) \end{aligned} \right\} \qquad (13.58)$$

Normally, we regard Equation 13.55b as solved if we can express q

17*

and its derivative I as functions of time, and a possible way of doing this is graphical: to plot the point (q, I) and see how it moves. Each point of the locus could be labelled with the time at which it occurred. If the system is stable, the values of q and I should in the long run decrease to zero, so that the point (q, I) describes a curve which approaches the origin.

Now let X be the total energy stored in the system, so that

$$X = q^2/2C + \tfrac{1}{2}LI^2 \tag{13.59}$$

Multiply the first of Equations 13.58 by q/C and the second by LI and add, and we obtain

$$\frac{\mathrm{d}X}{\mathrm{d}t} = V_0 I - RI^2 \tag{13.60}$$

The question under discussion is stability. If the system of Fig. 13.2 is disturbed, does it in the long run tend to return to its original quiescent or 'dead' state or not? Hence the first term $V_0 I$ on the right-hand side of Equation 13.60 is irrelevant—it is only present while the disturbance V_0 is still in progress. If this term is omitted, however, Equation 13.60 shows that $\dfrac{\mathrm{d}X}{\mathrm{d}t}$ is always negative ('negative-definite') for $R > 0$, whereas Equation 13.59 shows that X itself is always positive ('positive-definite'). The exceptional zero values for X and $\dfrac{\mathrm{d}X}{\mathrm{d}t}$ when q and I are both zero can be tolerated.

Now the essence of Liapunov's method is to be able to find a quantity like X, which is made up of the various dependent variables $\left(\text{here } q \text{ and } I, \text{ or rather } q \text{ and } \dfrac{\mathrm{d}q}{\mathrm{d}t}\right)$ and is itself positive-definite but such that its derivative with respect to time is negative-definite. If such a quantity can be found, the system is 'asymptotically stable'— if it is displaced, it will ultimately return to the equilibrium position. In the case just discussed, X was the total energy of the system, and this gives a useful clue to the kind of expression required for Liapunov's approach. Stability is proved from the facts that X is positive-definite and $\dfrac{\mathrm{d}X}{\mathrm{d}t}$ negative-definite alone; we do not need to obtain an explicit formula for X, q or I.

The system of Fig. 13.1 was obviously stable ab initio, and was only discussed as a means of making general principles clear.

Next therefore let us see whether we can by Liapunov's approach obtain the condition of stability for a third-order linear system

$$(p^3 + a_2 p^2 + a_1 p + a_0)\, I(t) = V_0(t) \tag{13.61}$$

which is that a_0, a_1, a_2 and $a_1 a_2 - a_0$ must all be positive (as mentioned at the beginning of this chapter). The first requirement is to get Equation 13.61 into a form in which it will be obvious how to find an expression analogous to X in Equation 13.59, so that X is positive-definite and $\dfrac{dX}{dt}$ is negative-definite, and it is not obvious how to do this. We therefore follow Parks[15] in first formulating an expression Y such that Y and $\dfrac{dY}{dt}$ can easily be tested for positive-and negative-definiteness respectively, and then seeing how we can relate Y to Equation 13.61. Consider therefore the system of linear first-order differential (or operational) equations somewhat analogous to Equations 13.58

$$\left.\begin{aligned}
pI &= I_1 \\
pI_1 &= -b_3 I + I_2 \\
pI_2 &= -b_2 I_1 - b_1 I_2 + V_0(t)
\end{aligned}\right\} \tag{13.62}$$

Multiply the first of Equations 13.62 by $2b_1 b_2 b_3 I$, the second by $2b_1 b_2 I_1$, and the last by $2b_1 I_2$, and add. We obtain

$$\begin{aligned}
pY &= p\{b_1 b_2 b_3 I^2 + b_1 b_2 I_1{}^2 + b_1 I_2{}^2\} \\
&= -2b_1{}^2 I_2{}^2 + 2b_1 I_2 V_0(t)
\end{aligned} \tag{13.63}$$

The expression on the right-hand side of Equation 13.63 is clearly negative definite (if, as when discussing Equation 13.60, we ignore the V_0-term, only present while the disturbance is in progress). The expression differentiated on the left-hand side is positive-definite if and only if all the quantities b_1, b_2 and b_3 are positive. Hence Y is just the sort of expression we require as a 'Liapunov function', provided that we can relate the system of equations 13.62 to the given equation 13.61. From the first two of Equations 13.62, we can express I_1 and I_2 in terms of I and its derivatives, and substituting into the last of Equations 13.62 gives

$$\{p^3 + b_1 p^2 + (b_2 + b_3)p + b_1 b_3\} I = V_0(t) \tag{13.64}$$

which is the same as Equation 13.61 if

$$b_1 = a_2; \quad b_2 + b_3 = a_1; \quad b_1 b_3 = a_0 \qquad (13.65)$$

so that

$$b_1 = a_2; \quad b_2 = a_1 - (a_0/a_2); \quad b_3 = a_0/a_2 \qquad (13.66)$$

and, since the b-terms must be positive for stability, we have arrived at the same stability rule for Equation 13.61 as before.

For a fourth-order linear system the procedure is similar, and the general case is easily inferred. If the given equation is

$$(p^4 + a_3 p^3 + a_2 p^2 + a_1 p + a_0)I = V_0(t) \qquad (13.67)$$

the set of equations analogous to Equations 13.62 is

$$\left.\begin{aligned}
pI &= I_1 \\
pI_1 &= -b_4 I + I_2 \\
pI_2 &= -b_3 I_1 + I_3 \\
pI_3 &= -b_2 I_2 - b_1 I_3 + V_0(t)
\end{aligned}\right\} \qquad (13.68)$$

Multiplying the first of Equations (13.68) by $2b_1 b_2 b_3 b_4 I$, the second by $2b_1 b_2 b_3 I_1$, the third by $2b_1 b_2 I_2$, and the last by $2b_1 I_3$ and adding, we obtain

$$\begin{aligned}
pZ &= p\{b_1 b_2 b_3 b_4 I^2 + b_1 b_2 b_3 I_1{}^2 + b_1 b_2 I_2{}^2 + b_1 I_3{}^2\} \\
&= -2b_1{}^2 I_3{}^2 + 2b_1 I_3 V_0(t) \qquad (13.69)
\end{aligned}$$

so that Z is satisfactory as a 'Liapunov function' provided that b_1, b_2, b_3 and b_4 are positive.

Eliminating I_1, I_2 and I_3 from Equations 13.68, we find that the equation which must be the same as Equation 13.67 is

$$\{p^4 + b_1 p^3 + (b_2 + b_3 + b_4)p^2 + b_1(b_3 + b_4)p + b_2 b_4\}I = V_0(t) \qquad (13.70)$$

so that

$$b_1 = a_3; \quad b_2 + b_3 + b_4 = a_2; \quad b_1(b_3 + b_4) = a_1;$$
$$b_2 b_4 = a_0 \qquad (13.71)$$

and expressing the b's in terms of a's:

$$b_1 = a_3; \quad b_2 = \frac{a_2 a_3 - a_1}{a_3}; \quad b_3 = \frac{a_1 a_2 a_3 - a_1{}^2 - a_0 a_3{}^2}{a_3(a_2 a_3 - a_1)};$$

$$b_4 = \frac{a_0 a_3}{a_2 a_3 - a_1} \tag{13.72}$$

Equations 13.72 involve the same expressions as arise when the conditions for a quartic equation to be free from roots with positive real parts were considered at the beginning of the chapter, but the Liapunov approach does throw new light on why these expressions are significant.

In the foregoing, we have only covered ground already well explored by a different route, and allowed Liapunov to shed new light on familiar results. But the Liapunov approach may also enable us to settle conclusively whether a system is stable or not when the equations governing the behaviour of the system are not explicitly soluble—when they contain nonlinear terms, for example. Parks[15] states that if the nonlinear terms are omitted from a system of equations, and the resulting linear equations are stable (i.e., a 'Liapunov function' which is positive-definite and which has a negative-definite time-derivative can be found) then the full non-linear system is also stable.

Thus, while Liapunov's approach throws very useful light on stability criteria obtained otherwise for linear systems associated with algebraic equations, its main usefulness is likely to lie in making stability criteria obtainable in cases (outside the scope of this book) where they could not otherwise be obtained at all.

REFERENCES

[1] Morris, J., 'An "Escalator" Process for the Solution of Linear Simultaneous Equations', *Phil. Mag.*, **37**, pp. 106–120 (1946).

[2] Shih-Nge Lin, 'A method of successive approximations of evaluating the real and complex roots of cubic and higher-order equations', *J. Maths and Phys.*, **20**, pp. 231–42 (1941). See also Morris, J. and Head, J. W., 'Note on Lin's Iteration Process for the Extraction of Complex Roots of Algebraic Equations', *Quart J. Mech. and Applied Math.*, **6**, Part 4, pp. 391-397 (1953).

[3] Attwood, C., *Practical Five-figure Mathematical Tables*, Macmillan (1950).

[4] Savant, C. J. Jr., *Basic Feedback Control System Design*, McGraw-Hill, Chapter 4, (1958). See also the following three references by Evans, W. R.:
Evans, W. R., *Control-System Dynamics*, McGraw-Hill (1954).
Evans, W. R., 'Control System Synthesis by Root-Locus Method', *Trans. Amer. Inst. Elect. Engrs*, **69**, pp. 66–69 (1950).
Evans, W. R., 'Graphical Analysis of Control Systems', *Trans. Amer. Inst. Elect. Engrs.*, **67**, pp. 547–551 (1948).

[5] Broadbent, D. T., Letter to *Electronic & Radio Engineer*, **35**, No. 3, p. 115, March 1958.

[6] Jordan, W. B., *Mathematical Tables and Aids to Computation*, **5**, p. 183, July 1961.

[7] Unified Circuit Theory (in preparation, Iliffe Books Ltd.). See also Wilson, W. Proctor, Mayo, C. G., and Head, J. W., 'The fundamental importance of the Heaviside Operational Calculus', *J. Brit. I.R.E.*, **24**, no. 6, pp. 461–77. Dec 1962 and Deards, S. R. (Ed.), *Recent Developments in Network Theory*, Pergamon Press: Oxford, pp. 31–55 (1963).

[8] Jolley, L. B. W., *Summation of Series*, Chapman & Hall, London (1925), Dover Publications, N.Y. (1960).

[9] Gouriet, G. G., *Two Theorems Concerning Group Delay with Practical Applications to Delay Correction*, I.E.E. Monograph no. 275R, December 1957.

[10] Wilson, W. Proctor, *Electronic & Radio Engineer*, **34**, no. 6, pp. 229–31, June 1957.

[11] Wilson, W. Proctor, *Electronic Technology*, **38**, no. 2, p. 69, February 1961.

[12] Jackson, Willis and Huxley, L. G. H., 'The Solution of Transmission-Line Problems by the Use of the Circle Diagram of Impedance', *J. Instn. Elec. Engrs.*, Part III, **91**, no. 15, pp. 105-116, September 1944.

[13] Mayo, C. G., and Head, J. W., 'Wide-Range RC Oscillator', *Electronic & Radio Engineer*, **35**, no. 11, pp. 412–416, November 1958.

[14] Jury, E. I., and Blanchard, J., 'A Stability Test for Linear Discrete Systems in Table Form', *Proc. Inst. Radio. Engrs.*, **49**, no. 12, pp. 1247–1948, December 1961. See also Jury, E. I., 'A Stability Test for Linear Discrete Systems using a Simple Division', *Proc. Inst. Radio. Engrs.*, **49**, no. 12, pp. 1948–1949. December 1961.

[15] Parks, P. C., 'Liapunov's Methods in Automatic Control Theory', *Control*, **5**, nos. 53 and 54, pp. 102–105 and 109-112, November and December 1962.

INDEX